MATHEMATICS

PART II

Textbook for Class XII

राष्ट्रीय शैक्षिक अनुसंधान और प्रशिक्षण परिषद्
NATIONAL COUNCIL OF EDUCATIONAL RESEARCH AND TRAINING

First Edition

January 2007 Magha 1928

Reprinted

October 2007 Kartika 1929
January 2009 Pausa 1930
December 2009 Agrahayana 1931
January 2012 Magha 1933
November 2012 Kartika 1934

PD 450T BS

₹ 105.00

Printed on 80 GSM paper with NCERT water mark

Published at the Publication Division by the Secretary, National Council of Educational Research and Training, Sri Aurobindo Marg, New Delhi 110 016 and printed at Amit Printing Press, D-12 & 132, Industrial Area, Site-A, Mathura (UP)

ISBN   81-7450-629-2 (Part-I)
81-7450-653-5 (Part-II)

OFFICES OF THE PUBLICATION DIVISION, NCERT

NCERT Campus
Sri Aurobindo Marg
New Delhi 110 016   Phone : 011-26562708

108, 100 Feet Road
Hosdakere Halli Extension
Banashankari III Stage
Bangalore 560 085   Phone : 080-26725740

Navjivan Trust Building
P.O. Navjivan
Ahmedabad 380 014   Phone : 079-27541446

CWC Campus
Opp. Dhankal Bus Stop
Panihati
Kolkata 700 114   Phone : 033-25530454

CWC Complex
Maligaon
Guwahati 781 021   Phone : 0361-2674869

Publication Team

Head, Publication Division	:	Ashok Srivastava
Chief Production Officer	:	Shiv Kumar
Chief Editor (Incharge)	:	Naresh Yadav
Chief Business Manager	:	Gautam Ganguly
Editor	:	Bijnan Sutar
Production Assistant	:	Rajesh Pippal

Cover and Illustration
Arvinder Chawla

Foreword

The National Curriculum Framework, 2005, recommends that children's life at school must be linked to their life outside the school. This principle marks a departure from the legacy of bookish learning which continues to shape our system and causes a gap between the school, home and community. The syllabi and textbooks developed on the basis of NCF signify an attempt to implement this basic idea. They also attempt to discourage rote learning and the maintenance of sharp boundaries between different subject areas. We hope these measures will take us significantly further in the direction of a child-centred system of education outlined in the National Policy on Education (1986).

The success of this effort depends on the steps that school principals and teachers will take to encourage children to reflect on their own learning and to pursue imaginative activities and questions. We must recognise that, given space, time and freedom, children generate new knowledge by engaging with the information passed on to them by adults. Treating the prescribed textbook as the sole basis of examination is one of the key reasons why other resources and sites of learning are ignored. Inculcating creativity and initiative is possible if we perceive and treat children as participants in learning, not as receivers of a fixed body of knowledge.

These aims imply considerable change in school routines and mode of functioning. Flexibility in the daily time-table is as necessary as rigour in implementing the annual calendar so that the required number of teaching days are actually devoted to teaching. The methods used for teaching and evaluation will also determine how effective this textbook proves for making children's life at school a happy experience, rather than a source of stress or boredom. Syllabus designers have tried to address the problem of curricular burden by restructuring and reorienting knowledge at different stages with greater consideration for child psychology and the time available for teaching. The textbook attempts to enhance this endeavour by giving higher priority and space to opportunities for contemplation and wondering, discussion in small groups, and activities requiring hands-on experience.

NCERT appreciates the hard work done by the textbook development committee responsible for this book. We wish to thank the Chairperson of the advisory group in Science and Mathematics, Professor J.V. Narlikar and the Chief Advisor for this book, Professor P.K. Jain for guiding the work of this committee. Several teachers contributed to the development of this textbook; we are grateful to their principals for making this possible. We are indebted to the institutions and organisations which have generously permitted us to draw upon their resources, material and personnel. As an organisation committed to systemic reform and continuous improvement in the quality of its products, NCERT welcomes comments and suggestions which will enable us to undertake further revision and refinement.

Director
New Delhi   National Council of Educational
20 November 2006   Research and Training

Preface

The National Council of Educational Research and Training (NCERT) had constituted 21 Focus Groups on Teaching of various subjects related to School Education, to review the National Curriculum Framework for School Education - 2000 (NCFSE - 2000) in face of new emerging challenges and transformations occurring in the fields of content and pedagogy under the contexts of National and International spectrum of school education. These Focus Groups made general and specific comments in their respective areas. Consequently, based on these reports of Focus Groups, National Curriculum Framework (NCF)-2005 was developed.

NCERT designed the new syllabi and constituted Textbook Development Teams for Classes XI and XII to prepare textbooks in Mathematics under the new guidelines and new syllabi. The textbook for Class XI is already in use, which was brought in 2005.

The first draft of the present book (Class XII) was prepared by the team consisting of NCERT faculty, experts and practicing teachers. The draft was refined by the development team in different meetings. This draft of the book was exposed to a group of practicing teachers teaching Mathematics at higher secondary stage in different parts of the country, in a review workshop organised by the NCERT at Delhi. The teachers made useful comments and suggestions which were incorporated in the draft textbook. The draft textbook was finalised by an editorial board constituted out of the development team. Finally, the Advisory Group in Science and Mathematics and the Monitoring Committee constituted by the HRD Ministry, Government of India have approved the draft of the textbook.

In the fitness of things, let us cite some of the essential features dominating the textbook. These characteristics have reflections in almost all the chapters. The existing textbook contains thirteen main chapters and two appendices. Each chapter contains the followings :

- Introduction: Highlighting the importance of the topic; connection with earlier studied topics; brief mention about the new concepts to be discussed in the chapter.
- Organisation of chapter into sections comprising one or more concepts/ subconcepts.
- Motivating and introducing the concepts/subconcepts. Illustrations have been provided wherever possible.

- Proofs/problem solving involving deductive or inductive reasoning, multiplicity of approaches wherever possible have been inducted.

- Geometric viewing / visualisation of concepts have been emphasized whenever needed.

- Applications of mathematical concepts have also been integrated with allied subjects like Science and Social Sciences.

- Adequate and variety of examples/exercises have been given in each section.

- For refocusing and strengthening the understanding and skill of problem solving and applicabilities, miscellaneous types of examples/exercises have been provided involving two or more subconcepts at a time at the end of the chapter. The scope of challenging problems to talented minority have been reflected conducive to the recommendation as reflected in NCF-2005.

- For more motivational purpose, brief historical background of topics have been provided at the end of the chapter and at the beginning of each chapter, relevant quotation and photograph of eminent mathematician who have contributed significantly in the development of the topic undertaken, are also provided.

- Lastly, for direct recapitulation of main concepts, formulas and results, brief summary of the chapter has also been provided.

I am thankful to Professor Krishan Kumar, Director, NCERT who constituted the team and invited me to join this national endeavour for the improvement of Mathematics education. He has provided us with an enlightened perspective and a very conducive environment. This made the task of preparing the book much more enjoyable and rewarding. I express my gratitude to Professor J.V. Narlikar, Chairperson of the Advisory Group in Science and Mathematics, for his specific suggestions and advice towards the improvement of the book from time to time. I, also, thank Professor G. Ravindra, Joint Director, NCERT for his help from time to time.

I express my sincere thanks to Professor Hukum Singh, Chief Coordinator and Head, DESM, Dr. V. P. Singh, Coordinator and Professor, S. K. Singh Gautam who have been helping for the success of this project academically as well as administratively. Also, I would like to place on records my appreciation and thanks to all the members of the team and the teachers who have been associated with this noble cause in one or the other form.

PAWAN K. JAIN
Chief Advisor

Textbook Development Committee

CHAIRPERSON, ADVISORY GROUP IN SCIENCE AND MATHEMATICS

J.V. Narlikar, *Emeritus Professor,* Inter-University Centre for Astronomy and Astrophysics (IUCAA), Ganeshkhind, Pune University, Pune

CHIEF ADVISOR

P.K. Jain, *Professor,* Department of Mathematics, University of Delhi, Delhi

CHIEF COORDINATOR

Hukum Singh, *Professor* and *Head,* DESM, NCERT, New Delhi

MEMBERS

A.K. Rajput, *Associate Professor,* RIE, Bhopal, M.P.

Arun Pal Singh, *Associate Professor,* Department of Mathematics, Dayal Singh College, University of Delhi, Delhi

B.S.P. Raju, *Professor,* RIE Mysore, Karnataka

C.R. Pradeep, *Assistant Professor,* Department of Mathematics, Indian Institute of Science, Bangalore, Karnataka

D.R. Sharma *P.G.T.,* Jawahar Navodaya Vidyalaya, Mungeshpur, Delhi

R.P. Maurya, *Associate Professor,* DESM, NCERT, New Delhi

Ram Avtar, *Professor* (Retd.) and *Consultant,* DESM, NCERT, New Delhi

S.K. Kaushik, *Associate Professor,* Department of Mathematics, Kirori Mal College, University of Delhi, Delhi

S.K.S. Gautam, *Professor,* DESM, NCERT, New Delhi

S.S. Khare, *Pro-Vice-Chancellor,* NEHU, Tura Campus, Meghalaya

Sangeeta Arora, *P.G.T.,* Apeejay School, Saket, New Delhi

Shailja Tewari, *P.G.T.,* Kendriya Vidyalaya, Barkakana, Hazaribagh, Jharkhand

Sunil Bajaj, *Sr. Specialist,* SCERT, Gurgaon, Haryana

Vinayak Bujade, *Lecturer,* Vidarbha Buniyadi Junior College, Sakkardara Chowk, Nagpur, Maharashtra

MEMBER-COORDINATOR

V.P. Singh, *Associate Professor,* DESM, NCERT, New Delhi

CONSTITUTION OF INDIA

Preamble

WE, THE PEOPLE OF INDIA, having solemnly resolved to constitute India into a **SOVEREIGN SOCIALIST SECULAR DEMOCRATIC REPUBLIC** and to secure to all its citizens:

JUSTICE, social, economic and political;

LIBERTY of thought, expression, belief, faith and worship;

EQUALITY of status and of opportunity and to promote among them all;

FRATERNITY assuring the dignity of the individual and the unity and integrity of the Nation;

IN OUR CONSTITUENT ASSEMBLY this twenty-sixth day of November, 1949, do **HEREBY ADOPT, ENACT AND GIVE TO OURSELVES THIS CONSTITUTION.**

Acknowledgements

The Council gratefully acknowledges the valuable contributions of the following participants of the Textbook Review Workshop: Jagdish Saran, *Professor,* Deptt. of Statistics, University of Delhi; Quddus Khan, *Lecturer*, Shibli National P.G. College, Azamgarh (U.P.); P.K. Tewari, *Assistant Commissioner* (Retd.), Kendriya Vidyalaya Sangathan; S.B. Tripathi, *Lecturer,* R.P.V.V., Surajmal Vihar, Delhi; O.N. Singh, *Reader,* RIE, Bhubaneswar, Orissa; Miss Saroj, *Lecturer,* Govt. Girls Senior Secondary School No.1, Roop Nagar, Delhi; P. Bhaskar Kumar, *P.G.T.,* Jawahar Navodaya Vidyalaya, Lepakshi, Anantapur, (A.P.); Mrs. S. Kalpagam, *P.G.T.,* K.V. NAL Campus, Bangalore; Rahul Sofat, *Lecturer,* Air Force Golden Jubilee Institute, Subroto Park, New Delhi; Vandita Kalra, *Lecturer,* Sarvodaya Kanya Vidyalaya, Vikaspuri, District Centre, New Delhi; Janardan Tripathi, *Lecturer,* Govt. R.H.S.S., Aizawl, Mizoram and Ms. Sushma Jaireth, *Reader*, DWS, NCERT, New Delhi.

The Council acknowledges the efforts of Deepak Kapoor, *Incharge,*Computer Station; Sajjad Haider Ansari, Rakesh Kumar and Nargis Islam, *D.T.P. Operators;* Monika Saxena, *Copy Editor;* and Abhimanu Mohanty, *Proof Reader.*

The contribution of APC-Office, administration of DESM and Publication Department is also duly acknowledged.

Contents of
MATHEMATICS PART I
For Class XII

Chapter 1	Relations and Functions	1 - 32
Chapter 2	Inverse Trigonometric Functions	33 - 55
Chapter 3	Matrices	56 - 102
Chapter 4	Determinants	103 - 146
Chapter 5	Continuity and Differentiability	147 - 193
Chapter 6	Application of Derivatives	194 - 246
	Appendix 1: Proofs in Mathematics	247 - 255
	Appendix 2: Mathematical Modelling	256 - 267
	Answers	268 - 286

Contents

PART II

Foreword		*iii*
Preface		*v*

7. Integrals — **287**

7.1	Introduction	288
7.2	Integration as an Inverse Process of Differentiation	288
7.3	Methods of Integration	300
7.4	Integrals of some Particular Functions	307
7.5	Integration by Partial Fractions	316
7.6	Integration by Parts	323
7.7	Definite Integral	331
7.8	Fundamental Theorem of Calculus	334
7.9	Evaluation of Definite Integrals by Substitution	338
7.10	Some Properties of Definite Integrals	341

8. Application of Integrals — **359**

8.1	Introduction	359
8.2	Area under Simple Curves	359
8.3	Area between Two Curves	366

9. Differential Equations — **379**

9.1	Introduction	379
9.2	Basic Concepts	379
9.3	General and Particular Solutions of a Differential Equation	383
9.4	Formation of a Differential Equation whose General Solution is given	385
9.5	Methods of Solving First order, First Degree Differential Equations	391

10. Vector Algebra — **424**

10.1	Introduction	424
10.2	Some Basic Concepts	424
10.3	Types of Vectors	427
10.4	Addition of Vectors	429

10.5	Multiplication of a Vector by a Scalar	432
10.6	Product of Two Vectors	441
11.	**Three Dimensional Geometry**	**463**
11.1	Introduction	463
11.2	Direction Cosines and Direction Ratios of a Line	463
11.3	Equation of a Line in Space	468
11.4	Angle between Two Lines	471
11.5	Shortest Distance between Two Lines	473
11.6	Plane	479
11.7	Coplanarity of Two Lines	487
11.8	Angle between Two Planes	488
11.9	Distance of a Point from a Plane	490
11.10	Angle between a Line and a Plane	492
12.	**Linear Programming**	**504**
12.1	Introduction	504
12.2	Linear Programming Problem and its Mathematical Formulation	505
12.3	Different Types of Linear Programming Problems	514
13.	**Probability**	**531**
13.1	Introduction	531
13.2	Conditional Probability	531
13.3	Multiplication Theorem on Probability	540
13.4	Independent Events	542
13.5	Bayes' Theorem	548
13.6	Random Variables and its Probability Distributions	557
13.7	Bernoulli Trials and Binomial Distribution	572
	Answers	**588**
	Supplementary Material	**613**

Chapter 7

INTEGRALS

❖ *Just as a mountaineer climbs a mountain – because it is there, so a good mathematics student studies new material because it is there. — JAMES B. BRISTOL* ❖

7.1 Introduction

Differential Calculus is centred on the concept of the derivative. The original motivation for the derivative was the problem of defining tangent lines to the graphs of functions and calculating the slope of such lines. Integral Calculus is motivated by the problem of defining and calculating the area of the region bounded by the graph of the functions.

If a function f is differentiable in an interval I, i.e., its derivative f' exists at each point of I, then a natural question arises that given f' at each point of I, can we determine the function? The functions that could possibly have given function as a derivative are called anti derivatives (or primitive) of the function. Further, the formula that gives

**G .W. Leibnitz
(1646 -1716)**

all these anti derivatives is called the ***indefinite integral*** of the function and such process of finding anti derivatives is called integration. Such type of problems arise in many practical situations. For instance, if we know the instantaneous velocity of an object at any instant, then there arises a natural question, i.e., can we determine the position of the object at any instant? There are several such practical and theoretical situations where the process of integration is involved. The development of integral calculus arises out of the efforts of solving the problems of the following types:

(a)   the problem of finding a function whenever its derivative is given,
(b)   the problem of finding the area bounded by the graph of a function under certain conditions.

These two problems lead to the two forms of the integrals, e.g., indefinite and definite integrals, which together constitute the ***Integral Calculus***.

There is a connection, known as the ***Fundamental Theorem of Calculus***, between indefinite integral and definite integral which makes the definite integral as a practical tool for science and engineering. The definite integral is also used to solve many interesting problems from various disciplines like economics, finance and probability.

In this Chapter, we shall confine ourselves to the study of indefinite and definite integrals and their elementary properties including some techniques of integration.

7.2 Integration as an Inverse Process of Differentiation

Integration is the inverse process of differentiation. Instead of differentiating a function, we are given the derivative of a function and asked to find its primitive, i.e., the original function. Such a process is called *integration* or *anti differentiation*.

Let us consider the following examples:

We know that
$$\frac{d}{dx}(\sin x) = \cos x \qquad \qquad \text{... (1)}$$

$$\frac{d}{dx}(\frac{x^3}{3}) = x^2 \qquad \qquad \text{... (2)}$$

and
$$\frac{d}{dx}(e^x) = e^x \qquad \qquad \text{... (3)}$$

We observe that in (1), the function $\cos x$ is the derived function of $\sin x$. We say that $\sin x$ is an anti derivative (or an integral) of $\cos x$. Similarly, in (2) and (3), $\frac{x^3}{3}$ and e^x are the anti derivatives (or integrals) of x^2 and e^x, respectively. Again, we note that for any real number C, treated as constant function, its derivative is zero and hence, we can write (1), (2) and (3) as follows :

$$\frac{d}{dx}(\sin x + C) = \cos x,\ \frac{d}{dx}(\frac{x^3}{3} + C) = x^2 \text{ and } \frac{d}{dx}(e^x + C) = e^x$$

Thus, anti derivatives (or integrals) of the above cited functions are not unique. Actually, there exist infinitely many anti derivatives of each of these functions which can be obtained by choosing C arbitrarily from the set of real numbers. For this reason C is customarily referred to as ***arbitrary constant***. In fact, C is the ***parameter*** by varying which one gets different anti derivatives (or integrals) of the given function.

More generally, if there is a function F such that $\frac{d}{dx}F(x) = f(x)$, $\forall x \in$ I (interval), then for any arbitrary real number C, (also called *constant of integration*)

$$\frac{d}{dx}[F(x) + C] = f(x), x \in I$$

Thus, $\{F + C, C \in \mathbf{R}\}$ denotes a family of anti derivatives of f.

Remark Functions with same derivatives differ by a constant. To show this, let g and h be two functions having the same derivatives on an interval I.

Consider the function $f = g - h$ defined by $f(x) = g(x) - h(x)$, $\forall x \in$ I

Then $\dfrac{df}{dx} = f' = g' - h'$ giving $f'(x) = g'(x) - h'(x)$ $\forall x \in$ I

or $f'(x) = 0$, $\forall x \in$ I by hypothesis,

i.e., the rate of change of f with respect to x is zero on I and hence f is constant.

In view of the above remark, it is justified to infer that the family $\{F + C, C \in \mathbf{R}\}$ provides all possible anti derivatives of f.

We introduce a new symbol, namely, $\int f(x)\,dx$ which will represent the entire class of anti derivatives read as the indefinite integral of f with respect to x.

Symbolically, we write $\int f(x)\,dx = F(x) + C$.

Notation Given that $\dfrac{dy}{dx} = f(x)$, we write $y = \int f(x)\,dx$.

For the sake of convenience, we mention below the following symbols/terms/phrases with their meanings as given in the Table (7.1).

Table 7.1

Symbols/Terms/Phrases	Meaning
$\int f(x)\,dx$	Integral of f with respect to x
$f(x)$ in $\int f(x)\,dx$	Integrand
x in $\int f(x)\,dx$	Variable of integration
Integrate	Find the integral
An integral of f	A function F such that $F'(x) = f(x)$
Integration	The process of finding the integral
Constant of Integration	Any real number C, considered as constant function

We already know the formulae for the derivatives of many important functions. From these formulae, we can write down immediately the corresponding formulae (referred to as standard formulae) for the integrals of these functions, as listed below which will be used to find integrals of other functions.

Derivatives

Integrals (Anti derivatives)

(i) $\dfrac{d}{dx}\left(\dfrac{x^{n+1}}{n+1}\right) = x^n$;

$\int x^n\, dx = \dfrac{x^{n+1}}{n+1} + C\, , \, n \neq -1$

Particularly, we note that

$\dfrac{d}{dx}(x) = 1$;

$\int dx = x + C$

(ii) $\dfrac{d}{dx}(\sin x) = \cos x$;

$\int \cos x\, dx = \sin x + C$

(iii) $\dfrac{d}{dx}(-\cos x) = \sin x$;

$\int \sin x\, dx = -\cos x + C$

(iv) $\dfrac{d}{dx}(\tan x) = \sec^2 x$;

$\int \sec^2 x\, dx = \tan x + C$

(v) $\dfrac{d}{dx}(-\cot x) = \operatorname{cosec}^2 x$;

$\int \operatorname{cosec}^2 x\, dx = -\cot x + C$

(vi) $\dfrac{d}{dx}(\sec x) = \sec x \tan x$;

$\int \sec x \tan x\, dx = \sec x + C$

(vii) $\dfrac{d}{dx}(-\operatorname{cosec} x) = \operatorname{cosec} x \cot x$;

$\int \operatorname{cosec} x \cot x\, dx = -\operatorname{cosec} x + C$

(viii) $\dfrac{d}{dx}(\sin^{-1} x) = \dfrac{1}{\sqrt{1-x^2}}$;

$\int \dfrac{dx}{\sqrt{1-x^2}} = \sin^{-1} x + C$

(ix) $\dfrac{d}{dx}(-\cos^{-1} x) = \dfrac{1}{\sqrt{1-x^2}}$;

$\int \dfrac{dx}{\sqrt{1-x^2}} = -\cos^{-1} x + C$

(x) $\dfrac{d}{dx}(\tan^{-1} x) = \dfrac{1}{1+x^2}$;

$\int \dfrac{dx}{1+x^2} = \tan^{-1} x + C$

(xi) $\dfrac{d}{dx}(-\cot^{-1} x) = \dfrac{1}{1+x^2}$;

$\int \dfrac{dx}{1+x^2} = -\cot^{-1} x + C$

(xii) $\dfrac{d}{dx}\left(\sec^{-1}x\right)=\dfrac{1}{x\sqrt{x^2-1}}$; $\qquad$ $\displaystyle\int\dfrac{dx}{x\sqrt{x^2-1}}=\sec^{-1}x+C$

(xiii) $\dfrac{d}{dx}\left(-\csc^{-1}x\right)=\dfrac{1}{x\sqrt{x^2-1}}$; $\qquad$ $\displaystyle\int\dfrac{dx}{x\sqrt{x^2-1}}=-\csc^{-1}x+C$

(xiv) $\dfrac{d}{dx}(e^x)=e^x$; $\qquad$ $\displaystyle\int e^x\,dx=e^x+C$

(xv) $\dfrac{d}{dx}(\log|x|)=\dfrac{1}{x}$; $\qquad$ $\displaystyle\int\dfrac{1}{x}\,dx=\log|x|+C$

(xvi) $\dfrac{d}{dx}\left(\dfrac{a^x}{\log a}\right)=a^x$; $\qquad$ $\displaystyle\int a^x\,dx=\dfrac{a^x}{\log a}+C$

> **Note** In practice, we normally do not mention the interval over which the various functions are defined. However, in any specific problem one has to keep it in mind.

7.2.1 Geometrical interpretation of indefinite integral

Let $f(x)=2x$. Then $\displaystyle\int f(x)\,dx=x^2+C$. For different values of C, we get different integrals. But these integrals are very similar geometrically.

Thus, $y=x^2+C$, where C is arbitrary constant, represents a family of integrals. By assigning different values to C, we get different members of the family. These together constitute the indefinite integral. In this case, each integral represents a parabola with its axis along y-axis.

Clearly, for C = 0, we obtain $y=x^2$, a parabola with its vertex on the origin. The curve $y=x^2+1$ for C = 1 is obtained by shifting the parabola $y=x^2$ one unit along y-axis in positive direction. For C = – 1, $y=x^2-1$ is obtained by shifting the parabola $y=x^2$ one unit along y-axis in the negative direction. Thus, for each positive value of C, each parabola of the family has its vertex on the positive side of the y-axis and for negative values of C, each has its vertex along the negative side of the y-axis. Some of these have been shown in the Fig 7.1.

Let us consider the intersection of all these parabolas by a line $x=a$. In the Fig 7.1, we have taken $a>0$. The same is true when $a<0$. If the line $x=a$ intersects the parabolas $y=x^2$, $y=x^2+1$, $y=x^2+2$, $y=x^2-1$, $y=x^2-2$ at P_0, P_1, P_2, P_{-1}, P_{-2} etc., respectively, then $\dfrac{dy}{dx}$ at these points equals $2a$. This indicates that the tangents to the curves at these points are parallel. Thus, $\displaystyle\int 2x\,dx=x^2+C=F_C(x)$ (say), implies that

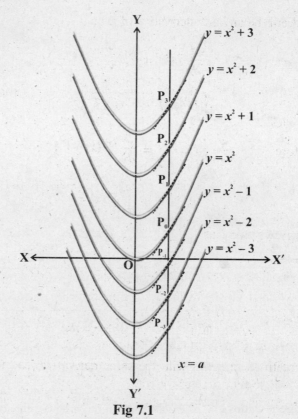

Fig 7.1

the tangents to all the curves $y = F_C(x)$, $C \in \mathbf{R}$, at the points of intersection of the curves by the line $x = a$, $(a \in \mathbf{R})$, are parallel.

Further, the following equation (statement) $\int f(x)\, dx = F(x) + C = y$ (say),

represents a family of curves. The different values of C will correspond to different members of this family and these members can be obtained by shifting any one of the curves parallel to itself. This is the geometrical interpretation of indefinite integral.

7.2.2 Some properties of indefinite integral

In this sub section, we shall derive some properties of indefinite integrals.

(I) The process of differentiation and integration are inverses of each other in the sense of the following results :

$$\frac{d}{dx}\int f(x)\, dx = f(x)$$

and $\qquad\qquad \int f'(x)\, dx = f(x) + C$, where C is any arbitrary constant.

Proof Let F be any anti derivative of f, i.e.,

$$\frac{d}{dx} F(x) = f(x)$$

Then $\int f(x)\, dx = F(x) + C$

Therefore $\frac{d}{dx} \int f(x)\, dx = \frac{d}{dx}(F(x) + C)$

$$= \frac{d}{dx} F(x) = f(x)$$

Similarly, we note that

$$f'(x) = \frac{d}{dx} f(x)$$

and hence $\int f'(x)\, dx = f(x) + C$

where C is arbitrary constant called constant of integration.

(II) Two indefinite integrals with the same derivative lead to the same family of curves and so they are equivalent.

   Proof Let f and g be two functions such that

$$\frac{d}{dx} \int f(x)\, dx = \frac{d}{dx} \int g(x)\, dx$$

or $\frac{d}{dx}\left[\int f(x)\, dx - \int g(x)\, dx\right] = 0$

Hence $\int f(x)\, dx - \int g(x)\, dx = $ C, where C is any real number   (Why?)

or $\int f(x)\, dx = \int g(x)\, dx + C$

So the families of curves $\left\{\int f(x)\, dx + C_1, C_1 \in R\right\}$

and $\left\{\int g(x)\, dx + C_2, C_2 \in R\right\}$ are identical.

Hence, in this sense, $\int f(x)\, dx$ and $\int g(x)\, dx$ are equivalent.

> **☞ Note** The equivalence of the families $\left\{ \int f(x)\,dx + C_1, C_1 \in \mathbf{R} \right\}$ and $\left\{ \int g(x)\,dx + C_2, C_2 \in \mathbf{R} \right\}$ is customarily expressed by writing $\int f(x)\,dx = \int g(x)\,dx$, without mentioning the parameter.

(III)　$\int [f(x) + g(x)]\,dx = \int f(x)\,dx + \int g(x)\,dx$

　　Proof　By Property (I), we have

$$\frac{d}{dx}\left[\int [f(x) + g(x)]\,dx \right] = f(x) + g(x) \qquad \ldots (1)$$

　　On the otherhand, we find that

$$\frac{d}{dx}\left[\int f(x)\,dx + \int g(x)\,dx \right] = \frac{d}{dx}\int f(x)\,dx + \frac{d}{dx}\int g(x)\,dx$$

$$= f(x) + g(x) \qquad \ldots (2)$$

　　Thus, in view of Property (II), it follows by (1) and (2) that

$$\int (f(x) + g(x))\,dx = \int f(x)\,dx + \int g(x)\,dx.$$

(IV)　For any real number k, $\int k\,f(x)\,dx = k \int f(x)\,dx$

　　Proof By the Property (I), $\dfrac{d}{dx}\int k\,f(x)\,dx = k\,f(x)$.

　　Also　$\dfrac{d}{dx}\left[k \int f(x)\,dx \right] = k\dfrac{d}{dx}\int f(x)\,dx = k\,f(x)$

　　Therefore, using the Property (II), we have $\int k\,f(x)\,dx = k \int f(x)\,dx$.

(V)　Properties (III) and (IV) can be generalised to a finite number of functions $f_1, f_2, \ldots, f_n$ and the real numbers, $k_1, k_2, \ldots, k_n$ giving

$$\int [k_1 f_1(x) + k_2 f_2(x) + \ldots + k_n f_n(x)]\,dx$$

$$= k_1 \int f_1(x)\,dx + k_2 \int f_2(x)\,dx + \ldots + k_n \int f_n(x)\,dx.$$

　　To find an anti derivative of a given function, we search intuitively for a function whose derivative is the given function. The search for the requisite function for finding an anti derivative is known as integration by the method of inspection. We illustrate it through some examples.

Example 1 Write an anti derivative for each of the following functions using the method of inspection:

(i) $\cos 2x$ (ii) $3x^2 + 4x^3$ (iii) $\dfrac{1}{x}, x \neq 0$

Solution

(i) We look for a function whose derivative is $\cos 2x$. Recall that

$$\frac{d}{dx} \sin 2x = 2 \cos 2x$$

or $\cos 2x = \dfrac{1}{2} \dfrac{d}{dx} (\sin 2x) = \dfrac{d}{dx}\left(\dfrac{1}{2} \sin 2x\right)$

Therefore, an anti derivative of $\cos 2x$ is $\dfrac{1}{2} \sin 2x$.

(ii) We look for a function whose derivative is $3x^2 + 4x^3$. Note that

$$\frac{d}{dx}\left(x^3 + x^4\right) = 3x^2 + 4x^3.$$

Therefore, an anti derivative of $3x^2 + 4x^3$ is $x^3 + x^4$.

(iii) We know that

$$\frac{d}{dx}(\log x) = \frac{1}{x}, x > 0 \text{ and } \frac{d}{dx}[\log(-x)] = \frac{1}{-x}(-1) = \frac{1}{x}; x < 0$$

Combining above, we get $\dfrac{d}{dx}\left(\log|x|\right) = \dfrac{1}{x}, x \neq 0$

Therefore, $\displaystyle\int \frac{1}{x} dx = \log|x|$ is one of the anti derivatives of $\dfrac{1}{x}$.

Example 2 Find the following integrals:

(i) $\displaystyle\int \frac{x^3 - 1}{x^2} dx$ (ii) $\displaystyle\int (x^{\frac{2}{3}} + 1)\, dx$ (iii) $\displaystyle\int (x^{\frac{3}{2}} + 2 e^x - \frac{1}{x})\, dx$

Solution

(i) We have

$$\int \frac{x^3 - 1}{x^2} dx = \int x\, dx - \int x^{-2}\, dx \qquad \text{(by Property V)}$$

$$= \left(\frac{x^{1+1}}{1+1} + C_1 \right) - \left(\frac{x^{-2+1}}{-2+1} + C_2 \right); \ C_1, C_2 \text{ are constants of integration}$$

$$= \frac{x^2}{2} + C_1 - \frac{x^{-1}}{-1} - C_2 = \frac{x^2}{2} + \frac{1}{x} + C_1 - C_2$$

$$= \frac{x^2}{2} + \frac{1}{x} + C, \text{ where } C = C_1 - C_2 \text{ is another constant of integration.}$$

Note From now onwards, we shall write only one constant of integration in the final answer.

(ii) We have

$$\int (x^{\frac{2}{3}} + 1) \, dx = \int x^{\frac{2}{3}} \, dx + \int dx$$

$$= \frac{x^{\frac{2}{3}+1}}{\frac{2}{3}+1} + x + C = \frac{3}{5} x^{\frac{5}{3}} + x + C$$

(iii) We have $\int (x^{\frac{3}{2}} + 2 \, e^x - \frac{1}{x}) \, dx = \int x^{\frac{3}{2}} \, dx + \int 2 \, e^x \, dx - \int \frac{1}{x} \, dx$

$$= \frac{x^{\frac{3}{2}+1}}{\frac{3}{2}+1} + 2 \, e^x - \log |x| + C$$

$$= \frac{2}{5} x^{\frac{5}{2}} + 2 \, e^x - \log |x| + C$$

Example 3 Find the following integrals:

(i) $\int (\sin x + \cos x) \, dx$ (ii) $\int \operatorname{cosec} x \, (\operatorname{cosec} x + \cot x) \, dx$

(iii) $\int \frac{1 - \sin x}{\cos^2 x} \, dx$

Solution

(i) We have

$$\int (\sin x + \cos x) \, dx = \int \sin x \, dx + \int \cos x \, dx$$

$$= -\cos x + \sin x + C$$

(ii) We have

$$\int (\operatorname{cosec} x \,(\operatorname{cosec} x + \cot x))\, dx = \int \operatorname{cosec}^2 x \, dx + \int \operatorname{cosec} x \cot x \, dx$$

$$= -\cot x - \operatorname{cosec} x + C$$

(iii) We have

$$\int \frac{1 - \sin x}{\cos^2 x}\, dx = \int \frac{1}{\cos^2 x}\, dx - \int \frac{\sin x}{\cos^2 x}\, dx$$

$$= \int \sec^2 x \, dx - \int \tan x \sec x \, dx$$

$$= \tan x - \sec x + C$$

Example 4 Find the anti derivative F of f defined by $f(x) = 4x^3 - 6$, where F $(0) = 3$

Solution One anti derivative of $f(x)$ is $x^4 - 6x$ since

$$\frac{d}{dx}(x^4 - 6x) = 4x^3 - 6$$

Therefore, the anti derivative F is given by

$$F(x) = x^4 - 6x + C, \text{ where C is constant.}$$

Given that   F$(0) = 3$, which gives,

$$3 = 0 - 6 \times 0 + C \quad \text{or} \quad C = 3$$

Hence, the required anti derivative is the unique function F defined by

$$F(x) = x^4 - 6x + 3.$$

Remarks

(i) We see that if F is an anti derivative of f, then so is F + C, where C is any constant. Thus, if we know one anti derivative F of a function f, we can write down an infinite number of anti derivatives of f by adding any constant to F expressed by F$(x) +$ C, C $\in$ **R**. In applications, it is often necessary to satisfy an additional condition which then determines a specific value of C giving unique anti derivative of the given function.

(ii) Sometimes, F is not expressible in terms of elementary functions viz., polynomial, logarithmic, exponential, trigonometric functions and their inverses etc. We are therefore blocked for finding $\int f(x)\, dx$. For example, it is not possible to find

$\int e^{-x^2}\, dx$ by inspection since we can not find a function whose derivative is e^{-x^2}

(iii) When the variable of integration is denoted by a variable other than x, the integral formulae are modified accordingly. For instance

$$\int y^4 \, dy = \frac{y^{4+1}}{4+1} + C = \frac{1}{5} y^5 + C$$

7.2.3 Comparison between differentiation and integration

1. Both are operations on functions.
2. Both satisfy the property of linearity, i.e.,

(i) $\dfrac{d}{dx}\left[k_1 \, f_1 \, (x) + k_2 \, f_2 \, (x)\right] = k_1 \, \dfrac{d}{dx} \, f_1 \, (x) + k_2 \, \dfrac{d}{dx} \, f_2 \, (x)$

(ii) $\displaystyle\int \left[k_1 \, f_1 \, (x) + k_2 \, f_2 \, (x)\right] dx = k_1 \int f_1 \, (x) \, dx + k_2 \int f_2 \, (x) \, dx$

Here k_1 and k_2 are constants.

3. We have already seen that all functions are not differentiable. Similarly, all functions are not integrable. We will learn more about nondifferentiable functions and nonintegrable functions in higher classes.

4. The derivative of a function, when it exists, is a unique function. The integral of a function is not so. However, they are unique upto an additive constant, i.e., any two integrals of a function differ by a constant.

5. When a polynomial function P is differentiated, the result is a polynomial whose degree is 1 less than the degree of P. When a polynomial function P is integrated, the result is a polynomial whose degree is 1 more than that of P.

6. We can speak of the derivative at a point. We never speak of the integral at a point, we speak of the integral of a function over an interval on which the integral is defined as will be seen in Section 7.7.

7. The derivative of a function has a geometrical meaning, namely, the slope of the tangent to the corresponding curve at a point. Similarly, the indefinite integral of a function represents geometrically, a family of curves placed parallel to each other having parallel tangents at the points of intersection of the curves of the family with the lines orthogonal (perpendicular) to the axis representing the variable of integration.

8. The derivative is used for finding some physical quantities like the velocity of a moving particle, when the distance traversed at any time t is known. Similarly, the integral is used in calculating the distance traversed when the velocity at time t is known.

9. Differentiation is a process involving limits. **So is integration,** as will be seen in Section 7.7.

10. The process of differentiation and integration are inverses of each other as discussed in Section 7.2.2 (i).

EXERCISE 7.1

Find an anti derivative (or integral) of the following functions by the method of inspection.

1. $\sin 2x$ 2. $\cos 3x$ 3. e^{2x}
4. $(ax + b)^2$ 5. $\sin 2x - 4\,e^{3x}$

Find the following integrals in Exercises 6 to 20:

6. $\int (4\,e^{3x} + 1)\,dx$ 7. $\int x^2 (1 - \dfrac{1}{x^2})\,dx$ 8. $\int (ax^2 + bx + c)\,dx$

9. $\int (2x^2 + e^x)\,dx$ 10. $\int \left(\sqrt{x} - \dfrac{1}{\sqrt{x}}\right)^2 dx$ 11. $\int \dfrac{x^3 + 5x^2 - 4}{x^2}\,dx$

12. $\int \dfrac{x^3 + 3x + 4}{\sqrt{x}}\,dx$ 13. $\int \dfrac{x^3 - x^2 + x - 1}{x - 1}\,dx$ 14. $\int (1 - x)\sqrt{x}\,dx$

15. $\int \sqrt{x}(3x^2 + 2x + 3)\,dx$ 16. $\int (2x - 3\cos x + e^x)\,dx$

17. $\int (2x^2 - 3\sin x + 5\sqrt{x})\,dx$ 18. $\int \sec x\,(\sec x + \tan x)\,dx$

19. $\int \dfrac{\sec^2 x}{\csc^2 x}\,dx$ 20. $\int \dfrac{2 - 3\sin x}{\cos^2 x}\,dx.$

Choose the correct answer in Exercises 21 and 22.

21. The anti derivative of $\left(\sqrt{x} + \dfrac{1}{\sqrt{x}}\right)$ equals

(A) $\dfrac{1}{3}x^{\frac{1}{3}} + 2x^{\frac{1}{2}} + C$ (B) $\dfrac{2}{3}x^{\frac{2}{3}} + \dfrac{1}{2}x^2 + C$

(C) $\dfrac{2}{3}x^{\frac{3}{2}} + 2x^{\frac{1}{2}} + C$ (D) $\dfrac{3}{2}x^{\frac{3}{2}} + \dfrac{1}{2}x^{\frac{1}{2}} + C$

22. If $\dfrac{d}{dx} f(x) = 4x^3 - \dfrac{3}{x^4}$ such that $f(2) = 0$. Then $f(x)$ is

(A) $x^4 + \dfrac{1}{x^3} - \dfrac{129}{8}$ (B) $x^3 + \dfrac{1}{x^4} + \dfrac{129}{8}$

(C) $x^4 + \dfrac{1}{x^3} + \dfrac{129}{8}$ (D) $x^3 + \dfrac{1}{x^4} - \dfrac{129}{8}$

7.3 Methods of Integration

In previous section, we discussed integrals of those functions which were readily obtainable from derivatives of some functions. It was based on inspection, i.e., on the search of a function F whose derivative is f which led us to the integral of f. However, this method, which depends on inspection, is not very suitable for many functions. Hence, we need to develop additional techniques or methods for finding the integrals by reducing them into standard forms. Prominent among them are methods based on:

1. Integration by Substitution
2. Integration using Partial Fractions
3. Integration by Parts

7.3.1 Integration by substitution

In this section, we consider the method of integration by substitution.

The given integral $\int f(x)\, dx$ can be transformed into another form by changing the independent variable x to t by substituting $x = g(t)$.

Consider $$I = \int f(x)\, dx$$

Put $x = g(t)$ so that $\dfrac{dx}{dt} = g'(t)$.

We write $$dx = g'(t)\, dt$$

Thus $$I = \int f(x)\, dx = \int f(g(t))\, g'(t)\, dt$$

This change of variable formula is one of the important tools available to us in the name of integration by substitution. It is often important to guess what will be the useful substitution. Usually, we make a substitution for a function whose derivative also occurs in the integrand as illustrated in the following examples.

Example 5 Integrate the following functions w.r.t. x:

(i) $\sin mx$

(ii) $2x \sin (x^2 + 1)$

(iii) $\dfrac{\tan^4 \sqrt{x} \sec^2 \sqrt{x}}{\sqrt{x}}$

(iv) $\dfrac{\sin (\tan^{-1} x)}{1 + x^2}$

Solution

(i)   We know that derivative of mx is m. Thus, we make the substitution $mx = t$ so that $m\, dx = dt$.

Therefore, $$\int \sin mx \, dx = \frac{1}{m} \int \sin t \, dt = -\frac{1}{m} \cos t + C = -\frac{1}{m} \cos mx + C$$

(ii) Derivative of $x^2 + 1$ is $2x$. Thus, we use the substitution $x^2 + 1 = t$ so that $2x \, dx = dt$.

Therefore, $\int 2x \sin (x^2 + 1) \, dx = \int \sin t \, dt \ = \ - \cos t + C \ = - \cos (x^2 + 1) + C$

(iii) Derivative of $\sqrt{x}$ is $\dfrac{1}{2} x^{-\frac{1}{2}} = \dfrac{1}{2\sqrt{x}}$. Thus, we use the substitution

$\sqrt{x} = t$ so that $\dfrac{1}{2\sqrt{x}} dx = dt$ giving $dx = 2t \, dt$.

Thus, $\displaystyle\int \frac{\tan^4 \sqrt{x} \sec^2 \sqrt{x}}{\sqrt{x}} \, dx = \int \frac{2t \tan^4 t \sec^2 t \, dt}{t} \ = \ 2 \int \tan^4 t \, \sec^2 t \, dt$

Again, we make another substitution $\tan t = u$ so that $\sec^2 t \, dt = du$

Therefore, $2 \displaystyle\int \tan^4 t \sec^2 t \, dt = 2 \int u^4 \, du \ = \ 2 \frac{u^5}{5} + C$

$$= \ \frac{2}{5} \tan^5 t + C \ \text{(since } u = \tan t\text{)}$$

$$= \ \frac{2}{5} \tan^5 \sqrt{x} + C \ \text{(since } t = \sqrt{x}\text{)}$$

Hence, $\displaystyle\int \frac{\tan^4 \sqrt{x} \sec^2 \sqrt{x}}{\sqrt{x}} \, dx \ = \ \frac{2}{5} \tan^5 \sqrt{x} + C$

Alternatively, make the substitution $\tan \sqrt{x} = t$

(iv) Derivative of $\tan^{-1} x = \dfrac{1}{1+x^2}$. Thus, we use the substitution

$\tan^{-1} x = t$ so that $\dfrac{dx}{1+x^2} = dt$.

Therefore , $\displaystyle\int \frac{\sin (\tan^{-1} x)}{1 + x^2} \, dx = \int \sin t \, dt \ = \ - \cos t + C = - \cos (\tan^{-1} x) + C$

Now, we discuss some important integrals involving trigonometric functions and their standard integrals using substitution technique. These will be used later without reference.

(i) $\displaystyle\int \tan x \, dx = \log|\sec x| + C$

We have

$$\int \tan x \, dx = \int \frac{\sin x}{\cos x} \, dx$$

Put $\cos x = t$ so that $\sin x \, dx = - \, dt$

Then $$\int \tan x \, dx = -\int \frac{dt}{t} = -\log|t| + C = -\log|\cos x| + C$$

or $$\int \tan x \, dx = \log|\sec x| + C$$

(ii) $\int \cot x \, dx = \log|\sin x| + C$

We have $\int \cot x \, dx = \int \dfrac{\cos x}{\sin x} \, dx$

Put $\sin x = t$ so that $\cos x \, dx = dt$

Then $$\int \cot x \, dx = \int \frac{dt}{t} = \log|t| + C = \log|\sin x| + C$$

(iii) $\int \sec x \, dx = \log|\sec x + \tan x| + C$

We have

$$\int \sec x \, dx = \int \frac{\sec x \, (\sec x + \tan x)}{\sec x + \tan x} \, dx$$

Put $\sec x + \tan x = t$ so that $\sec x \, (\tan x + \sec x) \, dx = dt$

Therefore, $\int \sec x \, dx = \int \dfrac{dt}{t} = \log|t| + C = \log|\sec x + \tan x| + C$

(iv) $\int \operatorname{cosec} x \, dx = \log|\operatorname{cosec} x - \cot x| + C$

We have

$$\int \operatorname{cosec} x \, dx = \int \frac{\operatorname{cosec} x \, (\operatorname{cosec} x + \cot x)}{(\operatorname{cosec} x + \cot x)} \, dx$$

Put $\operatorname{cosec} x + \cot x = t$ so that $-\operatorname{cosec} x \, (\operatorname{cosec} x + \cot x) \, dx = dt$

So $\int \operatorname{cosec} x \, dx = -\int \dfrac{dt}{t} = -\log|t| = -\log|\operatorname{cosec} x + \cot x| + C$

$$= -\log\left|\frac{\operatorname{cosec}^2 x - \cot^2 x}{\operatorname{cosec} x - \cot x}\right| + C$$

$$= \log|\operatorname{cosec} x - \cot x| + C$$

Example 6 Find the following integrals:

(i) $\displaystyle\int \sin^3 x \cos^2 x \, dx$ (ii) $\displaystyle\int \frac{\sin x}{\sin (x + a)} \, dx$ (iii) $\displaystyle\int \frac{1}{1 + \tan x} \, dx$

Solution

(i) We have

$$\int \sin^3 x \cos^2 x \, dx = \int \sin^2 x \cos^2 x \, (\sin x) \, dx$$

$$= \int (1 - \cos^2 x) \cos^2 x \, (\sin x) \, dx$$

Put $t = \cos x$ so that $dt = -\sin x \, dx$

Therefore, $\int \sin^2 x \cos^2 x \, (\sin x) \, dx = -\int (1 - t^2) \, t^2 \, dt$

$$= -\int (t^2 - t^4) \, dt = -\left(\frac{t^3}{3} - \frac{t^5}{5} \right) + C$$

$$= -\frac{1}{3} \cos^3 x + \frac{1}{5} \cos^5 x + C$$

(ii) Put $x + a = t$. Then $dx = dt$. Therefore

$$\int \frac{\sin x}{\sin (x+a)} \, dx = \int \frac{\sin (t-a)}{\sin t} \, dt$$

$$= \int \frac{\sin t \cos a - \cos t \sin a}{\sin t} \, dt$$

$$= \cos a \int dt - \sin a \int \cot t \, dt$$

$$= (\cos a) \, t - (\sin a) \left[\log |\sin t| + C_1 \right]$$

$$= (\cos a) \, (x+a) - (\sin a) \left[\log |\sin (x+a)| + C_1 \right]$$

$$= x \cos a + a \cos a - (\sin a) \log |\sin (x+a)| - C_1 \sin a$$

Hence, $\int \dfrac{\sin x}{\sin (x+a)} \, dx = x \cos a - \sin a \log |\sin (x+a)| + C,$

where, $C = -C_1 \sin a + a \cos a$, is another arbitrary constant.

(iii) $\int \dfrac{dx}{1 + \tan x} = \int \dfrac{\cos x \, dx}{\cos x + \sin x}$

$$= \frac{1}{2} \int \frac{(\cos x + \sin x + \cos x - \sin x) \, dx}{\cos x + \sin x}$$

$$= \frac{1}{2} \int dx + \frac{1}{2} \int \frac{\cos x - \sin x}{\cos x + \sin x} dx$$

$$= \frac{x}{2} + \frac{C_1}{2} + \frac{1}{2} \int \frac{\cos x - \sin x}{\cos x + \sin x} dx \qquad \ldots (1)$$

Now, consider $I = \int \frac{\cos x - \sin x}{\cos x + \sin x} dx$

Put $\cos x + \sin x = t$ so that $(\cos x - \sin x) \, dx = dt$

Therefore $I = \int \frac{dt}{t} = \log |t| + C_2 = \log |\cos x + \sin x| + C_2$

Putting it in (1), we get

$$\int \frac{dx}{1 + \tan x} = \frac{x}{2} + \frac{C_1}{2} + \frac{1}{2} \log |\cos x + \sin x| + \frac{C_2}{2}$$

$$= \frac{x}{2} + \frac{1}{2} \log |\cos x + \sin x| + \frac{C_1}{2} + \frac{C_2}{2}$$

$$= \frac{x}{2} + \frac{1}{2} \log |\cos x + \sin x| + C, \left(C = \frac{C_1}{2} + \frac{C_2}{2} \right)$$

EXERCISE 7.2

Integrate the functions in Exercises 1 to 37:

1. $\dfrac{2x}{1 + x^2}$

2. $\dfrac{(\log x)^2}{x}$

3. $\dfrac{1}{x + x \log x}$

4. $\sin x \sin (\cos x)$

5. $\sin (ax + b) \cos (ax + b)$

6. $\sqrt{ax + b}$

7. $x \sqrt{x + 2}$

8. $x \sqrt{1 + 2x^2}$

9. $(4x + 2) \sqrt{x^2 + x + 1}$

10. $\dfrac{1}{x - \sqrt{x}}$

11. $\dfrac{x}{\sqrt{x + 4}}, x > 0$

12. $(x^3 - 1)^{\frac{1}{3}} x^5$

13. $\dfrac{x^2}{(2 + 3x^3)^3}$

14. $\dfrac{1}{x (\log x)^m}, x > 0, m \neq 1$

15. $\dfrac{x}{9 - 4x^2}$

16. $e^{2x + 3}$

17. $\dfrac{x}{e^{x^2}}$

18. $\dfrac{e^{\tan^{-1}x}}{1+x^2}$

19. $\dfrac{e^{2x}-1}{e^{2x}+1}$

20. $\dfrac{e^{2x}-e^{-2x}}{e^{2x}+e^{-2x}}$

21. $\tan^2(2x-3)$

22. $\sec^2(7-4x)$

23. $\dfrac{\sin^{-1}x}{\sqrt{1-x^2}}$

24. $\dfrac{2\cos x - 3\sin x}{6\cos x + 4\sin x}$

25. $\dfrac{1}{\cos^2 x\,(1-\tan x)^2}$

26. $\dfrac{\cos\sqrt{x}}{\sqrt{x}}$

27. $\sqrt{\sin 2x}\,\cos 2x$

28. $\dfrac{\cos x}{\sqrt{1+\sin x}}$

29. $\cot x\,\log\sin x$

30. $\dfrac{\sin x}{1+\cos x}$

31. $\dfrac{\sin x}{(1+\cos x)^2}$

32. $\dfrac{1}{1+\cot x}$

33. $\dfrac{1}{1-\tan x}$

34. $\dfrac{\sqrt{\tan x}}{\sin x\cos x}$

35. $\dfrac{(1+\log x)^2}{x}$

36. $\dfrac{(x+1)(x+\log x)^2}{x}$

37. $\dfrac{x^3\sin\left(\tan^{-1}x^4\right)}{1+x^8}$

Choose the correct answer in Exercises 38 and 39.

38. $\displaystyle\int\dfrac{10x^9+10^x\log_e 10\ dx}{x^{10}+10^x}$ equals

    (A) $10^x - x^{10} + C$ (B) $10^x + x^{10} + C$

    (C) $(10^x - x^{10})^{-1} + C$ (D) $\log(10^x + x^{10}) + C$

39. $\displaystyle\int\dfrac{dx}{\sin^2 x\cos^2 x}$ equals

    (A) $\tan x + \cot x + C$ (B) $\tan x - \cot x + C$

    (C) $\tan x\cot x + C$ (D) $\tan x - \cot 2x + C$

7.3.2 *Integration using trigonometric identities*

When the integrand involves some trigonometric functions, we use some known identities to find the integral as illustrated through the following example.

Example 7 Find (i) $\displaystyle\int\cos^2 x\,dx$ (ii) $\displaystyle\int\sin 2x\cos 3x\,dx$ (iii) $\displaystyle\int\sin^3 x\,dx$

Solution

(i)   Recall the identity $\cos 2x = 2 \cos^2 x - 1$, which gives

$$\cos^2 x = \frac{1 + \cos 2x}{2}$$

Therefore, $\int \cos^2 x \, dx = \frac{1}{2} \int (1 + \cos 2x) \, dx = \frac{1}{2} \int dx + \frac{1}{2} \int \cos 2x \, dx$

$$= \frac{x}{2} + \frac{1}{4} \sin 2x + C$$

(ii)   Recall the identity $\sin x \cos y = \frac{1}{2} [\sin (x + y) + \sin (x - y)]$ (Why?)

Then $\int \sin 2x \cos 3x \, dx = \frac{1}{2} \left[\int \sin 5x \, dx - \int \sin x \, dx \right]$

$$= \frac{1}{2} \left[-\frac{1}{5} \cos 5x + \cos x \right] + C$$

$$= -\frac{1}{10} \cos 5x + \frac{1}{2} \cos x + C$$

(iii)   From the identity $\sin 3x = 3 \sin x - 4 \sin^3 x$, we find that

$$\sin^3 x = \frac{3 \sin x - \sin 3x}{4}$$

Therefore, $\int \sin^3 x \, dx = \frac{3}{4} \int \sin x \, dx - \frac{1}{4} \int \sin 3x \, dx$

$$= -\frac{3}{4} \cos x + \frac{1}{12} \cos 3x + C$$

Alternatively, $\int \sin^3 x \, dx = \int \sin^2 x \sin x \, dx = \int (1 - \cos^2 x) \sin x \, dx$

Put $\cos x = t$ so that $- \sin x \, dx = dt$

Therefore, $\int \sin^3 x \, dx = -\int (1 - t^2) \, dt = -\int dt + \int t^2 \, dt = -t + \frac{t^3}{3} + C$

$$= - \cos x + \frac{1}{3} \cos^3 x + C$$

Remark It can be shown using trigonometric identities that both answers are equivalent

EXERCISE 7.3

Find the integrals of the functions in Exercises 1 to 22:

1. $\sin^2 (2x + 5)$
2. $\sin 3x \cos 4x$
3. $\cos 2x \cos 4x \cos 6x$

4. $\sin^3 (2x + 1)$
5. $\sin^3 x \cos^3 x$
6. $\sin x \sin 2x \sin 3x$

7. $\sin 4x \sin 8x$
8. $\dfrac{1 - \cos x}{1 + \cos x}$
9. $\dfrac{\cos x}{1 + \cos x}$

10. $\sin^4 x$
11. $\cos^4 2x$
12. $\dfrac{\sin^2 x}{1 + \cos x}$

13. $\dfrac{\cos 2x - \cos 2\alpha}{\cos x - \cos \alpha}$
14. $\dfrac{\cos x - \sin x}{1 + \sin 2x}$
15. $\tan^3 2x \sec 2x$

16. $\tan^4 x$
17. $\dfrac{\sin^3 x + \cos^3 x}{\sin^2 x \cos^2 x}$
18. $\dfrac{\cos 2x + 2\sin^2 x}{\cos^2 x}$

19. $\dfrac{1}{\sin x \cos^3 x}$
20. $\dfrac{\cos 2x}{\left(\cos x + \sin x\right)^2}$
21. $\sin^{-1} (\cos x)$

22. $\dfrac{1}{\cos (x - a) \cos (x - b)}$

Choose the correct answer in Exercises 23 and 24.

23. $\displaystyle\int \dfrac{\sin^2 x - \cos^2 x}{\sin^2 x \cos^2 x} dx$ is equal to

(A) $\tan x + \cot x + C$ (B) $\tan x + \csc x + C$

(C) $-\tan x + \cot x + C$ (D) $\tan x + \sec x + C$

24. $\displaystyle\int \dfrac{e^x (1 + x)}{\cos^2 (e^x x)} dx$ equals

(A) $-\cot (e x^x) + C$ (B) $\tan (x e^x) + C$

(C) $\tan (e^x) + C$ (D) $\cot (e^x) + C$

7.4 Integrals of Some Particular Functions

In this section, we mention below some important formulae of integrals and apply them for integrating many other related standard integrals:

(1) $\displaystyle\int \dfrac{dx}{x^2 - a^2} = \dfrac{1}{2a} \log \left| \dfrac{x - a}{x + a} \right| + C$

(2) $\int \dfrac{dx}{a^2 - x^2} = \dfrac{1}{2a} \log \left| \dfrac{a+x}{a-x} \right| + C$

(3) $\int \dfrac{dx}{x^2 + a^2} = \dfrac{1}{a} \tan^{-1} \dfrac{x}{a} + C$

(4) $\int \dfrac{dx}{\sqrt{x^2 - a^2}} = \log \left| x + \sqrt{x^2 - a^2} \right| + C$

(5) $\int \dfrac{dx}{\sqrt{a^2 - x^2}} = \sin^{-1} \dfrac{x}{a} + C$

(6) $\int \dfrac{dx}{\sqrt{x^2 + a^2}} = \log \left| x + \sqrt{x^2 + a^2} \right| + C$

We now prove the above results:

(1) We have $\dfrac{1}{x^2 - a^2} = \dfrac{1}{(x-a)(x+a)}$

$$= \dfrac{1}{2a} \left[\dfrac{(x+a)-(x-a)}{(x-a)(x+a)} \right] = \dfrac{1}{2a} \left[\dfrac{1}{x-a} - \dfrac{1}{x+a} \right]$$

Therefore, $\int \dfrac{dx}{x^2 - a^2} = \dfrac{1}{2a} \left[\int \dfrac{dx}{x-a} - \int \dfrac{dx}{x+a} \right]$

$$= \dfrac{1}{2a} \left[\log | (x-a) | - \log | (x+a) | \right] + C$$

$$= \dfrac{1}{2a} \log \left| \dfrac{x-a}{x+a} \right| + C$$

(2) In view of (1) above, we have

$$\dfrac{1}{a^2 - x^2} = \dfrac{1}{2a} \left[\dfrac{(a+x)+(a-x)}{(a+x)(a-x)} \right] = \dfrac{1}{2a} \left[\dfrac{1}{a-x} + \dfrac{1}{a+x} \right]$$

Therefore, $\displaystyle\int \frac{dx}{a^2 - x^2} = \frac{1}{2a}\left[\int \frac{dx}{a-x} + \int \frac{dx}{a+x}\right]$

$$= \frac{1}{2a}\left[-\log|a-x| + \log|a+x|\right] + C$$

$$= \frac{1}{2a}\log\left|\frac{a+x}{a-x}\right| + C$$

Note The technique used in (1) will be explained in Section 7.5.

(3) Put $x = a \tan\theta$. Then $dx = a \sec^2\theta \, d\theta$.

Therefore, $\displaystyle\int \frac{dx}{x^2 + a^2} = \int \frac{a \sec^2\theta \, d\theta}{a^2 \tan^2\theta + a^2}$

$$= \frac{1}{a}\int d\theta = \frac{1}{a}\theta + C = \frac{1}{a}\tan^{-1}\frac{x}{a} + C$$

(4) Let $x = a \sec\theta$. Then $dx = a \sec\theta \tan\theta \, d\theta$.

Therefore, $\displaystyle\int \frac{dx}{\sqrt{x^2 - a^2}} = \int \frac{a \sec\theta \tan\theta \, d\theta}{\sqrt{a^2 \sec^2\theta - a^2}}$

$$= \int \sec\theta \, d\theta = \log|\sec\theta + \tan\theta| + C_1$$

$$= \log\left|\frac{x}{a} + \sqrt{\frac{x^2}{a^2} - 1}\right| + C_1$$

$$= \log\left|x + \sqrt{x^2 - a^2}\right| - \log|a| + C_1$$

$$= \log\left|x + \sqrt{x^2 - a^2}\right| + C, \text{ where } C = C_1 - \log|a|$$

(5) Let $x = a \sin\theta$. Then $dx = a \cos\theta \, d\theta$.

Therefore, $\displaystyle\int \frac{dx}{\sqrt{a^2 - x^2}} = \int \frac{a \cos\theta \, d\theta}{\sqrt{a^2 - a^2 \sin^2\theta}}$

$$= \int d\theta = \theta + C = \sin^{-1}\frac{x}{a} + C$$

(6) Let $x = a \tan\theta$. Then $dx = a \sec^2\theta \, d\theta$.

Therefore, $\displaystyle\int \frac{dx}{\sqrt{x^2 + a^2}} = \int \frac{a \sec^2\theta \, d\theta}{\sqrt{a^2 \tan^2\theta + a^2}}$

$$= \int \sec\theta \, d\theta = \log|(\sec\theta + \tan\theta)| + C_1$$

$$= \log \left| \frac{x}{a} + \sqrt{\frac{x^2}{a^2} + 1} \right| + C_1$$

$$= \log \left| x + \sqrt{x^2 + a^2} \right| - \log |a| + C_1$$

$$= \log \left| x + \sqrt{x^2 + a^2} \right| + C, \text{ where } C = C_1 - \log |a|$$

Applying these standard formulae, we now obtain some more formulae which are useful from applications point of view and can be applied directly to evaluate other integrals.

(7) To find the integral $\int \dfrac{dx}{ax^2 + bx + c}$, we write

$$ax^2 + bx + c = a \left[x^2 + \frac{b}{a} x + \frac{c}{a} \right] = a \left[\left(x + \frac{b}{2a} \right)^2 + \left(\frac{c}{a} - \frac{b^2}{4a^2} \right) \right]$$

Now, put $x + \dfrac{b}{2a} = t$ so that $dx = dt$ and writing $\dfrac{c}{a} - \dfrac{b^2}{4a^2} = \pm k^2$. We find the

integral reduced to the form $\dfrac{1}{a} \int \dfrac{dt}{t^2 \pm k^2}$ depending upon the sign of $\left(\dfrac{c}{a} - \dfrac{b^2}{4a^2} \right)$

and hence can be evaluated.

(8) To find the integral of the type $\int \dfrac{dx}{\sqrt{ax^2 + bx + c}}$, proceeding as in (7), we

obtain the integral using the standard formulae.

(9) To find the integral of the type $\int \dfrac{px + q}{ax^2 + bx + c} dx$, where p, q, a, b, c are

constants, we are to find real numbers A, B such that

$$px + q = A \frac{d}{dx} (ax^2 + bx + c) + B = A (2ax + b) + B$$

To determine A and B, we equate from both sides the coefficients of x and the constant terms. A and B are thus obtained and hence the integral is reduced to one of the known forms.

(10) **For the evaluation of the integral of the type** $\int \dfrac{(px+q)\,dx}{\sqrt{ax^2+bx+c}}$, we proceed

as in (9) and transform the integral into known standard forms.

Let us illustrate the above methods by some examples.

Example 8 Find the following integrals:

(i) $\int \dfrac{dx}{x^2-16}$ (ii) $\int \dfrac{dx}{\sqrt{2x-x^2}}$

Solution

(i) We have $\int \dfrac{dx}{x^2-16} = \int \dfrac{dx}{x^2-4^2} = \dfrac{1}{8}\log\left|\dfrac{x-4}{x+4}\right| + C$ [by 7.4 (1)]

(ii) $\int \dfrac{dx}{\sqrt{2x-x^2}} = \int \dfrac{dx}{\sqrt{1-(x-1)^2}}$

Put $x-1 = t$. Then $dx = dt$.

Therefore, $\int \dfrac{dx}{\sqrt{2x-x^2}} = \int \dfrac{dt}{\sqrt{1-t^2}} = \sin^{-1}(t) + C$ [by 7.4 (5)]

$$= \sin^{-1}(x-1) + C$$

Example 9 Find the following integrals :

(i) $\int \dfrac{dx}{x^2-6x+13}$ (ii) $\int \dfrac{dx}{3x^2+13x-10}$ (iii) $\int \dfrac{dx}{\sqrt{5x^2-2x}}$

Solution

(i) We have $x^2-6x+13 = x^2-6x+3^2-3^2+13 = (x-3)^2+4$

So, $\int \dfrac{dx}{x^2-6x+13} = \int \dfrac{1}{(x-3)^2+2^2}\,dx$

Let $x-3 = t$. Then $dx = dt$

Therefore, $\int \dfrac{dx}{x^2-6x+13} = \int \dfrac{dt}{t^2+2^2} = \dfrac{1}{2}\tan^{-1}\dfrac{t}{2} + C$ [by 7.4 (3)]

$$= \dfrac{1}{2}\tan^{-1}\dfrac{x-3}{2} + C$$

(ii)   The given integral is of the form 7.4 (7). We write the denominator of the integrand,

$$3x^2 + 13x - 10 = 3\left(x^2 + \frac{13x}{3} - \frac{10}{3}\right)$$

$$= 3\left[\left(x + \frac{13}{6}\right)^2 - \left(\frac{17}{6}\right)^2\right] \quad \text{(completing the square)}$$

Thus $\displaystyle\int \frac{dx}{3x^2 + 13x - 10} = \frac{1}{3}\int \frac{dx}{\left(x + \frac{13}{6}\right)^2 - \left(\frac{17}{6}\right)^2}$

Put $x + \dfrac{13}{6} = t$. Then $dx = dt$.

Therefore, $\displaystyle\int \frac{dx}{3x^2 + 13x - 10} = \frac{1}{3}\int \frac{dt}{t^2 - \left(\frac{17}{6}\right)^2}$

$$= \frac{1}{3 \times 2 \times \frac{17}{6}} \log\left|\frac{t - \frac{17}{6}}{t + \frac{17}{6}}\right| + C_1 \qquad \text{[by 7.4 (i)]}$$

$$= \frac{1}{17} \log\left|\frac{x + \frac{13}{6} - \frac{17}{6}}{x + \frac{13}{6} + \frac{17}{6}}\right| + C_1$$

$$= \frac{1}{17} \log\left|\frac{6x - 4}{6x + 30}\right| + C_1$$

$$= \frac{1}{17} \log\left|\frac{3x - 2}{x + 5}\right| + C_1 + \frac{1}{17} \log\frac{1}{3}$$

$$= \frac{1}{17} \log\left|\frac{3x - 2}{x + 5}\right| + C, \text{ where } C = C_1 + \frac{1}{17} \log\frac{1}{3}$$

(iii)   We have $\int \dfrac{dx}{\sqrt{5x^2 - 2x}} = \int \dfrac{dx}{\sqrt{5\left(x^2 - \dfrac{2x}{5}\right)}}$

$$= \frac{1}{\sqrt{5}} \int \frac{dx}{\sqrt{\left(x - \dfrac{1}{5}\right)^2 - \left(\dfrac{1}{5}\right)^2}} \qquad \text{(completing the square)}$$

Put $x - \dfrac{1}{5} = t$. Then $dx = dt$.

Therefore, $\displaystyle \int \frac{dx}{\sqrt{5x^2 - 2x}} = \frac{1}{\sqrt{5}} \int \frac{dt}{\sqrt{t^2 - \left(\dfrac{1}{5}\right)^2}}$

$$= \frac{1}{\sqrt{5}} \log \left| t + \sqrt{t^2 - \left(\frac{1}{5}\right)^2} \right| + C \qquad \text{[by 7.4 (4)]}$$

$$= \frac{1}{\sqrt{5}} \log \left| x - \frac{1}{5} + \sqrt{x^2 - \frac{2x}{5}} \right| + C$$

Example 10 Find the following integrals:

(i) $\displaystyle \int \frac{x+2}{2x^2 + 6x + 5}\, dx$ (ii) $\displaystyle \int \frac{x+3}{\sqrt{5 - 4x + x^2}}\, dx$

Solution

(i) Using the formula 7.4 (9), we express

$$x + 2 = A \frac{d}{dx}\left(2x^2 + 6x + 5\right) + B = A\,(4x + 6) + B$$

Equating the coefficients of x and the constant terms from both sides, we get

$4A = 1$ and $6A + B = 2$ or $A = \dfrac{1}{4}$ and $B = \dfrac{1}{2}$.

Therefore, $\displaystyle \int \frac{x+2}{2x^2 + 6x + 5} = \frac{1}{4} \int \frac{4x+6}{2x^2 + 6x + 5}\, dx + \frac{1}{2} \int \frac{dx}{2x^2 + 6x + 5}$

$$= \frac{1}{4} I_1 + \frac{1}{2} I_2 \quad \text{(say)} \qquad \qquad \dots (1)$$

In I_1, put $2x^2 + 6x + 5 = t$, so that $(4x + 6)\,dx = dt$

Therefore, $I_1 = \int \dfrac{dt.}{t} = \log|t| + C_1$

$$= \log|2x^2 + 6x + 5| + C_1 \qquad \text{... (2)}$$

and $I_2 = \int \dfrac{dx}{2x^2 + 6x + 5} = \dfrac{1}{2} \int \dfrac{dx}{x^2 + 3x + \dfrac{5}{2}}$

$$= \dfrac{1}{2} \int \dfrac{dx}{\left(x + \dfrac{3}{2}\right)^2 + \left(\dfrac{1}{2}\right)^2}$$

Put $x + \dfrac{3}{2} = t$, so that $dx = dt$, we get

$$I_2 = \dfrac{1}{2} \int \dfrac{dt}{t^2 + \left(\dfrac{1}{2}\right)^2} = \dfrac{1}{2 \times \dfrac{1}{2}} \tan^{-1} 2t + C_2 \qquad \text{[by 7.4 (3)]}$$

$$= \tan^{-1} 2 \left(x + \dfrac{3}{2}\right) + C_2 = \tan^{-1}(2x + 3) + C_2 \qquad \text{... (3)}$$

Using (2) and (3) in (1), we get

$$\int \dfrac{x + 2}{2x^2 + 6x + 5}\,dx = \dfrac{1}{4} \log|2x^2 + 6x + 5| + \dfrac{1}{2} \tan^{-1}(2x + 3) + C$$

where, $C = \dfrac{C_1}{4} + \dfrac{C_2}{2}$

(ii) This integral is of the form given in 7.4 (10). Let us express

$$x + 3 = A \dfrac{d}{dx}(5 - 4x - x^2) + B = A(-4 - 2x) + B$$

Equating the coefficients of x and the constant terms from both sides, we get

$$-2A = 1 \text{ and } -4A + B = 3, \text{ i.e., } A = -\dfrac{1}{2} \text{ and } B = 1$$

Therefore, $\displaystyle\int\frac{x+3}{\sqrt{5-4x-x^2}}\,dx = -\frac{1}{2}\int\frac{(-4-2x)\,dx}{\sqrt{5-4x-x^2}}+\int\frac{dx}{\sqrt{5-4x-x^2}}$

$$= -\frac{1}{2}\,I_1 + I_2 \qquad\qquad ...\,(1)$$

In I_1, put $5 - 4x - x^2 = t$, so that $(-4 - 2x)\,dx = dt$.

Therefore, $\displaystyle I_1 = \int\frac{(-4-2x)\,dx}{\sqrt{5-4x-x^2}} = \int\frac{dt}{\sqrt{t}} = 2\sqrt{t} + C_1$

$$= 2\sqrt{5-4x-x^2} + C_1 \qquad\qquad ...\,(2)$$

Now consider $\displaystyle I_2 = \int\frac{dx}{\sqrt{5-4x-x^2}} = \int\frac{dx}{\sqrt{9-(x+2)^2}}$

Put $x + 2 = t$, so that $dx = dt$.

Therefore, $\displaystyle I_2 = \int\frac{dt}{\sqrt{3^2-t^2}} = \sin^{-1}\frac{t}{3} + C_2 \qquad$ [by 7.4 (5)]

$$= \sin^{-1}\frac{x+2}{3} + C_2 \qquad\qquad ...\,(3)$$

Substituting (2) and (3) in (1), we obtain

$$\int\frac{x+3}{\sqrt{5-4x-x^2}} = -\sqrt{5-4x-x^2} + \sin^{-1}\frac{x+2}{3} + C,\ \text{where}\ C = C_2 - \frac{C_1}{2}$$

EXERCISE 7.4

Integrate the functions in Exercises 1 to 23.

1. $\dfrac{3x^2}{x^6+1}$

2. $\dfrac{1}{\sqrt{1+4x^2}}$

3. $\dfrac{1}{\sqrt{(2-x)^2+1}}$

4. $\dfrac{1}{\sqrt{9-25x^2}}$

5. $\dfrac{3x}{1+2x^4}$

6. $\dfrac{x^2}{1-x^6}$

7. $\dfrac{x-1}{\sqrt{x^2-1}}$

8. $\dfrac{x^2}{\sqrt{x^6+a^6}}$

9. $\dfrac{\sec^2 x}{\sqrt{\tan^2 x+4}}$

10. $\dfrac{1}{\sqrt{x^2+2x+2}}$ **11.** $\dfrac{1}{9x^2+6x+5}$ **12.** $\dfrac{1}{\sqrt{7-6x-x^2}}$

13. $\dfrac{1}{\sqrt{(x-1)(x-2)}}$ **14.** $\dfrac{1}{\sqrt{8+3x-x^2}}$ **15.** $\dfrac{1}{\sqrt{(x-a)(x-b)}}$

16. $\dfrac{4x+1}{\sqrt{2x^2+x-3}}$ **17.** $\dfrac{x+2}{\sqrt{x^2-1}}$ **18.** $\dfrac{5x-2}{1+2x+3x^2}$

19. $\dfrac{6x+7}{\sqrt{(x-5)(x-4)}}$ **20.** $\dfrac{x+2}{\sqrt{4x-x^2}}$ **21.** $\dfrac{x+2}{\sqrt{x^2+2x+3}}$

22. $\dfrac{x+3}{x^2-2x-5}$ **23.** $\dfrac{5x+3}{\sqrt{x^2+4x+10}}$.

Choose the correct answer in Exercises 24 and 25.

24. $\displaystyle\int \dfrac{dx}{x^2+2x+2}$ equals

(A) $x\tan^{-1}(x+1)+C$ (B) $\tan^{-1}(x+1)+C$

(C) $(x+1)\tan^{-1}x+C$ (D) $\tan^{-1}x+C$

25. $\displaystyle\int \dfrac{dx}{\sqrt{9x-4x^2}}$ equals

(A) $\dfrac{1}{9}\sin^{-1}\left(\dfrac{9x-8}{8}\right)+C$ (B) $\dfrac{1}{2}\sin^{-1}\left(\dfrac{8x-9}{9}\right)+C$

(C) $\dfrac{1}{3}\sin^{-1}\left(\dfrac{9x-8}{8}\right)+C$ (D) $\dfrac{1}{2}\sin^{-1}\left(\dfrac{9x-8}{9}\right)+C$

7.5 Integration by Partial Fractions

Recall that a rational function is defined as the ratio of two polynomials in the form

$\dfrac{P(x)}{Q(x)}$, where P (x) and Q(x) are polynomials in x and $Q(x) \neq 0$. If the degree of P(x)

is less than the degree of Q(x), then the rational function is called proper, otherwise, it is called improper. The improper rational functions can be reduced to the proper rational functions by long division process. Thus, if $\dfrac{P(x)}{Q(x)}$ is improper, then $\dfrac{P(x)}{Q(x)} = T(x) + \dfrac{P_1(x)}{Q(x)}$,

where $T(x)$ is a polynomial in x and $\dfrac{P_1(x)}{Q(x)}$ is a proper rational function. As we know how to integrate polynomials, the integration of any rational function is reduced to the integration of a proper rational function. The rational functions which we shall consider here for integration purposes will be those whose denominators can be factorised into linear and quadratic factors. Assume that we want to evaluate $\displaystyle\int \dfrac{P(x)}{Q(x)} dx$, where $\dfrac{P(x)}{Q(x)}$ is proper rational function. It is always possible to write the integrand as a sum of simpler rational functions by a method called partial fraction decomposition. After this, the integration can be carried out easily using the already known methods. The following Table 7.2 indicates the types of simpler partial fractions that are to be associated with various kind of rational functions.

Table 7.2

S.No.	Form of the rational function	Form of the partial fraction
1.	$\dfrac{px+q}{(x-a)(x-b)}$, $a \neq b$	$\dfrac{A}{x-a} + \dfrac{B}{x-b}$
2.	$\dfrac{px+q}{(x-a)^2}$	$\dfrac{A}{x-a} + \dfrac{B}{(x-a)^2}$
3.	$\dfrac{px^2+qx+r}{(x-a)(x-b)(x-c)}$	$\dfrac{A}{x-a} + \dfrac{B}{x-b} + \dfrac{C}{x-c}$
4.	$\dfrac{px^2+qx+r}{(x-a)^2(x-b)}$	$\dfrac{A}{x-a} + \dfrac{B}{(x-a)^2} + \dfrac{C}{x-b}$
5.	$\dfrac{px^2+qx+r}{(x-a)(x^2+bx+c)}$	$\dfrac{A}{x-a} + \dfrac{Bx+C}{x^2+bx+c}$
	where x^2+bx+c cannot be factorised further	

In the above table, A, B and C are real numbers to be determined suitably.

Example 11 Find $\int \dfrac{dx}{(x+1)(x+2)}$

Solution The integrand is a proper rational function. Therefore, by using the form of partial fraction [Table 7.2 (i)], we write

$$\frac{1}{(x+1)(x+2)} = \frac{A}{x+1} + \frac{B}{x+2} \qquad \text{... (1)}$$

where, real numbers A and B are to be determined suitably. This gives

$$1 = A(x+2) + B(x+1).$$

Equating the coefficients of x and the constant term, we get

$$A + B = 0$$

and $$2A + B = 1$$

Solving these equations, we get A = 1 and B = – 1.

Thus, the integrand is given by

$$\frac{1}{(x+1)(x+2)} = \frac{1}{x+1} + \frac{-1}{x+2}$$

Therefore,

$$\int \frac{dx}{(x+1)(x+2)} = \int \frac{dx}{x+1} - \int \frac{dx}{x+2}$$

$$= \log|x+1| - \log|x+2| + C$$

$$= \log \left| \frac{x+1}{x+2} \right| + C$$

Remark The equation (1) above is an identity, i.e. a statement true for all (permissible) values of x. Some authors use the symbol '≡' to indicate that the statement is an identity and use the symbol '=' to indicate that the statement is an equation, i.e., to indicate that the statement is true only for certain values of x.

Example 12 Find $\int \dfrac{x^2 + 1}{x^2 - 5x + 6}\, dx$

Solution Here the integrand $\dfrac{x^2 + 1}{x^2 - 5x + 6}$ is not proper rational function, so we divide

$x^2 + 1$ by $x^2 - 5x + 6$ and find that

$$\frac{x^2+1}{x^2-5x+6} = 1 + \frac{5x-5}{x^2-5x+6} = 1 + \frac{5x-5}{(x-2)(x-3)}$$

Let

$$\frac{5x-5}{(x-2)(x-3)} = \frac{A}{x-2} + \frac{B}{x-3}$$

So that

$$5x - 5 = A(x-3) + B(x-2)$$

Equating the coefficients of x and constant terms on both sides, we get $A + B = 5$ and $3A + 2B = 5$. Solving these equations, we get $A = -5$ and $B = 10$

Thus,

$$\frac{x^2+1}{x^2-5x+6} = 1 - \frac{5}{x-2} + \frac{10}{x-3}$$

Therefore,

$$\int \frac{x^2+1}{x^2-5x+6}dx = \int dx - 5\int \frac{1}{x-2}dx + 10\int \frac{dx}{x-3}$$

$$= x - 5\log|x-2| + 10\log|x-3| + C.$$

Example 13 Find $\int \frac{3x-2}{(x+1)^2(x+3)}dx$

Solution The integrand is of the type as given in Table 7.2 (4). We write

$$\frac{3x-2}{(x+1)^2(x+3)} = \frac{A}{x+1} + \frac{B}{(x+1)^2} + \frac{C}{x+3}$$

So that

$$3x - 2 = A(x+1)(x+3) + B(x+3) + C(x+1)^2$$

$$= A(x^2+4x+3) + B(x+3) + C(x^2+2x+1)$$

Comparing coefficient of x^2, x and constant term on both sides, we get $A + C = 0$, $4A + B + 2C = 3$ and $3A + 3B + C = -2$. Solving these equations, we get $A = \frac{11}{4}$, $B = \frac{-5}{2}$ and $C = \frac{-11}{4}$. Thus the integrand is given by

$$\frac{3x-2}{(x+1)^2(x+3)} = \frac{11}{4(x+1)} - \frac{5}{2(x+1)^2} - \frac{11}{4(x+3)}$$

Therefore,

$$\int \frac{3x-2}{(x+1)^2(x+3)} = \frac{11}{4}\int \frac{dx}{x+1} - \frac{5}{2}\int \frac{dx}{(x+1)^2} - \frac{11}{4}\int \frac{dx}{x+3}$$

$$= \frac{11}{4}\log|x+1| + \frac{5}{2(x+1)} - \frac{11}{4}\log|x+3| + C$$

$$= \frac{11}{4}\log\left|\frac{x+1}{x+3}\right| + \frac{5}{2(x+1)} + C$$

Example 14 Find $\int \dfrac{x^2}{(x^2+1)(x^2+4)} dx$

Solution Consider $\dfrac{x^2}{(x^2+1)(x^2+4)}$ and put $x^2 = y$.

Then
$$\dfrac{x^2}{(x^2+1)(x^2+4)} = \dfrac{y}{(y+1)(y+4)}$$

Write
$$\dfrac{y}{(y+1)(y+4)} = \dfrac{A}{y+1} + \dfrac{B}{y+4}$$

So that
$$y = A(y+4) + B(y+1)$$

Comparing coefficients of y and constant terms on both sides, we get $A + B = 1$ and $4A + B = 0$, which give

$$A = -\dfrac{1}{3} \quad \text{and} \quad B = \dfrac{4}{3}$$

Thus,
$$\dfrac{x^2}{(x^2+1)(x^2+4)} = -\dfrac{1}{3(x^2+1)} + \dfrac{4}{3(x^2+4)}$$

Therefore,
$$\int \dfrac{x^2 dx}{(x^2+1)(x^2+4)} = -\dfrac{1}{3}\int \dfrac{dx}{x^2+1} + \dfrac{4}{3}\int \dfrac{dx}{x^2+4}$$

$$= -\dfrac{1}{3}\tan^{-1}x + \dfrac{4}{3}\times\dfrac{1}{2}\tan^{-1}\dfrac{x}{2} + C$$

$$= -\dfrac{1}{3}\tan^{-1}x + \dfrac{2}{3}\tan^{-1}\dfrac{x}{2} + C$$

In the above example, the substitution was made only for the partial fraction part and not for the integration part. Now, we consider an example, where the integration involves a combination of the substitution method and the partial fraction method.

Example 15 Find $\int \dfrac{(3\sin\phi - 2)\cos\phi}{5 - \cos^2\phi - 4\sin\phi} d\phi$

Solution Let $y = \sin\phi$

Then
$$dy = \cos\phi \, d\phi$$

Therefore, $\displaystyle\int \frac{(3\sin\phi - 2)\cos\phi}{5 - \cos^2\phi - 4\sin\phi}\, d\phi = \int \frac{(3y - 2)\, dy}{5 - (1 - y^2) - 4y}$

$$= \int \frac{3y - 2}{y^2 - 4y + 4}\, dy$$

$$= \int \frac{3y - 2}{(y - 2)^2} = \mathrm{I}\,(\text{say})$$

Now, we write $\displaystyle\frac{3y - 2}{(y - 2)^2} = \frac{A}{y - 2} + \frac{B}{(y - 2)^2}$ [by Table 7.2 (2)]

Therefore, $\qquad\qquad\qquad 3y - 2 = A\,(y - 2) + B$

Comparing the coefficients of y and constant term, we get A = 3 and B − 2A = − 2, which gives A = 3 and B = 4.

Therefore, the required integral is given by

$$\mathrm{I} = \int [\frac{3}{y - 2} + \frac{4}{(y - 2)^2}]\, dy = 3\int \frac{dy}{y - 2} + 4\int \frac{dy}{(y - 2)^2}$$

$$= 3\log|\, y - 2\,| + 4\left(-\frac{1}{y - 2}\right) + C$$

$$= 3\log|\,\sin\phi - 2\,| + \frac{4}{2 - \sin\phi} + C$$

$$= 3\log\,(2 - \sin\phi) + \frac{4}{2 - \sin\phi} + C \ \ (\text{since, } 2 - \sin\phi \text{ is always positive})$$

Example 16 Find $\displaystyle\int \frac{x^2 + x + 1\, dx}{(x + 2)\,(x^2 + 1)}$

Solution The integrand is a proper rational function. Decompose the rational function into partial fraction [Table 2.2(5)]. Write

$$\frac{x^2 + x + 1}{(x^2 + 1)\,(x + 2)} = \frac{A}{x + 2} + \frac{Bx + C}{(x^2 + 1)}$$

Therefore, $\qquad\qquad x^2 + x + 1 = A\,(x^2 + 1) + (Bx + C)\,(x + 2)$

Equating the coefficients of x^2, x and of constant term of both sides, we get
$A + B = 1$, $2B + \textit{c}C = 1$ and $A + 2C = 1$. Solving these equations, we get

$$A = \frac{3}{5}, B = \frac{2}{5} \text{ and } C = \frac{1}{5}$$

Thus, the integrand is given by

$$\frac{x^2 + x + 1}{(x^2 + 1)(x + 2)} = \frac{3}{5(x + 2)} + \frac{\frac{2}{5}x + \frac{1}{5}}{x^2 + 1} = \frac{3}{5(x + 2)} + \frac{1}{5}\left(\frac{2x + 1}{x^2 + 1}\right)$$

Therefore, $$\int \frac{x^2 + x + 1}{(x^2 + 1)(x + 2)} dx = \frac{3}{5} \int \frac{dx}{x + 2} + \frac{1}{5} \int \frac{2x}{x^2 + 1} dx + \frac{1}{5} \int \frac{1}{x^2 + 1} dx$$

$$= \frac{3}{5} \log|x + 2| + \frac{1}{5} \log|x^2 + 1| + \frac{1}{5} \tan^{-1} x + C$$

EXERCISE 7.5

Integrate the rational functions in Exercises 1 to 21.

1. $\dfrac{x}{(x + 1)(x + 2)}$

2. $\dfrac{1}{x^2 - 9}$

3. $\dfrac{3x - 1}{(x - 1)(x - 2)(x - 3)}$

4. $\dfrac{x}{(x - 1)(x - 2)(x - 3)}$

5. $\dfrac{2x}{x^2 + 3x + 2}$

6. $\dfrac{1 - x^2}{x(1 - 2x)}$

7. $\dfrac{x}{(x^2 + 1)(x - 1)}$

8. $\dfrac{x}{(x - 1)^2 (x + 2)}$

9. $\dfrac{3x + 5}{x^3 - x^2 - x + 1}$

10. $\dfrac{2x - 3}{(x^2 - 1)(2x + 3)}$

11. $\dfrac{5x}{(x + 1)(x^2 - 4)}$

12. $\dfrac{x^3 + x + 1}{x^2 - 1}$

13. $\dfrac{2}{(1 - x)(1 + x^2)}$

14. $\dfrac{3x - 1}{(x + 2)^2}$

15. $\dfrac{1}{x^4 - 1}$

16. $\dfrac{1}{x(x^n + 1)}$ [Hint: multiply numerator and denominator by x^{n-1} and put $x^n = t$]

17. $\dfrac{\cos x}{(1 - \sin x)(2 - \sin x)}$ [Hint : Put $\sin x = t$]

18. $\dfrac{(x^2+1)\,(x^2+2)}{(x^2+3)\,(x^2+4)}$ **19.** $\dfrac{2x}{(x^2+1)\,(x^2+3)}$ **20.** $\dfrac{1}{x\,(x^4-1)}$

21. $\dfrac{1}{(e^x-1)}$ [Hint : Put $e^x = t$]

Choose the correct answer in each of the Exercises 22 and 23.

22. $\displaystyle\int \dfrac{x\,dx}{(x-1)\,(x-2)}$ equals

(A) $\log\left|\dfrac{(x-1)^2}{x-2}\right|+C$

(B) $\log\left|\dfrac{(x-2)^2}{x-1}\right|+C$

(C) $\log\left|\left(\dfrac{x-1}{x-2}\right)^2\right|+C$

(D) $\log\left|(x-1)\,(x-2)\right|+C$

23. $\displaystyle\int \dfrac{dx}{x\,(x^2+1)}$ equals

(A) $\log|x|-\dfrac{1}{2}\log(x^2+1)+C$

(B) $\log|x|+\dfrac{1}{2}\log(x^2+1)+C$

(C) $-\log|x|+\dfrac{1}{2}\log(x^2+1)+C$

(D) $\dfrac{1}{2}\log|x|+\log(x^2+1)+C$

7.6 Integration by Parts

In this section, we describe one more method of integration, that is found quite useful in integrating products of functions.

If u and v are any two differentiable functions of a single variable x (say). Then, by the product rule of differentiation, we have

$$\frac{d}{dx}(uv) = u\frac{dv}{dx}+v\frac{du}{dx}$$

Integrating both sides, we get

$$uv = \int u\frac{dv}{dx}\,dx+\int v\frac{du}{dx}\,dx$$

or

$$\int u\frac{dv}{dx}\,dx = uv-\int v\frac{du}{dx}\,dx \qquad \text{... (1)}$$

Let

$$u = f(x) \text{ and } \frac{dv}{dx}=g(x). \text{ Then}$$

$$\frac{du}{dx}=f'(x) \text{ and } v = \int g(x)\,dx$$

Therefore, expression (1) can be rewritten as

$$\int f(x)\, g(x)\, dx \;=\; f(x)\int g(x)\, dx - \int [\int g(x)\, dx]\, f'(x)\, dx$$

i.e., $$\int f(x)\, g\,(x)\, dx \;=\; f(x)\int g\,(x)\, dx - \int [\, f'\,(x)\int g(x)\, dx]\, dx$$

If we take f as the first function and g as the second function, then this formula may be stated as follows:

"**The integral of the product of two functions = (first function) × (integral of the second function) – Integral of [(differential coefficient of the first function) × (integral of the second function)]**"

Example 17 Find $\int x \cos x\, dx$

Solution Put $f\,(x) = x$ (first function) and $g\,(x) = \cos x$ (second function).
Then, integration by parts gives

$$\int x \cos x\, dx \;=\; x \int \cos x\, dx - \int [\frac{d}{dx}(x)\int \cos x\, dx]\, dx$$

$$=\; x \sin x - \int \sin x\, dx \;=\; x \sin x + \cos x + C$$

Suppose, we take $f(x) = \cos x$ and $g(x) = x$. Then

$$\int x \cos x\, dx \;=\; \cos x \int x\, dx - \int [\frac{d}{dx}(\cos x)\int x\, dx]\, dx$$

$$=\; (\cos x)\frac{x^2}{2} + \int \sin x\, \frac{x^2}{2}\, dx$$

Thus, it shows that the integral $\int x \cos x\, dx$ is reduced to the comparatively more complicated integral having more power of x. Therefore, the proper choice of the first function and the second function is significant.

Remarks

(i) It is worth mentioning that integration by parts is not applicable to product of functions in all cases. For instance, the method does not work for $\int \sqrt{x} \sin x\, dx$. The reason is that there does not exist any function whose derivative is $\sqrt{x}\, \sin x$.

(ii) Observe that while finding the integral of the second function, we did not add any constant of integration. If we write the integral of the second function $\cos x$

as sin $x + k$, where k is any constant, then

$$\int x \cos x \, dx = x (\sin x + k) - \int (\sin x + k) \, dx$$

$$= x (\sin x + k) - \int (\sin x \, dx - \int k \, dx$$

$$= x (\sin x + k) - \cos x - kx + C = x \sin x + \cos x + C$$

This shows that adding a constant to the integral of the second function is superfluous so far as the final result is concerned while applying the method of integration by parts.

(iii) Usually, if any function is a power of x or a polynomial in x, then we take it as the first function. However, in cases where other function is inverse trigonometric function or logarithmic function, then we take them as first function.

Example 18 Find $\int \log x \, dx$

Solution To start with, we are unable to guess a function whose derivative is $\log x$. We take $\log x$ as the first function and the constant function 1 as the second function. Then, the integral of the second function is x.

Hence,

$$\int (\log x . 1) \, dx = \log x \int 1 \, dx - \int [\frac{d}{dx} (\log x) \int 1 \, dx] \, dx$$

$$= (\log x) \cdot x - \int \frac{1}{x} x \, dx = x \log x - x + C.$$

Example 19 Find $\int x \, e^x dx$

Solution Take first function as x and second function as e^x. The integral of the second function is e^x.

Therefore,

$$\int x \, e^x dx = x \, e^x - \int 1 \cdot e^x dx = xe^x - e^x + C.$$

Example 20 Find $\int \frac{x \sin^{-1} x}{\sqrt{1 - x^2}} \, dx$

Solution Let first function be $\sin^{-1} x$ and second function be $\dfrac{x}{\sqrt{1 - x^2}}$.

First we find the integral of the second function, i.e., $\int \dfrac{x \, dx}{\sqrt{1 - x^2}}$.

Put $t = 1 - x^2$. Then $dt = -2x \, dx$

Therefore,
$$\int \frac{x\,dx}{\sqrt{1-x^2}} = -\frac{1}{2}\int \frac{dt}{\sqrt{t}} = -\sqrt{t} = -\sqrt{1-x^2}$$

Hence,
$$\int \frac{x\sin^{-1}x}{\sqrt{1-x^2}}dx = (\sin^{-1}x)\left(-\sqrt{1-x^2}\right) - \int \frac{1}{\sqrt{1-x^2}}(-\sqrt{1-x^2})\,dx$$

$$= -\sqrt{1-x^2}\,\sin^{-1}x + x + C = x - \sqrt{1-x^2}\,\sin^{-1}x + C$$

Alternatively, this integral can also be worked out by making substitution $\sin^{-1}x = \theta$ and then integrating by parts.

Example 21 Find $\int e^x \sin x\,dx$

Solution Take e^x as the first function and $\sin x$ as second function. Then, integrating by parts, we have

$$I = \int e^x \sin x\,dx = e^x(-\cos x) + \int e^x \cos x\,dx$$

$$= -e^x \cos x + I_1 \text{ (say)} \qquad \qquad \dots (1)$$

Taking e^x and $\cos x$ as the first and second functions, respectively, in I_1, we get

$$I_1 = e^x \sin x - \int e^x \sin x\,dx$$

Substituting the value of I_1 in (1), we get

$$I = -e^x \cos x + e^x \sin x - I \quad \text{or} \quad 2I = e^x(\sin x - \cos x)$$

Hence,
$$I = \int e^x \sin x\,dx = \frac{e^x}{2}(\sin x - \cos x) + C$$

Alternatively, above integral can also be determined by taking $\sin x$ as the first function and e^x the second function.

7.6.1 *Integral of the type* $\int e^x[f(x) + f'(x)]\,dx$

We have
$$I = \int e^x[f(x) + f'(x)]\,dx = \int e^x f(x)\,dx + \int e^x f'(x)\,dx$$

$$= I_1 + \int e^x f'(x)\,dx, \text{ where } I_1 = \int e^x f(x)\,dx \qquad \qquad \dots (1)$$

Taking $f(x)$ and e^x as the first function and second function, respectively, in I_1 and integrating it by parts, we have $I_1 = f(x)\,e^x - \int f'(x)\,e^x\,dx + C$

Substituting I_1 in (1), we get

$$I = e^x f(x) - \int f'(x)\,e^x\,dx + \int e^x f'(x)\,dx + C = e^x f(x) + C$$

Thus, $$\int e^x [f(x) + f'(x)] dx = e^x f(x) + C$$

Example 22 Find (i) $\int e^x (\tan^{-1} x + \dfrac{1}{1+x^2}) dx$ (ii) $\int \dfrac{(x^2 + 1) e^x}{(x+1)^2} dx$

Solution

(i) We have $I = \int e^x (\tan^{-1} x + \dfrac{1}{1+x^2}) dx$

Consider $f(x) = \tan^{-1} x$, then $f'(x) = \dfrac{1}{1+x^2}$

Thus, the given integrand is of the form $e^x [f(x) + f'(x)]$.

Therefore, $I = \int e^x (\tan^{-1} x + \dfrac{1}{1+x^2}) dx = e^x \tan^{-1} x + C$

(ii) We have $I = \int \dfrac{(x^2 + 1) e^x}{(x+1)^2} dx = \int e^x [\dfrac{x^2 - 1 + 1 + 1)}{(x+1)^2}] dx$

$= \int e^x [\dfrac{x^2 - 1}{(x+1)^2} + \dfrac{2}{(x+1)^2}] dx = \int e^x [\dfrac{x-1}{x+1} + \dfrac{2}{(x+1)^2}] dx$

Consider $f(x) = \dfrac{x-1}{x+1}$, then $f'(x) = \dfrac{2}{(x+1)^2}$

Thus, the given integrand is of the form $e^x [f(x) + f'(x)]$.

Therefore, $\int \dfrac{x^2 + 1}{(x+1)^2} e^x dx = \dfrac{x-1}{x+1} e^x + C$

EXERCISE 7.6

Integrate the functions in Exercises 1 to 22.

1. $x \sin x$
2. $x \sin 3x$
3. $x^2 e^x$
4. $x \log x$

5. $x \log 2x$
6. $x^2 \log x$
7. $x \sin^{-1} x$
8. $x \tan^{-1} x$

9. $x \cos^{-1} x$
10. $(\sin^{-1} x)^2$
11. $\dfrac{x \cos^{-1} x}{\sqrt{1-x^2}}$
12. $x \sec^2 x$

13. $\tan^{-1} x$
14. $x (\log x)^2$
15. $(x^2 + 1) \log x$

16. $e^x (\sin x + \cos x)$ 17. $\dfrac{x\,e^x}{(1+x)^2}$ 18. $e^x \left(\dfrac{1+\sin x}{1+\cos x} \right)$

19. $e^x \left(\dfrac{1}{x} - \dfrac{1}{x^2} \right)$ 20. $\dfrac{(x-3)\,e^x}{(x-1)^3}$ 21. $e^{2x} \sin x$

22. $\sin^{-1} \left(\dfrac{2x}{1+x^2} \right)$

Choose the correct answer in Exercises 23 and 24.

23. $\int x^2 e^{x^3} dx$ equals

(A) $\dfrac{1}{3} e^{x^3} + C$ (B) $\dfrac{1}{3} e^{x^2} + C$

(C) $\dfrac{1}{2} e^{x^3} + C$ (D) $\dfrac{1}{2} e^{x^2} + C$

24. $\int e^x \sec x\,(1+\tan x)\,dx$ equals

(A) $e^x \cos x + C$ (B) $e^x \sec x + C$

(C) $e^x \sin x + C$ (D) $e^x \tan x + C$

7.6.2 Integrals of some more types

Here, we discuss some special types of standard integrals based on the technique of integration by parts :

(i) $\displaystyle \int \sqrt{x^2 - a^2}\, dx$ (ii) $\displaystyle \int \sqrt{x^2 + a^2}\, dx$ (iii) $\displaystyle \int \sqrt{a^2 - x^2}\, dx$

(i)   Let $I = \displaystyle \int \sqrt{x^2 - a^2}\, dx$

Taking constant function 1 as the second function and integrating by parts, we have

$$I = x\sqrt{x^2 - a^2} - \int \frac{1}{2} \frac{2x}{\sqrt{x^2 - a^2}} x\,dx$$

$$= x\sqrt{x^2 - a^2} - \int \frac{x^2}{\sqrt{x^2 - a^2}}\,dx = x\sqrt{x^2 - a^2} - \int \frac{x^2 - a^2 + a^2}{\sqrt{x^2 - a^2}}\,dx$$

$$= x\sqrt{x^2 - a^2} - \int\sqrt{x^2 - a^2}\, dx - a^2\int\frac{dx}{\sqrt{x^2 - a^2}}$$

$$= x\sqrt{x^2 - a^2} - I - a^2\int\frac{dx}{\sqrt{x^2 - a^2}}$$

or $$2I = x\sqrt{x^2 - a^2} - a^2\int\frac{dx}{\sqrt{x^2 - a^2}}$$

or $$\mathbf{I} = \int\sqrt{x^2 - a^2}\, dx = \frac{x}{2}\sqrt{x^2 - a^2} - \frac{a^2}{2}\log\left| x + \sqrt{x^2 - a^2} \right| + \mathbf{C}$$

Similarly, integrating other two integrals by parts, taking constant function 1 as the second function, we get

(ii) $$\int\sqrt{x^2 + a^2}\, dx = \frac{1}{2}x\sqrt{x^2 + a^2} + \frac{a^2}{2}\log\left| x + \sqrt{x^2 + a^2} \right| + \mathbf{C}$$

(iii) $$\int\sqrt{a^2 - x^2}\, dx = \frac{1}{2}x\sqrt{a^2 - x^2} + \frac{a^2}{2}\sin^{-1}\frac{x}{a} + \mathbf{C}$$

Alternatively, integrals (i), (ii) and (iii) can also be found by making trigonometric substitution $x = a\sec\theta$ in (i), $x = a\tan\theta$ in (ii) and $x = a\sin\theta$ in (iii) respectively.

Example 23 Find $\int\sqrt{x^2 + 2x + 5}\, dx$

Solution Note that

$$\int\sqrt{x^2 + 2x + 5}\, dx = \int\sqrt{(x+1)^2 + 4}\, dx$$

Put $x + 1 = y$, so that $dx = dy$. Then

$$\int\sqrt{x^2 + 2x + 5}\, dx = \int\sqrt{y^2 + 2^2}\, dy$$

$$= \frac{1}{2}y\sqrt{y^2 + 4} + \frac{4}{2}\log\left| y + \sqrt{y^2 + 4} \right| + \mathbf{C} \qquad \text{[using 7.6.2 (ii)]}$$

$$= \frac{1}{2}(x+1)\sqrt{x^2 + 2x + 5} + 2\log\left| x + 1 + \sqrt{x^2 + 2x + 5} \right| + \mathbf{C}$$

Example 24 Find $\int\sqrt{3 - 2x - x^2}\, dx$

Solution Note that $\int\sqrt{3 - 2x - x^2}\, dx = \int\sqrt{4 - (x+1)^2}\, dx$

Put $x + 1 = y$ so that $dx = dy$.

Thus $\qquad \int \sqrt{3 - 2x - x^2}\, dx = \int \sqrt{4 - y^2}\, dy$

$$= \frac{1}{2} y \sqrt{4 - y^2} + \frac{4}{2} \sin^{-1} \frac{y}{2} + C \qquad \text{[using 7.6.2 (iii)]}$$

$$= \frac{1}{2} (x + 1) \sqrt{3 - 2x - x^2} + 2 \sin^{-1}\left(\frac{x+1}{2}\right) + C$$

EXERCISE 7.7

Integrate the functions in Exercises 1 to 9.

1. $\sqrt{4 - x^2}$ 　　　　　 2. $\sqrt{1 - 4x^2}$ 　　　　　 3. $\sqrt{x^2 + 4x + 6}$

4. $\sqrt{x^2 + 4x + 1}$ 　　　 5. $\sqrt{1 - 4x - x^2}$ 　　　 6. $\sqrt{x^2 + 4x - 5}$

7. $\sqrt{1 + 3x - x^2}$ 　　　 8. $\sqrt{x^2 + 3x}$ 　　　　 9. $\sqrt{1 + \dfrac{x^2}{9}}$

Choose the correct answer in Exercises 10 to 11.

10. $\int \sqrt{1 + x^2}\, dx$ is equal to

(A) $\dfrac{x}{2} \sqrt{1 + x^2} + \dfrac{1}{2} \log\left|\left(x + \sqrt{1 + x^2}\right)\right| + C$

(B) $\dfrac{2}{3} (1 + x^2)^{\frac{3}{2}} + C$ 　　　　　 (C) $\dfrac{2}{3} x (1 + x^2)^{\frac{3}{2}} + C$

(D) $\dfrac{x^2}{2} \sqrt{1 + x^2} + \dfrac{1}{2} x^2 \log\left|x + \sqrt{1 + x^2}\right| + C$

11. $\int \sqrt{x^2 - 8x + 7}\, dx$ is equal to

(A) $\dfrac{1}{2} (x - 4)\sqrt{x^2 - 8x + 7} + 9\log\left|x - 4 + \sqrt{x^2 - 8x + 7}\right| + C$

(B) $\dfrac{1}{2} (x + 4)\sqrt{x^2 - 8x + 7} + 9\log\left|x + 4 + \sqrt{x^2 - 8x + 7}\right| + C$

(C) $\dfrac{1}{2} (x - 4)\sqrt{x^2 - 8x + 7} - 3\sqrt{2}\log\left|x - 4 + \sqrt{x^2 - 8x + 7}\right| + C$

(D) $\dfrac{1}{2} (x - 4)\sqrt{x^2 - 8x + 7} - \dfrac{9}{2}\log\left|x - 4 + \sqrt{x^2 - 8x + 7}\right| + C$

7.7 Definite Integral
In the previous sections, we have studied about the indefinite integrals and discussed few methods of finding them including integrals of some special functions. In this section, we shall study what is called definite integral of a function. The definite integral has a unique value. A definite integral is denoted by $\int_a^b f(x)\,dx$, where a is called the lower limit of the integral and b is called the upper limit of the integral. The definite integral is introduced either as the limit of a sum or if it has an anti derivative F in the interval $[a, b]$, then its value is the difference between the values of F at the end points, i.e., $F(b) - F(a)$. Here, we shall consider these two cases separately as discussed below:

7.7.1 Definite integral as the limit of a sum
Let f be a continuous function defined on close interval $[a, b]$. Assume that all the values taken by the function are non negative, so the graph of the function is a curve above the x-axis.

The definite integral $\int_a^b f(x)\,dx$ is the area bounded by the curve $y = f(x)$, the ordinates $x = a$, $x = b$ and the x-axis. To evaluate this area, consider the region PRSQP between this curve, x-axis and the ordinates $x = a$ and $x = b$ (Fig 7.2).

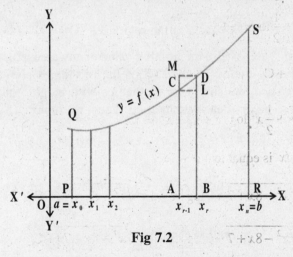

Fig 7.2

Divide the interval $[a, b]$ into n equal subintervals denoted by $[x_0, x_1]$, $[x_1, x_2]$,...., $[x_{r-1}, x_r]$, ..., $[x_{n-1}, x_n]$, where $x_0 = a$, $x_1 = a + h$, $x_2 = a + 2h$, ... , $x_r = a + rh$ and $x_n = b = a + nh$ or $n = \dfrac{b-a}{h}$. We note that as $n \to \infty$, $h \to 0$.

The region PRSQP under consideration is the sum of n subregions, where each subregion is defined on subintervals $[x_{r-1}, x_r]$, $r = 1, 2, 3, ..., n$.

From Fig 7.2, we have

area of the rectangle (ABLC) < area of the region (ABDCA) < area of the rectangle (ABDM) ... (1)

Evidently as $x_r - x_{r-1} \to 0$, i.e., $h \to 0$ all the three areas shown in (1) become nearly equal to each other. Now we form the following sums.

$$s_n = h \, [f(x_0) + ... + f(x_{n-1})] = h \sum_{r=0}^{n-1} f(x_r) \qquad ... (2)$$

and $$S_n = h [f(x_1) + f(x_2) + ... + f(x_n)] = h \sum_{r=1}^{n} f(x_r) \qquad ... (3)$$

Here, s_n and S_n denote the sum of areas of all lower rectangles and upper rectangles raised over subintervals $[x_{r-1}, x_r]$ for $r = 1, 2, 3, ..., n$, respectively.

In view of the inequality (1) for an arbitrary subinterval $[x_{r-1}, x_r]$, we have

$$s_n < \text{area of the region PRSQP} < S_n \qquad ... (4)$$

As $n \to \infty$ strips become narrower and narrower, it is assumed that the limiting values of (2) and (3) are the same in both cases and the common limiting value is the required area under the curve.

Symbolically, we write

$$\lim_{n \to \infty} S_n = \lim_{n \to \infty} s_n = \text{area of the region PRSQP} = \int_a^b f(x) dx \qquad ... (5)$$

It follows that this area is also the limiting value of any area which is between that of the rectangles below the curve and that of the rectangles above the curve. For the sake of convenience, we shall take rectangles with height equal to that of the curve at the left hand edge of each subinterval. Thus, we rewrite (5) as

$$\int_a^b f(x) dx = \lim_{h \to 0} h [f(a) + f(a+h) + ... + f(a + (n-1) h]$$

or $$\int_a^b f(x) dx = (b-a) \lim_{n \to \infty} \frac{1}{n} [f(a) + f(a+h) + ... + f(a + (n-1) h] \qquad ... (6)$$

where $$h = \frac{b-a}{n} \to 0 \text{ as } n \to \infty$$

The above expression (6) is known as the definition of definite integral as the *limit of sum*.

Remark The value of the definite integral of a function over any particular interval depends on the function and the interval, but not on the variable of integration that we choose to represent the independent variable. If the independent variable is denoted by t or u instead of x, we simply write the integral as $\int_a^b f(t)\, dt$ or $\int_a^b f(u)\, du$ instead of $\int_a^b f(x)\, dx$. Hence, the variable of integration is called a *dummy variable*.

Example 25 Find $\int_0^2 (x^2 + 1)\, dx$ as the limit of a sum.

Solution By definition

$$\int_a^b f(x)\, dx = (b-a) \lim_{n\to\infty} \frac{1}{n}[f(a) + f(a+h) + ... + f(a+(n-1)h],$$

where, $h = \dfrac{b-a}{n}$

In this example, $a = 0$, $b = 2$, $f(x) = x^2 + 1$, $h = \dfrac{2-0}{n} = \dfrac{2}{n}$

Therefore,

$$\int_0^2 (x^2 + 1)\, dx = 2 \lim_{n\to\infty} \frac{1}{n}[f(0) + f(\frac{2}{n}) + f(\frac{4}{n}) + ... + f(\frac{2(n-1)}{n})]$$

$$= 2 \lim_{n\to\infty} \frac{1}{n}[1 + (\frac{2^2}{n^2}+1) + (\frac{4^2}{n^2}+1) + ... + \left(\frac{(2n-2)^2}{n^2}+1\right)]$$

$$= 2 \lim_{n\to\infty} \frac{1}{n}[\underbrace{(1+1+...+1)}_{n\text{-}terms} + \frac{1}{n^2}(2^2 + 4^2 + ... + (2n-2)^2]$$

$$= 2 \lim_{n\to\infty} \frac{1}{n}[n + \frac{2^2}{n^2}(1^2 + 2^2 + ... + (n-1)^2]$$

$$= 2 \lim_{n\to\infty} \frac{1}{n}[n + \frac{4}{n^2} \frac{(n-1)\, n\, (2n-1)}{6}]$$

$$= 2 \lim_{n\to\infty} \frac{1}{n}[n + \frac{2}{3} \frac{(n-1)\, (2n-1)}{n}]$$

$$= 2 \lim_{n\to\infty} [1 + \frac{2}{3}(1-\frac{1}{n})\, (2-\frac{1}{n})] = 2[1+\frac{4}{3}] = \frac{14}{3}$$

Example 26 Evaluate $\int_0^2 e^x \, dx$ as the limit of a sum.

Solution By definition

$$\int_0^2 e^x \, dx = (2-0) \lim_{n \to \infty} \frac{1}{n} \left[e^0 + e^{\frac{2}{n}} + e^{\frac{4}{n}} + \dots + e^{\frac{2n-2}{n}} \right]$$

Using the sum to n terms of a G.P., where $a = 1$, $r = e^{\frac{2}{n}}$, we have

$$\int_0^2 e^x \, dx = 2 \lim_{n \to \infty} \frac{1}{n} \left[\frac{e^{\frac{2n}{n}} - 1}{e^{\frac{2}{n}} - 1} \right] = 2 \lim_{n \to \infty} \frac{1}{n} \left[\frac{e^2 - 1}{e^{\frac{2}{n}} - 1} \right]$$

$$= \frac{2(e^2 - 1)}{\lim_{n \to \infty} \left[\frac{e^{\frac{2}{n}} - 1}{\frac{2}{n}} \right] \cdot 2} = e^2 - 1 \qquad [\text{using } \lim_{h \to 0} \frac{(e^h - 1)}{h} = 1]$$

EXERCISE 7.8

Evaluate the following definite integrals as limit of sums.

1. $\int_a^b x \, dx$ 2. $\int_0^5 (x+1) \, dx$ 3. $\int_2^3 x^2 \, dx$

4. $\int_1^4 (x^2 - x) \, dx$ 5. $\int_{-1}^1 e^x \, dx$ 6. $\int_0^4 (x + e^{2x}) \, dx$

7.8 Fundamental Theorem of Calculus

7.8.1 *Area function*

We have defined $\int_a^b f(x) \, dx$ as the area of

the region bounded by the curve $y = f(x)$, the ordinates $x = a$ and $x = b$ and x-axis. Let x

be a given point in $[a, b]$. Then $\int_a^x f(x) \, dx$

represents the area of the light shaded region

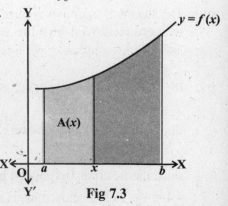

Fig 7.3

in Fig 7.3 [Here it is assumed that $f(x) > 0$ for $x \in [a, b]$, the assertion made below is equally true for other functions as well]. The area of this shaded region depends upon the value of x.

In other words, the area of this shaded region is a function of x. We denote this function of x by A(x). We call the function A(x) as *Area function* and is given by

$$A(x) = \int_a^x f(x)\, dx \qquad \qquad ...\,(1)$$

Based on this definition, the two basic fundamental theorems have been given. However, we only state them as their proofs are beyond the scope of this text book.

7.8.2 *First fundamental theorem of integral calculus*

Theorem 1 Let f be a continuous function on the closed interval $[a, b]$ and let A (x) be the area function. Then $A'(x) = f(x)$, for all $x \in [a, b]$.

7.8.3 *Second fundamental theorem of integral calculus*

We state below an important theorem which enables us to evaluate definite integrals by making use of anti derivative.

Theorem 2 Let f be continuous function defined on the closed interval $[a, b]$ and F be

an anti derivative of f. Then $\int_a^b f(x)\, dx = [F(x)]_a^b = F(b) - F(a)$.

Remarks

(i)   In words, the Theorem 2 tells us that $\int_a^b f(x)\, dx = $ (value of the anti derivative F of f at the upper limit b – value of the same anti derivative at the lower limit a).

(ii) This theorem is very useful, because it gives us a method of calculating the definite integral more easily, without calculating the limit of a sum.

(iii) The crucial operation in evaluating a definite integral is that of finding a function whose derivative is equal to the integrand. This strengthens the relationship between differentiation and integration.

(iv) In $\int_a^b f(x)\, dx$, the function f needs to be well defined and continuous in $[a, b]$.

For instance, the consideration of definite integral $\int_{-2}^3 x(x^2 - 1)^{\frac{1}{2}}\, dx$ is erroneous

since the function f expressed by $f(x) = x(x^2 - 1)^{\frac{1}{2}}$ is not defined in a portion $-1 < x < 1$ of the closed interval $[-2, 3]$.

Steps for calculating $\int_a^b f(x)\,dx$.

(i) Find the indefinite integral $\int f(x)\,dx$. Let this be F(x). There is no need to keep integration constant C because if we consider F(x) + C instead of F(x), we get

$$\int_a^b f(x)\,dx = [F(x)+C]_a^b = [F(b)+C]-[\dot{F}(a)+C] = F(b)-F(a).$$

Thus, the arbitrary constant disappears in evaluating the value of the definite integral.

(ii) Evaluate F(b) − F(a) = $[F(x)]_a^b$, which is the value of $\int_a^b f(x)\,dx$.

We now consider some examples

Example 27 Evaluate the following integrals:

(i) $\displaystyle\int_2^3 x^2\,dx$

(ii) $\displaystyle\int_4^9 \frac{\sqrt{x}}{(30-x^{\frac{3}{2}})^2}\,dx$

(iii) $\displaystyle\int_1^2 \frac{x\,dx}{(x+1)(x+2)}$

(iv) $\displaystyle\int_0^{\frac{\pi}{4}} \sin^3 2t\,\cos 2t\,dt$

Solution

(i) Let $I = \displaystyle\int_2^3 x^2\,dx$. Since $\int x^2\,dx = \dfrac{x^3}{3} = F(x)$,

Therefore, by the second fundamental theorem, we get

$$I = F(3) - F(2) = \frac{27}{3} - \frac{8}{3} = \frac{19}{3}$$

(ii) Let $I = \displaystyle\int_4^9 \frac{\sqrt{x}}{(30-x^{\frac{3}{2}})^2}\,dx$. We first find the anti derivative of the integrand.

Put $30 - x^{\frac{3}{2}} = t$. Then $-\dfrac{3}{2}\sqrt{x}\,dx = dt$ or $\sqrt{x}\,dx = -\dfrac{2}{3}dt$

Thus, $\displaystyle\int \frac{\sqrt{x}}{(30-x^{\frac{3}{2}})^2}\,dx = -\frac{2}{3}\int \frac{dt}{t^2} = \frac{2}{3}\left[\frac{1}{t}\right] = \frac{2}{3}\left[\frac{1}{(30-x^{\frac{3}{2}})}\right] = F(x)$

Therefore, by the second fundamental theorem of calculus, we have

$$I = F(9) - F(4) = \frac{2}{3} \left[\frac{1}{(30-x^2)^{\frac{3}{3}}} \right]_4^9$$

$$= \frac{2}{3} \left[\frac{1}{(30-27)} - \frac{1}{30-8} \right] = \frac{2}{3} \left[\frac{1}{3} - \frac{1}{22} \right] = \frac{19}{99}$$

(iii) Let $I = \int_1^2 \frac{x\,dx}{(x+1)\,(x+2)}$

Using partial fraction, we get $\dfrac{x}{(x+1)\,(x+2)} = \dfrac{-1}{x+1} + \dfrac{2}{x+2}$

So $\int \dfrac{x\,dx}{(x+1)\,(x+2)} = -\log|x+1| + 2\log|x+2| = F(x)$

Therefore, by the second fundamental theorem of calculus, we have

$$I = F(2) - F(1) = [-\log 3 + 2\log 4] - [-\log 2 + 2\log 3]$$

$$= -3\log 3 + \log 2 + 2\log 4 = \log\left(\frac{32}{27}\right)$$

(iv) Let $I = \int_0^{\frac{\pi}{4}} \sin^3 2t \cos 2t\, dt$. Consider $\int \sin^3 2t \cos 2t\, dt$

Put $\sin 2t = u$ so that $2\cos 2t\, dt = du$ or $\cos 2t\, dt = \dfrac{1}{2}\, du$

So $\int \sin^3 2t \cos 2t\, dt = \dfrac{1}{2} \int u^3 du$

$$= \frac{1}{8}[u^4] = \frac{1}{8}\sin^4 2t = F(t)\text{ say}$$

Therefore, by the second fundamental theorem of integral calculus

$$I = F\left(\frac{\pi}{4}\right) - F(0) = \frac{1}{8}[\sin^4\frac{\pi}{2} - \sin^4 0] = \frac{1}{8}$$

EXERCISE 7.9

Evaluate the definite integrals in Exercises 1 to 20.

1. $\int_{-1}^{1} (x+1)\, dx$ **2.** $\int_{2}^{3} \frac{1}{x}\, dx$ **3.** $\int_{1}^{2} (4x^3 - 5x^2 + 6x + 9)\, dx$

4. $\int_{0}^{\frac{\pi}{4}} \sin 2x\, dx$ **5.** $\int_{0}^{\frac{\pi}{2}} \cos 2x\, dx$ **6.** $\int_{4}^{5} e^x\, dx$ **7.** $\int_{0}^{\frac{\pi}{4}} \tan x\, dx$

8. $\int_{\frac{\pi}{6}}^{\frac{\pi}{4}} \csc x\, dx$ **9.** $\int_{0}^{1} \frac{dx}{\sqrt{1-x^2}}$ **10.** $\int_{0}^{1} \frac{dx}{1+x^2}$ **11.** $\int_{2}^{3} \frac{dx}{x^2 - 1}$

12. $\int_{0}^{\frac{\pi}{2}} \cos^2 x\, dx$ **13.** $\int_{2}^{3} \frac{x\, dx}{x^2 + 1}$ **14.** $\int_{0}^{1} \frac{2x+3}{5x^2 + 1}\, dx$ **15.** $\int_{0}^{1} x\, e^{x^2}\, dx$

16. $\int_{1}^{2} \frac{5x^2}{x^2 + 4x + 3}$ **17.** $\int_{0}^{\frac{\pi}{4}} (2\sec^2 x + x^3 + 2)\, dx$ **18.** $\int_{0}^{\pi} (\sin^2 \frac{x}{2} - \cos^2 \frac{x}{2})\, dx$

19. $\int_{0}^{2} \frac{6x+3}{x^2 + 4}\, dx$ **20.** $\int_{0}^{1} (x\, e^x + \sin \frac{\pi x}{4})\, dx$

Choose the correct answer in Exercises 21 and 22.

21. $\int_{1}^{\sqrt{3}} \frac{dx}{1+x^2}$ equals

   (A) $\frac{\pi}{3}$ (B) $\frac{2\pi}{3}$ (C) $\frac{\pi}{6}$ (D) $\frac{\pi}{12}$

22. $\int_{0}^{\frac{2}{3}} \frac{dx}{4+9x^2}$ equals

   (A) $\frac{\pi}{6}$ (B) $\frac{\pi}{12}$ (C) $\frac{\pi}{24}$ (D) $\frac{\pi}{4}$

7.9 Evaluation of Definite Integrals by Substitution

In the previous sections, we have discussed several methods for finding the indefinite integral. One of the important methods for finding the indefinite integral is the method of substitution.

To evaluate $\int_a^b f(x)\,dx$, by substitution, the steps could be as follows:

1. Consider the integral without limits and substitute, $y = f(x)$ or $x = g(y)$ to reduce the given integral to a known form.

2. Integrate the new integrand with respect to the new variable without mentioning the constant of integration.

3. Resubstitute for the new variable and write the answer in terms of the original variable.

4. Find the values of answers obtained in (3) at the given limits of integral and find the difference of the values at the upper and lower limits.

> **☞ Note** In order to quicken this method, we can proceed as follows: After performing steps 1, and 2, there is no need of step 3. Here, the integral will be kept in the new variable itself, and the limits of the integral will accordingly be changed, so that we can perform the last step.

Let us illustrate this by examples.

Example 28 Evaluate $\int_{-1}^{1} 5x^4 \sqrt{x^5 + 1}\,dx$.

Solution Put $t = x^5 + 1$, then $dt = 5x^4\,dx$.

Therefore,
$$\int 5x^4 \sqrt{x^5 + 1}\,dx = \int \sqrt{t}\,dt = \frac{2}{3} t^{\frac{3}{2}} = \frac{2}{3}(x^5 + 1)^{\frac{3}{2}}$$

Hence,
$$\int_{-1}^{1} 5x^4 \sqrt{x^5 + 1}\,dx = \frac{2}{3}\left[(x^5 + 1)^{\frac{3}{2}} \right]_{-1}^{1}$$

$$= \frac{2}{3}\left[(1^5 + 1)^{\frac{3}{2}} - \left((-1)^5 + 1 \right)^{\frac{3}{2}} \right]$$

$$= \frac{2}{3}\left[2^{\frac{3}{2}} - 0^{\frac{3}{2}} \right] = \frac{2}{3}(2\sqrt{2}) = \frac{4\sqrt{2}}{3}$$

Alternatively, first we transform the integral and then evaluate the transformed integral with new limits.

Let $t = x^5 + 1$. Then $dt = 5\,x^4\,dx$.

Note that, when $x = -1, t = 0$ and when $x = 1, t = 2$

Thus, as x varies from -1 to 1, t varies from 0 to 2

Therefore $\int_{-1}^{1} 5x^4 \sqrt{x^5+1}\, dx = \int_0^2 \sqrt{t}\, dt$

$$= \frac{2}{3}\left[t^{\frac{3}{2}}\right]_0^2 = \frac{2}{3}\left[2^{\frac{3}{2}} - 0^{\frac{3}{2}}\right] = \frac{2}{3}(2\sqrt{2}) = \frac{4\sqrt{2}}{3}$$

Example 29 Evaluate $\int_0^1 \frac{\tan^{-1}x}{1+x^2}\, dx$

Solution Let $t = \tan^{-1}x$, then $dt = \frac{1}{1+x^2}\, dx$. The new limits are, when $x = 0, t = 0$ and

when $x = 1, t = \dfrac{\pi}{4}$. Thus, as x varies from 0 to 1, t varies from 0 to $\dfrac{\pi}{4}$.

Therefore $\int_0^1 \frac{\tan^{-1}x}{1+x^2}\, dx = \int_0^{\frac{\pi}{4}} t\, dt \left[\frac{t^2}{2}\right]_0^{\frac{\pi}{4}} = \frac{1}{2}\left[\frac{\pi^2}{16} - 0\right] = \frac{\pi^2}{32}$

EXERCISE 7.10

Evaluate the integrals in Exercises 1 to 8 using substitution.

1. $\displaystyle\int_0^1 \frac{x}{x^2+1}\, dx$ 2. $\displaystyle\int_0^{\frac{\pi}{2}} \sqrt{\sin\phi}\,\cos^5\phi\, d\phi$ 3. $\displaystyle\int_0^1 \sin^{-1}\left(\frac{2x}{1+x^2}\right) dx$

4. $\displaystyle\int_0^2 x\sqrt{x+2}$ (Put $x + 2 = t^2$)   5. $\displaystyle\int_0^{\frac{\pi}{2}} \frac{\sin x}{1+\cos^2 x}\, dx$

6. $\displaystyle\int_0^2 \frac{dx}{x+4-x^2}$ 7. $\displaystyle\int_{-1}^1 \frac{dx}{x^2+2x+5}$ 8. $\displaystyle\int_1^2 \left(\frac{1}{x} - \frac{1}{2x^2}\right) e^{2x}\, dx$

Choose the correct answer in Exercises 9 and 10.

9. The value of the integral $\displaystyle\int_{\frac{1}{3}}^1 \frac{(x-x^3)^{\frac{1}{3}}}{x^4}\, dx$ is

   (A) 6   (B) 0   (C) 3   (D) 4

10. If $f(x) = \displaystyle\int_0^x t \sin t\, dt$, then $f'(x)$ is

   (A) $\cos x + x \sin x$ (B) $x \sin x$

   (C) $x \cos x$ (D) $\sin x + x \cos x$

7.10 Some Properties of Definite Integrals

We list below some important properties of definite integrals. These will be useful in evaluating the definite integrals more easily.

P_0 : $\int_a^b f(x)\,dx = \int_a^b f(t)\,dt$

P_1 : $\int_a^b f(x)\,dx = -\int_b^a f(x)\,dx$. In particular, $\int_a^a f(x)\,dx = 0$

P_2 : $\int_a^b f(x)\,dx = \int_a^c f(x)\,dx + \int_c^b f(x)\,dx$

P_3 : $\int_a^b f(x)\,dx = \int_a^b f(a+b-x)\,dx$

P_4 : $\int_0^a f(x)\,dx = \int_0^a f(a-x)\,dx$

(Note that P_4 is a particular case of P_3)

P_5 : $\int_0^{2a} f(x)\,dx = \int_0^a f(x)\,dx + \int_0^a f(2a-x)\,dx$

P_6 : $\int_0^{2a} f(x)\,dx = 2\int_0^a f(x)\,dx$, if $f(2a-x) = f(x)$ and

0 if $f(2a-x) = -f(x)$

P_7 : (i) $\int_{-a}^a f(x)\,dx = 2\int_0^a f(x)\,dx$, if f is an even function, i.e., if $f(-x) = f(x)$.

(ii) $\int_{-a}^a f(x)\,dx = 0$, if f is an odd function, i.e., if $f(-x) = -f(x)$.

We give the proofs of these properties one by one.

Proof of P_0 It follows directly by making the substitution $x = t$.

Proof of P_1 Let F be anti derivative of f. Then, by the second fundamental theorem of calculus, we have $\int_a^b f(x)\,dx = F(b) - F(a) = -[F(a) - F(b)] = -\int_b^a f(x)\,dx$

Here, we observe that, if $a = b$, then $\int_a^a f(x)\,dx = 0$.

Proof of P_2 Let F be anti derivative of f. Then

$$\int_a^b f(x)\,dx = F(b) - F(a) \qquad \text{... (1)}$$

$$\int_a^c f(x)\,dx = F(c) - F(a) \qquad \text{... (2)}$$

and $$\int_c^b f(x)\,dx = F(b) - F(c) \qquad \text{... (3)}$$

Adding (2) and (3), we get $\int_a^c f(x)\,dx + \int_c^b f(x)\,dx = F(b) - F(a) = \int_a^b f(x)\,dx$

This proves the property P_2.

Proof of P_3 Let $t = a + b - x$. Then $dt = -dx$. When $x = a$, $t = b$ and when $x = b$, $t = a$. Therefore

$$\int_a^b f(x)\,dx = -\int_b^a f(a+b-t)\,dt$$

$$= \int_a^b f(a+b-t)\,dt \quad \text{(by } P_1)$$

$$= \int_a^b f(a+b-x)\,dx \quad \text{by } P_0$$

Proof of P_4 Put $t = a - x$. Then $dt = -dx$. When $x = 0$, $t = a$ and when $x = a$, $t = 0$. Now proceed as in P_3.

Proof of P_5 Using P_2, we have $\int_0^{2a} f(x)\,dx = \int_0^a f(x)\,dx + \int_a^{2a} f(x)\,dx$.

Let $\quad\quad\quad\quad\quad t = 2a - x$ in the second integral on the right hand side. Then $dt = -dx$. When $x = a$, $t = a$ and when $x = 2a$, $t = 0$. Also $x = 2a - t$.
Therefore, the second integral becomes

$$\int_a^{2a} f(x)\,dx = -\int_a^0 f(2a-t)\,dt = \int_0^a f(2a-t)\,dt = \int_0^a f(2a-x)\,dx$$

Hence $\quad \int_0^{2a} f(x)\,dx = \int_0^a f(x)\,dx + \int_0^a f(2a-x)\,dx$

Proof of P_6 Using P_5, we have $\int_0^{2a} f(x)\,dx = \int_0^a f(x)\,dx + \int_0^a f(2a-x)\,dx$ ... (1)

Now, if $\quad\quad\quad\quad\quad f(2a - x) = f(x)$, then (1) becomes

$$\int_0^{2a} f(x)\,dx = \int_0^a f(x)\,dx + \int_0^a f(x)\,dx = 2\int_0^a f(x)\,dx,$$

and if $\quad\quad\quad\quad f(2a - x) = -f(x)$, then (1) becomes

$$\int_0^{2a} f(x)\,dx = \int_0^a f(x)\,dx - \int_0^a f(x)\,dx = 0$$

Proof of P_7 Using P_2, we have

$$\int_{-a}^a f(x)\,dx = \int_{-a}^0 f(x)\,dx + \int_0^a f(x)\,dx. \text{ Then}$$

Let $\quad\quad\quad\quad\quad\quad\quad\quad\quad\quad t = -x$ in the first integral on the right hand side. $dt = -dx$. When $x = -a$, $t = a$ and when $x = 0$, $t = 0$. Also $x = -t$.

Therefore
$$\int_{-a}^{a} f(x)\, dx = -\int_{a}^{0} f(-t)\, dt + \int_{0}^{a} f(x)\, dx$$

$$= \int_{0}^{a} f(-x)\, dx + \int_{0}^{a} f(x)\, dx \qquad \text{(by } P_0) \ \dots (1)$$

(i) Now, if f is an even function, then $f(-x) = f(x)$ and so (1) becomes

$$\int_{-a}^{a} f(x)\, dx = \int_{0}^{a} f(x)\, dx + \int_{0}^{a} f(x)\, dx = 2\int_{0}^{a} f(x)\, dx$$

(ii) If f is an odd function, then $f(-x) = -f(x)$ and so (1) becomes

$$\int_{-a}^{a} f(x)\, dx = -\int_{0}^{a} f(x)\, dx + \int_{0}^{a} f(x)\, dx = 0$$

Example 30 Evaluate $\displaystyle\int_{-1}^{2} \left| x^3 - x \right| dx$

Solution We note that $x^3 - x \geq 0$ on $[-1, 0]$ and $x^3 - x \leq 0$ on $[0, 1]$ and that $x^3 - x \geq 0$ on $[1, 2]$. So by P_2 we write

$$\int_{-1}^{2} \left| x^3 - x \right| dx = \int_{-1}^{0} (x^3 - x)\, dx + \int_{0}^{1} -(x^3 - x)\, dx + \int_{1}^{2} (x^3 - x)\, dx$$

$$= \int_{-1}^{0} (x^3 - x)\, dx + \int_{0}^{1} (x - x^3)\, dx + \int_{1}^{2} (x^3 - x)\, dx$$

$$= \left[\frac{x^4}{4} - \frac{x^2}{2} \right]_{-1}^{0} + \left[\frac{x^2}{2} - \frac{x^4}{4} \right]_{0}^{1} + \left[\frac{x^4}{4} - \frac{x^2}{2} \right]_{1}^{2}$$

$$= -\left(\frac{1}{4} - \frac{1}{2} \right) + \left(\frac{1}{2} - \frac{1}{4} \right) + (4 - 2) - \left(\frac{1}{4} - \frac{1}{2} \right)$$

$$= -\frac{1}{4} + \frac{1}{2} + \frac{1}{2} - \frac{1}{4} + 2 - \frac{1}{4} + \frac{1}{2} = \frac{3}{2} - \frac{3}{4} + 2 = \frac{11}{4}$$

Example 31 Evaluate $\displaystyle\int_{-\frac{\pi}{4}}^{\frac{\pi}{4}} \sin^2 x\, dx$

Solution We observe that $\sin^2 x$ is an even function. Therefore, by P_7 (i), we get

$$\int_{-\frac{\pi}{4}}^{\frac{\pi}{4}} \sin^2 x\, dx = 2\int_{0}^{\frac{\pi}{4}} \sin^2 x\, dx$$

$$= 2\int_0^{\frac{\pi}{4}} \frac{(1-\cos 2x)}{2}\, dx = \int_0^{\frac{\pi}{4}}(1-\cos 2x)\, dx$$

$$= \left[x - \frac{1}{2}\sin 2x\right]_0^{\frac{\pi}{4}} = \left(\frac{\pi}{4} - \frac{1}{2}\sin\frac{\pi}{2}\right) - 0 = \frac{\pi}{4} - \frac{1}{2}$$

Example 32 Evaluate $\displaystyle\int_0^{\pi} \frac{x\sin x}{1+\cos^2 x}\, dx$

Solution Let $I = \displaystyle\int_0^{\pi} \frac{x\sin x}{1+\cos^2 x}\, dx$. Then, by P_4, we have

$$I = \int_0^{\pi} \frac{(\pi-x)\sin(\pi-x)\, dx}{1+\cos^2(\pi-x)}$$

$$= \int_0^{\pi} \frac{(\pi-x)\sin x\, dx}{1+\cos^2 x} = \pi\int_0^{\pi} \frac{\sin x\, dx}{1+\cos^2 x} - I$$

or $$2\,I = \pi\int_0^{\pi} \frac{\sin x\, dx}{1+\cos^2 x}$$

or $$I = \frac{\pi}{2}\int_0^{\pi} \frac{\sin x\, dx}{1+\cos^2 x}$$

Put $\cos x = t$ so that $-\sin x\, dx = dt$. When $x = 0$, $t = 1$ and when $x = \pi$, $t = -1$. Therefore, (by P_1) we get

$$I = \frac{-\pi}{2}\int_1^{-1} \frac{dt}{1+t^2} = \frac{-\pi}{2}\int_1^{-1} \frac{dt}{1+t^2}$$

$$= \pi\int_0^1 \frac{dt}{1+t^2} \text{ (by } P_7, \text{ since } \frac{1}{1+t^2} \text{ is even function)}$$

$$= \pi\left[\tan^{-1} t\right]_0^1 = \pi\left[\tan^{-1} 1 - \tan^{-1} 0\right] = \pi\left[\frac{\pi}{4} - 0\right] = \frac{\pi^2}{4}$$

Example 33 Evaluate $\displaystyle\int_{-1}^{1} \sin^5 x \cos^4 x\, dx$

Solution Let $I = \displaystyle\int_{-1}^{1} \sin^5 x\cos^4 x\, dx$. Let $f(x) = \sin^5 x\cos^4 x$. Then

$f(-x) = \sin^5(-x)\cos^4(-x) = -\sin^5 x\cos^4 x = -f(x)$, i.e., f is an odd function.
Therefore, by P_7 (ii), $I = 0$

Example 34 Evaluate $\int_0^{\frac{\pi}{2}} \dfrac{\sin^4 x}{\sin^4 x + \cos^4 x} \, dx$

Solution Let $I = \int_0^{\frac{\pi}{2}} \dfrac{\sin^4 x}{\sin^4 x + \cos^4 x} \, dx$ ... (1)

Then, by P_4

$$I = \int_0^{\frac{\pi}{2}} \frac{\sin^4 \left(\frac{\pi}{2} - x\right)}{\sin^4 \left(\frac{\pi}{2} - x\right) + \cos^4 \left(\frac{\pi}{2} - x\right)} \, dx = \int_0^{\frac{\pi}{2}} \frac{\cos^4 x}{\cos^4 x + \sin^4 x} \, dx \quad ... (2)$$

Adding (1) and (2), we get

$$2I = \int_0^{\frac{\pi}{2}} \frac{\sin^4 x + \cos^4 x}{\sin^4 x + \cos^4 x} \, dx = \int_0^{\frac{\pi}{2}} dx = [x]_0^{\frac{\pi}{2}} = \frac{\pi}{2}$$

Hence $I = \dfrac{\pi}{4}$

Example 35 Evaluate $\int_{\frac{\pi}{6}}^{\frac{\pi}{3}} \dfrac{dx}{1 + \sqrt{\tan x}}$

Solution Let $I = \int_{\frac{\pi}{6}}^{\frac{\pi}{3}} \dfrac{dx}{1 + \sqrt{\tan x}} = \int_{\frac{\pi}{6}}^{\frac{\pi}{3}} \dfrac{\sqrt{\cos x}\, dx}{\sqrt{\cos x} + \sqrt{\sin x}}$ ... (1)

Then, by P_3 $I = \int_{\frac{\pi}{6}}^{\frac{\pi}{3}} \dfrac{\sqrt{\cos\left(\frac{\pi}{3} + \frac{\pi}{6} - x\right)}\, dx}{\sqrt{\cos\left(\frac{\pi}{3} + \frac{\pi}{6} - x\right)} + \sqrt{\sin\left(\frac{\pi}{3} + \frac{\pi}{6} - x\right)}}$

$$= \int_{\frac{\pi}{6}}^{\frac{\pi}{3}} \frac{\sqrt{\sin x}}{\sqrt{\sin x} + \sqrt{\cos x}} \, dx \quad ... (2)$$

Adding (1) and (2), we get

$$2I = \int_{\frac{\pi}{6}}^{\frac{\pi}{3}} dx = [x]_{\frac{\pi}{6}}^{\frac{\pi}{3}} = \frac{\pi}{3} - \frac{\pi}{6} = \frac{\pi}{6}. \text{ Hence } I = \frac{\pi}{12}$$

Example 36 Evaluate $\int_0^{\frac{\pi}{2}} \log \sin x \, dx$

Solution Let $I = \int_0^{\frac{\pi}{2}} \log \sin x \, dx$

Then, by P_4

$$I = \int_0^{\frac{\pi}{2}} \log \sin \left(\frac{\pi}{2} - x \right) dx = \int_0^{\frac{\pi}{2}} \log \cos x \, dx$$

Adding the two values of I, we get

$$2I = \int_0^{\frac{\pi}{2}} \left(\log \sin x + \log \cos x \right) dx$$

$$= \int_0^{\frac{\pi}{2}} \left(\log \sin x \cos x + \log 2 - \log 2 \right) dx \text{ (by adding and subtracting } \log 2)$$

$$= \int_0^{\frac{\pi}{2}} \log \sin 2x \, dx - \int_0^{\frac{\pi}{2}} \log 2 \, dx \quad \text{(Why?)}$$

Put $2x = t$ in the first integral. Then $2 \, dx = dt$, when $x = 0$, $t = 0$ and when $x = \frac{\pi}{2}$,
$t = \pi$.

Therefore $$2I = \frac{1}{2} \int_0^{\pi} \log \sin t \, dt - \frac{\pi}{2} \log 2$$

$$= \frac{2}{2} \int_0^{\frac{\pi}{2}} \log \sin t \, dt - \frac{\pi}{2} \log 2 \text{ [by } P_6 \text{ as } \sin (\pi - t) = \sin t)$$

$$= \int_0^{\frac{\pi}{2}} \log \sin x \, dx - \frac{\pi}{2} \log 2 \text{ (by changing variable } t \text{ to } x)$$

$$= I - \frac{\pi}{2} \log 2$$

Hence $$\int_0^{\frac{\pi}{2}} \log \sin x \, dx = \frac{-\pi}{2} \log 2.$$

EXERCISE 7.11

By using the properties of definite integrals, evaluate the integrals in Exercises 1 to 19.

1. $\int_0^{\frac{\pi}{2}} \cos^2 x \, dx$

2. $\int_0^{\frac{\pi}{2}} \frac{\sqrt{\sin x}}{\sqrt{\sin x} + \sqrt{\cos x}} \, dx$

3. $\int_0^{\frac{\pi}{2}} \frac{\sin^{\frac{3}{2}} x \, dx}{\sin^{\frac{3}{2}} x + \cos^{\frac{3}{2}} x}$

4. $\int_0^{\frac{\pi}{2}} \frac{\cos^5 x \, dx}{\sin^5 x + \cos^5 x}$

5. $\int_{-5}^{5} |x+2| \, dx$

6. $\int_2^8 |x-5| \, dx$

7. $\int_0^1 x(1-x)^n \, dx$

8. $\int_0^{\frac{\pi}{4}} \log(1+\tan x) \, dx$

9. $\int_0^2 x\sqrt{2-x} \, dx$

10. $\int_0^{\frac{\pi}{2}} (2\log \sin x - \log \sin 2x) \, dx$

11. $\int_{-\frac{\pi}{2}}^{\frac{\pi}{2}} \sin^2 x \, dx$

12. $\int_0^{\pi} \frac{x \, dx}{1+\sin x}$

13. $\int_{-\frac{\pi}{2}}^{\frac{\pi}{2}} \sin^7 x \, dx$

14. $\int_0^{2\pi} \cos^5 x \, dx$

15. $\int_0^{\frac{\pi}{2}} \frac{\sin x - \cos x}{1+\sin x \cos x} \, dx$

16. $\int_0^{\pi} \log(1+\cos x) \, dx$

17. $\int_0^a \frac{\sqrt{x}}{\sqrt{x} + \sqrt{a-x}} \, dx$

18. $\int_0^4 |x-1| \, dx$

19. Show that $\int_0^a f(x)g(x) \, dx = 2\int_0^a f(x) \, dx$, if f and g are defined as $f(x) = f(a-x)$ and $g(x) + g(a-x) = 4$

Choose the correct answer in Exercises 20 and 21.

20. The value of $\int_{-\frac{\pi}{2}}^{\frac{\pi}{2}} (x^3 + x\cos x + \tan^5 x + 1) \, dx$ is

(A) 0   (B) 2   (C) π (D) 1

21. The value of $\int_0^{\frac{\pi}{2}} \log\left(\frac{4+3\sin x}{4+3\cos x}\right) dx$ is

(A) 2   (B) $\frac{3}{4}$ (C) 0   (D) –2

Miscellaneous Examples

Example 37 Find $\int \cos 6x \sqrt{1+\sin 6x}\ dx$

Solution Put $t = 1 + \sin 6x$, so that $dt = 6 \cos 6x\ dx$

Therefore $\int \cos 6x \sqrt{1+\sin 6x}\ dx = \dfrac{1}{6}\int t^{\frac{1}{2}} dt$

$$= \frac{1}{6} \times \frac{2}{3}(t)^{\frac{3}{2}} + C = \frac{1}{9}(1+\sin 6x)^{\frac{3}{2}} + C$$

Example 38 Find $\int \dfrac{(x^4 - x)^{\frac{1}{4}}}{x^5}\ dx$

Solution We have $\int \dfrac{(x^4 - x)^{\frac{1}{4}}}{x^5}\ dx = \int \dfrac{(1-\frac{1}{x^3})^{\frac{1}{4}}}{x^4}\ dx$

Put $1 - \dfrac{1}{x^3} = 1 - x^{-3} = t$, so that $\dfrac{3}{x^4} dx = dt$

Therefore $\int \dfrac{(x^4 - x)^{\frac{1}{4}}}{x^5}\ dx = \dfrac{1}{3}\int t^{\frac{1}{4}}\ dt = \dfrac{1}{3}\times\dfrac{4}{5} t^{\frac{5}{4}} + C = \dfrac{4}{15}\left(1-\dfrac{1}{x^3}\right)^{\frac{5}{4}} + C$

Example 39 Find $\int \dfrac{x^4\ dx}{(x-1)(x^2+1)}$

Solution We have

$$\frac{x^4}{(x-1)(x^2+1)} = (x+1) + \frac{1}{x^3 - x^2 + x - 1}$$

$$= (x+1) + \frac{1}{(x-1)(x^2+1)} \qquad \dots (1)$$

Now express $\dfrac{1}{(x-1)(x^2+1)} = \dfrac{A}{(x-1)} + \dfrac{Bx+C}{(x^2+1)} \qquad \dots (2)$

So
$$1 = A (x^2 + 1) + (Bx + C) (x - 1)$$
$$= (A + B) x^2 + (C - B) x + A - C$$

Equating coefficients on both sides, we get $A + B = 0$, $C - B = 0$ and $A - C = 1$,

which give $A = \dfrac{1}{2}$, $B = C = -\dfrac{1}{2}$. Substituting values of A, B and C in (2), we get

$$\frac{1}{(x-1)(x^2+1)} = \frac{1}{2(x-1)} - \frac{1}{2}\frac{x}{(x^2+1)} - \frac{1}{2(x^2+1)} \qquad \dots (3)$$

Again, substituting (3) in (1), we have

$$\frac{x^4}{(x-1)(x^2+x+1)} = (x+1) + \frac{1}{2(x-1)} - \frac{1}{2}\frac{x}{(x^2+1)} - \frac{1}{2(x^2+1)}$$

Therefore

$$\int \frac{x^4}{(x-1)(x^2+x+1)} dx = \frac{x^2}{2} + x + \frac{1}{2}\log|x-1| - \frac{1}{4}\log(x^2+1) - \frac{1}{2}\tan^{-1}x + C$$

Example 40 Find $\displaystyle\int \left[\log(\log x) + \frac{1}{(\log x)^2} \right] dx$

Solution Let $I = \displaystyle\int \left[\log(\log x) + \frac{1}{(\log x)^2} \right] dx$

$$= \int \log(\log x)\, dx + \int \frac{1}{(\log x)^2}\, dx$$

In the first integral, let us take 1 as the second function. Then integrating it by parts, we get

$$I = x\log(\log x) - \int \frac{1}{x\log x} x\, dx + \int \frac{dx}{(\log x)^2}$$

$$= x\log(\log x) - \int \frac{dx}{\log x} + \int \frac{dx}{(\log x)^2} \qquad \dots (1)$$

Again, consider $\displaystyle\int \frac{dx}{\log x}$, take 1 as the second function and integrate it by parts,

we have $\displaystyle\int \frac{dx}{\log x} = \left[\frac{x}{\log x} - \int x \left\{ -\frac{1}{(\log x)^2} \left(\frac{1}{x} \right) \right\} dx \right] \qquad \dots (2)$

Putting (2) in (1), we get

$$I = x\log(\log x) - \frac{x}{\log x} - \int\frac{dx}{(\log x)^2} + \int\frac{dx}{(\log x)^2} = x\log(\log x) - \frac{x}{\log x} + C$$

Example 41 Find $\int\left[\sqrt{\cot x} + \sqrt{\tan x}\right]dx$

Solution We have

$$I = \int\left[\sqrt{\cot x} + \sqrt{\tan x}\right]dx = \int\sqrt{\tan x}(1 + \cot x)\,dx$$

Put $\tan x = t^2$, so that $\sec^2 x\,dx = 2t\,dt$

or $$dx = \frac{2t\,dt}{1 + t^4}$$

Then $$I = \int t\left(1 + \frac{1}{t^2}\right)\frac{2t}{(1+t^4)}\,dt$$

$$= 2\int\frac{(t^2+1)}{t^4+1}\,dt = 2\int\frac{\left(1+\dfrac{1}{t^2}\right)dt}{\left(t^2+\dfrac{1}{t^2}\right)} = 2\int\frac{\left(1+\dfrac{1}{t^2}\right)dt}{\left(t-\dfrac{1}{t}\right)^2+2}$$

Put $t - \dfrac{1}{t} = y$, so that $\left(1 + \dfrac{1}{t^2}\right)dt = dy$. Then

$$I = 2\int\frac{dy}{y^2 + \left(\sqrt{2}\right)^2} = \sqrt{2}\,\tan^{-1}\frac{y}{\sqrt{2}} + C = \sqrt{2}\,\tan^{-1}\frac{\left(t-\dfrac{1}{t}\right)}{\sqrt{2}} + C$$

$$= \sqrt{2}\,\tan^{-1}\left(\frac{t^2-1}{\sqrt{2}\,t}\right) + C = \sqrt{2}\,\tan^{-1}\left(\frac{\tan x - 1}{\sqrt{2\tan x}}\right) + C$$

Example 42 Find $\displaystyle\int\frac{\sin 2x\cos 2x\,dx}{\sqrt{9 - \cos^4(2x)}}$

Solution Let $I = \displaystyle\int\frac{\sin 2x\cos 2x}{\sqrt{9 - \cos^4 2x}}\,dx$

Put $\cos^2 (2x) = t$ so that $4 \sin 2x \cos 2x \, dx = -\, dt$

Therefore $\quad I = -\dfrac{1}{4}\displaystyle\int \dfrac{dt}{\sqrt{9-t^2}} = -\dfrac{1}{4}\sin^{-1}\left(\dfrac{t}{3}\right) + C = -\dfrac{1}{4}\sin^{-1}\left[\dfrac{1}{3}\cos^2 2x\right] + C$

Example 43 Evaluate $\displaystyle\int_{-1}^{\frac{3}{2}} |x \sin (\pi x)| \, dx$

Solution Here $f(x) = |x \sin \pi x| = \begin{cases} x \sin \pi x \text{ for } -1 \le x \le 1 \\ -x \sin \pi x \text{ for } 1 \le x \le \dfrac{3}{2} \end{cases}$

Therefore $\quad \displaystyle\int_{-1}^{\frac{3}{2}} |x \sin \pi x| \, dx = \int_{-1}^{1} x \sin \pi x \, dx + \int_{1}^{\frac{3}{2}} - x \sin \pi x \, dx$

$$= \int_{-1}^{1} x \sin \pi x \, dx - \int_{1}^{\frac{3}{2}} x \sin \pi x \, dx$$

Integrating both integrals on righthand side, we get

$$\int_{-1}^{\frac{3}{2}} |x \sin \pi x| \, dx = \left[\dfrac{-x \cos \pi x}{\pi} + \dfrac{\sin \pi x}{\pi^2}\right]_{-1}^{1} - \left[\dfrac{-x \cos \pi x}{\pi} + \dfrac{\sin \pi x}{\pi^2}\right]_{1}^{\frac{3}{2}}$$

$$= \dfrac{2}{\pi} - \left[-\dfrac{1}{\pi^2} - \dfrac{1}{\pi}\right] = \dfrac{3}{\pi} + \dfrac{1}{\pi^2}$$

Example 44 Evaluate $\displaystyle\int_{0}^{\pi} \dfrac{x \, dx}{a^2 \cos^2 x + b^2 \sin^2 x}$

Solution Let $I = \displaystyle\int_{0}^{\pi} \dfrac{x \, dx}{a^2 \cos^2 x + b^2 \sin^2 x} = \int_{0}^{\pi} \dfrac{(\pi - x)\, dx}{a^2 \cos^2 (\pi - x) + b^2 \sin^2 (\pi - x)}$ (using P_4)

$$= \pi \int_{0}^{\pi} \dfrac{dx}{a^2 \cos^2 x + b^2 \sin^2 x} - \int_{0}^{\pi} \dfrac{x \, dx}{a^2 \cos^2 x + b^2 \sin^2 x}$$

$$= \pi \int_{0}^{\pi} \dfrac{dx}{a^2 \cos^2 x + b^2 \sin^2 x} - I$$

Thus $\quad 2I = \pi \displaystyle\int_{0}^{\pi} \dfrac{dx}{a^2 \cos^2 x + b^2 \sin^2 x}$

or
$$I = \frac{\pi}{2} \int_0^\pi \frac{dx}{a^2 \cos^2 x + b^2 \sin^2 x} = \frac{\pi}{2} \cdot 2 \int_0^{\frac{\pi}{2}} \frac{dx}{a^2 \cos^2 x + b^2 \sin^2 x} \ (\text{using } P_6)$$

$$= \pi \left[\int_0^{\frac{\pi}{4}} \frac{dx}{a^2 \cos^2 x + b^2 \sin^2 x} + \int_{\frac{\pi}{4}}^{\frac{\pi}{2}} \frac{dx}{a^2 \cos^2 x + b^2 \sin^2 x} \right]$$

$$= \pi \left[\int_0^{\frac{\pi}{4}} \frac{\sec^2 x \, dx}{a^2 + b^2 \tan^2 x} + \int_{\frac{\pi}{4}}^{\frac{\pi}{2}} \frac{\cosec^2 x \, dx}{a^2 \cot^2 x + b^2} \right]$$

$$= \pi \left[\int_0^1 \frac{dt}{a^2 + b^2 t^2} - \int_1^0 \frac{du}{a^2 u^2 + b^2} \right] (\text{put} \tan x = t \text{ and } \cot x = u)$$

$$= \frac{\pi}{ab} \left[\tan^{-1} \frac{bt}{a} \right]_0^1 - \frac{\pi}{ab} \left[\tan^{-1} \frac{au}{b} \right]_1^0 = \frac{\pi}{ab} \left[\tan^{-1} \frac{b}{a} + \tan^{-1} \frac{a}{b} \right] = \frac{\pi^2}{2ab}$$

Miscellaneous Exercise on Chapter 7

Integrate the functions in Exercises 1 to 24.

1. $\dfrac{1}{x - x^3}$

2. $\dfrac{1}{\sqrt{x+a} + \sqrt{x+b}}$

3. $\dfrac{1}{x\sqrt{ax - x^2}}$ [Hint: Put $x = \dfrac{a}{t}$]

4. $\dfrac{1}{x^2 (x^4 + 1)^{\frac{3}{4}}}$

5. $\dfrac{1}{x^{\frac{1}{2}} + x^{\frac{1}{3}}}$ [Hint: $\dfrac{1}{x^{\frac{1}{2}} + x^{\frac{1}{3}}} = \dfrac{1}{x^{\frac{1}{3}} \left(1 + x^{\frac{1}{6}} \right)}$, put $x = t^6$]

6. $\dfrac{5x}{(x+1)(x^2 + 9)}$

7. $\dfrac{\sin x}{\sin (x - a)}$

8. $\dfrac{e^{5 \log x} - e^{4 \log x}}{e^{3 \log x} - e^{2 \log x}}$

9. $\dfrac{\cos x}{\sqrt{4 - \sin^2 x}}$

10. $\dfrac{\sin^8 - \cos^8 x}{1 - 2 \sin^2 x \cos^2 x}$

11. $\dfrac{1}{\cos (x+a) \cos (x+b)}$

12. $\dfrac{x^3}{\sqrt{1 - x^8}}$

13. $\dfrac{e^x}{(1 + e^x)(2 + e^x)}$

14. $\dfrac{1}{(x^2 + 1)(x^2 + 4)}$

15. $\cos^3 x \ e^{\log \sin x}$

16. $e^{3 \log x} (x^4 + 1)^{-1}$

17. $f'(ax + b) [f(ax + b)]^n$

18. $\dfrac{1}{\sqrt{\sin^3 x \sin (x + \alpha)}}$

19. $\dfrac{\sin^{-1} \sqrt{x} - \cos^{-1} \sqrt{x}}{\sin^{-1} \sqrt{x} + \cos^{-1} \sqrt{x}}$, $x \in [0, 1]$

20. $\sqrt{\dfrac{1-\sqrt{x}}{1+\sqrt{x}}}$

21. $\dfrac{2+\sin 2x}{1+\cos 2x}e^x$

22. $\dfrac{x^2+x+1}{(x+1)^2\,(x+2)}$

23. $\tan^{-1}\sqrt{\dfrac{1-x}{1+x}}$,

24. $\dfrac{\sqrt{x^2+1}\left[\log(x^2+1)-2\log x\right]}{x^4}$

Evaluate the definite integrals in Exercises 25 to 33.

25. $\displaystyle\int_{\frac{\pi}{2}}^{\pi} e^x\left(\dfrac{1-\sin x}{1-\cos x}\right)dx$

26. $\displaystyle\int_0^{\frac{\pi}{4}}\dfrac{\sin x\,\cos x}{\cos^4 x+\sin^4 x}dx$

27. $\displaystyle\int_0^{\frac{\pi}{2}}\dfrac{\cos^2 x\,dx}{\cos^2 x+4\sin^2 x}$

28. $\displaystyle\int_{\frac{\pi}{6}}^{\frac{\pi}{3}}\dfrac{\sin x+\cos x}{\sqrt{\sin 2x}}dx$

29. $\displaystyle\int_0^1\dfrac{dx}{\sqrt{1+x}-\sqrt{x}}$

30. $\displaystyle\int_0^{\frac{\pi}{4}}\dfrac{\sin x+\cos x}{9+16\sin 2x}dx$

31. $\displaystyle\int_0^{\frac{\pi}{2}}\sin 2x\tan^{-1}(\sin x)\,dx$

32. $\displaystyle\int_0^{\pi}\dfrac{x\tan x}{\sec x+\tan x}dx$

33. $\displaystyle\int_1^4[\,|x-1|+|x-2|+|x-3|\,]\,dx$

Prove the following (Exercises 34 to 39)

34. $\displaystyle\int_1^3\dfrac{dx}{x^2(x+1)}=\dfrac{2}{3}+\log\dfrac{2}{3}$

35. $\displaystyle\int_0^1 x\,e^x\,dx=1$

36. $\displaystyle\int_{-1}^1 x^{17}\cos^4 x\,dx=0$

37. $\displaystyle\int_0^{\frac{\pi}{2}}\sin^3 x\,dx=\dfrac{2}{3}$

38. $\displaystyle\int_0^{\frac{\pi}{4}}2\tan^3 x\,dx=1-\log 2$

39. $\displaystyle\int_0^1\sin^{-1}x\,dx=\dfrac{\pi}{2}-1$

40. Evaluate $\displaystyle\int_0^1 e^{2-3x}dx$ as a limit of a sum.

Choose the correct answers in Exercises 41 to 44.

41. $\displaystyle\int\dfrac{dx}{e^x+e^{-x}}$ is equal to

(A) $\tan^{-1}(e^x)+C$

(B) $\tan^{-1}(e^{-x})+C$

(C) $\log(e^x-e^{-x})+C$

(D) $\log(e^x+e^{-x})+C$

42. $\displaystyle\int\dfrac{\cos 2x}{(\sin x+\cos x)^2}dx$ is equal to

(A) $\dfrac{-1}{\sin x+\cos x}+C$

(B) $\log|\sin x+\cos x|+C$

(C) $\log|\sin x-\cos x|+C$

(D) $\dfrac{1}{(\sin x+\cos x)^2}$

3. If $f(a+b-x) = f(x)$, then $\int_a^b x\, f(x)\, dx$ is equal to

(A) $\dfrac{a+b}{2} \int_a^b f(b-x)\, dx$

(B) $\dfrac{a+b}{2} \int_a^b f(b+x)\, dx$

(C) $\dfrac{b-a}{2} \int_a^b f(x)\, dx$

(D) $\dfrac{a+b}{2} \int_a^b f(x)\, dx$

4. The value of $\int_0^1 \tan^{-1}\left(\dfrac{2x-1}{1+x-x^2}\right) dx$ is

(A) 1   (B) 0   (C) −1   (D) $\dfrac{\pi}{4}$

Summary

◆ Integration is the inverse process of differentiation. In the differential calculus, we are given a function and we have to find the derivative or differential of this function, but in the integral calculus, we are to find a function whose differential is given. Thus, integration is a process which is the inverse of differentiation.

Let $\dfrac{d}{dx} F(x) = f(x)$. Then we write $\int f(x)\, dx = F(x) + C$. These integrals are called indefinite integrals or general integrals, C is called constant of integration. All these integrals differ by a constant.

◆ From the geometric point of view, an indefinite integral is collection of family of curves, each of which is obtained by translating one of the curves parallel to itself upwards or downwards along the y-axis.

◆ Some properties of indefinite integrals are as follows:

1. $\int [f(x) + g(x)]\, dx = \int f(x)\, dx + \int g(x)\, dx$

2. For any real number k, $\int k\, f(x)\, dx = k \int f(x)\, dx$

More generally, if $f_1, f_2, f_3, \dots, f_n$ are functions and $k_1, k_2, \dots, k_n$ are real numbers. Then

$\int [k_1 f_1(x) + k_2 f_2(x) + \dots + k_n f_n(x)]\, dx$

$= k_1 \int f_1(x)\, dx + k_2 \int f_2(x)\, dx + \dots + k_n \int f_n(x)\, dx$

◆ **Some standard integrals**

(i) $\int x^n dx = \dfrac{x^{n+1}}{n+1} + C, \ n \neq -1.$ Particularly, $\int dx = x + C$

(ii) $\int \cos x \, dx = \sin x + C$ (iii) $\int \sin x \, dx = -\cos x + C$

(iv) $\int \sec^2 x \, dx = \tan x + C$ (v) $\int \mathrm{cosec}^2 x \, dx = -\cot x + C$

(vi) $\int \sec x \tan x \, dx = \sec x + C$

(vii) $\int \mathrm{cosec}\, x \cot x \, dx = -\mathrm{cosec}\, x + C$ (viii) $\int \dfrac{dx}{\sqrt{1-x^2}} = \sin^{-1} x + C$

(ix) $\int \dfrac{dx}{\sqrt{1-x^2}} = -\cos^{-1} x + C$ (x) $\int \dfrac{dx}{1+x^2} = \tan^{-1} x + C$

(xi) $\int \dfrac{dx}{1+x^2} = -\cot^{-1} x + C$ (xii) $\int e^x dx = e^x + C$

(xiii) $\int a^x dx = \dfrac{a^x}{\log a} + C$ (xiv) $\int \dfrac{dx}{x\sqrt{x^2-1}} = \sec^{-1} x + C$

(xv) $\int \dfrac{dx}{x\sqrt{x^2-1}} = -\mathrm{cosec}^{-1} x + C$ (xvi) $\int \dfrac{1}{x} dx = \log |x| + C$

◆ **Integration by partial fractions**

Recall that a rational function is ratio of two polynomials of the form $\dfrac{P(x)}{Q(x)}$, where $P(x)$ and $Q(x)$ are polynomials in x and $Q(x) \neq 0$. If degree of the polynomial $P(x)$ is greater than the degree of the polynomial $Q(x)$, then we may divide $P(x)$ by $Q(x)$ so that $\dfrac{P(x)}{Q(x)} = T(x) + \dfrac{P_1(x)}{Q(x)}$, where $T(x)$ is a polynomial in x and degree of $P_1(x)$ is less than the degree of $Q(x)$. $T(x)$ being polynomial can be easily integrated. $\dfrac{P_1(x)}{Q(x)}$ can be integrated by expressing $\dfrac{P_1(x)}{Q(x)}$ as the sum of partial fractions of the following type:

1. $\dfrac{px+q}{(x-a)(x-b)} = \dfrac{A}{x-a} + \dfrac{B}{x-b}, \; a \neq b$

2. $\dfrac{px+q}{(x-a)^2} = \dfrac{A}{x-a} + \dfrac{B}{(x-a)^2}$

3. $\dfrac{px^2+qx+r}{(x-a)(x-b)(x-c)} = \dfrac{A}{x-a} + \dfrac{B}{x-b} + \dfrac{C}{x-c}$

4. $\dfrac{px^2+qx+r}{(x-a)^2(x-b)} = \dfrac{A}{x-a} + \dfrac{B}{(x-a)^2} + \dfrac{C}{x-b}$

5. $\dfrac{px^2+qx+r}{(x-a)(x^2+bx+c)} = \dfrac{A}{x-a} + \dfrac{Bx+C}{x^2+bx+c}$

where $x^2 + bx + c$ can not be factorised further.

◆ **Integration by substitution**

A change in the variable of integration often reduces an integral to one of the fundamental integrals. The method in which we change the variable to some other variable is called the method of substitution. When the integrand involves some trigonometric functions, we use some well known identities to find the integrals. Using substitution technique, we obtain the following standard integrals.

(i) $\displaystyle\int \tan x \, dx = \log|\sec x| + C$ 　　　(ii) $\displaystyle\int \cot x \, dx = \log|\sin x| + C$

(iii) $\displaystyle\int \sec x \, dx = \log|\sec x + \tan x| + C$

(iv) $\displaystyle\int \operatorname{cosec} x \, dx = \log|\operatorname{cosec} x - \cot x| + C$

◆ **Integrals of some special functions**

(i) $\displaystyle\int \dfrac{dx}{x^2-a^2} = \dfrac{1}{2a} \log\left|\dfrac{x-a}{x+a}\right| + C$

(ii) $\displaystyle\int \dfrac{dx}{a^2-x^2} = \dfrac{1}{2a} \log\left|\dfrac{a+x}{a-x}\right| + C$ 　　　(iii) $\displaystyle\int \dfrac{dx}{x^2+a^2} = \dfrac{1}{a} \tan^{-1}\dfrac{x}{a} + C$

(iv) $\int \dfrac{dx}{\sqrt{x^2 - a^2}} = \log\left|x + \sqrt{x^2 - a^2}\right| + C$ (v) $\int \dfrac{dx}{\sqrt{a^2 - x^2}} = \sin^{-1}\dfrac{x}{a} + C$

(vi) $\int \dfrac{dx}{\sqrt{x^2 + a^2}} = \log\left|x + \sqrt{x^2 + a^2}\right| + C$

◆ **Integration by parts**

For given functions f_1 and f_2, we have

$$\int f_1(x) \cdot f_2(x)\, dx = f_1(x) \int f_2(x)\, dx - \int\left[\dfrac{d}{dx} f_1(x) \cdot \int f_2(x)\, dx\right] dx \,, \quad \text{i.e., the}$$

integral of the product of two functions = first function × integral of the second function – integral of {differential coefficient of the first function × integral of the second function}. Care must be taken in choosing the first function and the second function. Obviously, we must take that function as the second function whose integral is well known to us.

◆ $\int e^x[f(x) + f'(x)]\, dx = \int e^x f(x)\, dx + C$

◆ **Some special types of integrals**

(i) $\int \sqrt{x^2 - a^2}\, dx = \dfrac{x}{2}\sqrt{x^2 - a^2} - \dfrac{a^2}{2}\log\left|x + \sqrt{x^2 - a^2}\right| + C$

(ii) $\int \sqrt{x^2 + a^2}\, dx = \dfrac{x}{2}\sqrt{x^2 + a^2} + \dfrac{a^2}{2}\log\left|x + \sqrt{x^2 + a^2}\right| + C$

(iii) $\int \sqrt{a^2 - x^2}\, dx = \dfrac{x}{2}\sqrt{a^2 - x^2} + \dfrac{a^2}{2}\sin^{-1}\dfrac{x}{a} + C$

(iv) Integrals of the types $\int \dfrac{dx}{ax^2 + bx + c}$ or $\int \dfrac{dx}{\sqrt{ax^2 + bx + c}}$ can be transformed into standard form by expressing

$$ax^2 + bx + c = a\left[x^2 + \dfrac{b}{a}x + \dfrac{c}{a}\right] = a\left[\left(x + \dfrac{b}{2a}\right)^2 + \left(\dfrac{c}{a} - \dfrac{b^2}{4a^2}\right)\right]$$

(v) Integrals of the types $\int \dfrac{px + q\, dx}{ax^2 + bx + c}$ or $\int \dfrac{px + q\, dx}{\sqrt{ax^2 + bx + c}}$ can be transformed into standard form by expressing

$$px + q = A\frac{d}{dx}(ax^2 + bx + c) + B = A(2ax + b) + B, \text{ where A and B are}$$

determined by comparing coefficients on both sides.

◆ We have defined $\int_a^b f(x)\,dx$ as the area of the region bounded by the curve

$y = f(x)$, $a \le x \le b$, the x-axis and the ordinates $x = a$ and $x = b$. Let x be a

given point in $[a, b]$. Then $\int_a^x f(x)\,dx$ represents the **Area function** A (x).

This concept of area function leads to the Fundamental Theorems of Integral Calculus.

◆ **First fundamental theorem of integral calculus**

Let the area function be defined by A$(x) = \int_a^x f(x)\,dx$ for all $x \ge a$, where

the function f is assumed to be continuous on $[a, b]$. Then A$'(x) = f(x)$ for all $x \in [a, b]$.

◆ **Second fundamental theorem of integral calculus**
Let f be a continuous function of x defined on the closed interval $[a, b]$ and

let F be another function such that $\dfrac{d}{dx}F(x) = f(x)$ for all x in the domain of

f, then $\int_a^b f(x)\,dx = \left[F(x) + C\right]_a^b = F(b) - F(a)$.

This is called the definite integral of f over the range $[a, b]$, where a and b are called the limits of integration, a being the lower limit and b the upper limit.

—◈—

Chapter 8

APPLICATION OF INTEGRALS

❖ *One should study Mathematics because it is only through Mathematics that nature can be conceived in harmonious form. – BIRKHOFF* ❖

8.1 Introduction

In geometry, we have learnt formulae to calculate areas of various geometrical figures including triangles, rectangles, trapezias and circles. Such formulae are fundamental in the applications of mathematics to many real life problems. The formulae of elementary geometry allow us to calculate areas of many simple figures. However, they are inadequate for calculating the areas enclosed by curves. For that we shall need some concepts of Integral Calculus.

In the previous chapter, we have studied to find the area bounded by the curve $y = f(x)$, the ordinates $x = a$, $x = b$ and x-axis, while calculating definite integral as the limit of a sum. Here, in this chapter, we shall study a specific application of integrals to find the area under simple curves, area between lines and arcs of circles, parabolas and ellipses (standard forms only). We shall also deal with finding the area bounded by the above said curves.

A.L. Cauchy
(1789-1857)

8.2 Area under Simple Curves

In the previous chapter, we have studied definite integral as the limit of a sum and how to evaluate definite integral using Fundamental Theorem of Calculus. Now, we consider the easy and intuitive way of finding the area bounded by the curve $y = f(x)$, x-axis and the ordinates $x = a$ and $x = b$. From Fig 8.1, we can think of area under the curve as composed of large number of very thin vertical strips. Consider an arbitrary strip of height y and width dx, then dA (area of the elementary strip)$= ydx$, where, $y = f(x)$.

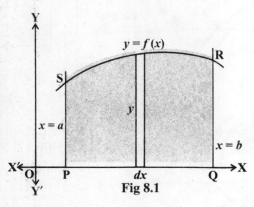

Fig 8.1

This area is called the *elementary area* which is located at an arbitrary position within the region which is specified by some value of x between a and b. We can think of the total area A of the region between x-axis, ordinates $x = a$, $x = b$ and the curve $y = f(x)$ as the result of adding up the elementary areas of thin strips across the region PQRSP. Symbolically, we express

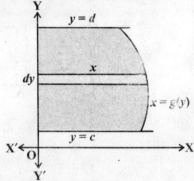

$$A = \int_a^b dA = \int_a^b y\,dx = \int_a^b f(x)\,dx$$

The area A of the region bounded by the curve $x = g(y)$, y-axis and the lines $y = c$, $y = d$ is given by

$$A = \int_c^d x\,dy = \int_c^d g(y)\,dy$$

Here, we consider horizontal strips as shown in the Fig 8.2

Fig 8.2

Remark If the position of the curve under consideration is below the x-axis, then since $f(x) < 0$ from $x = a$ to $x = b$, as shown in Fig 8.3, the area bounded by the curve, x-axis and the ordinates $x = a$, $x = b$ come out to be negative. But, it is only the numerical value of the area which is taken into consideration. Thus, if the area is negative, we take its absolute value, i.e., $\left| \int_a^b f(x)\,dx \right|$.

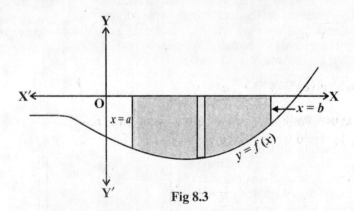

Fig 8.3

Generally, it may happen that some portion of the curve is above x-axis and some is below the x-axis as shown in the Fig 8.4. Here, $A_1 < 0$ and $A_2 > 0$. Therefore, the area A bounded by the curve $y = f(x)$, x-axis and the ordinates $x = a$ and $x = b$ is given by $A = |A_1| + A_2$.

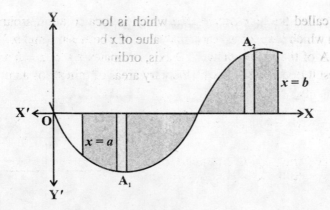

Fig 8.4

Example 1 Find the area enclosed by the circle $x^2 + y^2 = a^2$.

Solution From Fig 8.5, the whole area enclosed by the given circle

= 4 (area of the region AOBA bounded by the curve, x-axis and the ordinates $x = 0$ and $x = a$) [as the circle is symmetrical about both x-axis and y-axis]

$= 4 \int vdx$ (taking vertical strips)

$= 4 \int_0 \sqrt{a^2 - x^2}\ dx$

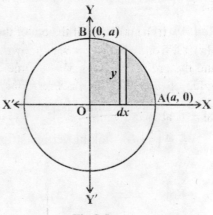

Fig 8.5

Since $x^2 + y^2 = a^2$ gives $\quad y = \pm\sqrt{a^2 - x^2}$

As the region AOBA lies in the first quadrant, y is taken as positive. Integrating, we get the whole area enclosed by the given circle

$$= 4\left[\frac{x}{2}\sqrt{a^2 - x^2} + \frac{a^2}{2}\sin^{-1}\frac{x}{a}\right]_0^a$$

$$= 4\left[\left(\frac{a}{2}\times 0 + \frac{a^2}{2}\sin^{-1}1\right) - 0\right] = 4\left(\frac{a^2}{2}\right)\left(\frac{\pi}{2}\right) = \pi a^2$$

Alternatively, considering horizontal strips as shown in Fig 8.6, the whole area of the region enclosed by circle

$$= 4\int_0^a x dy = 4\int_0^a \sqrt{a^2 - y^2}\, dy \quad \text{(Why?)}$$

$$= 4\left[\frac{y}{2}\sqrt{a^2 - y^2} + \frac{a^2}{2}\sin^{-1}\frac{y}{a}\right]_0^a$$

$$= 4\left[\left(\frac{a}{2}\times 0 + \frac{a^2}{2}\sin^{-1}1\right) - 0\right]$$

$$= 4\frac{a^2}{2}\frac{\pi}{2} = \pi a^2$$

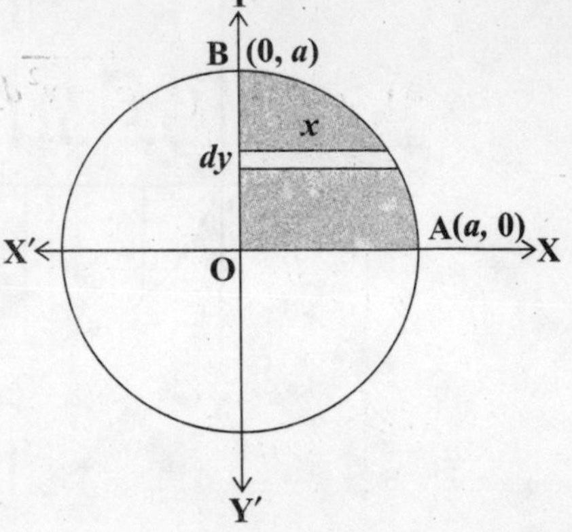

Fig 8.6

Example 2 Find the area enclosed by the ellipse $\dfrac{x^2}{a^2} + \dfrac{y^2}{b^2} = 1$

Solution From Fig 8.7, the area of the region ABA′B′A bounded by the ellipse

$$= 4 \begin{pmatrix} \text{area of the region } AOBA \text{ in } \textit{the first quadrant bounded} \\ \textit{by the curve, } x - \textit{axis and the ordinates } x = 0, x = a \end{pmatrix}$$

(as the ellipse is symmetrical about both x-axis and y-axis)

$$= 4\int_0^a y dx \quad \text{(taking vertical strips)}$$

Now $\dfrac{x^2}{a^2} + \dfrac{y^2}{b^2} = 1$ gives $y = \pm\dfrac{b}{a}\sqrt{a^2 - x^2}$, but as the region AOBA lies in the first

quadrant, y is taken as positive. So, the required area is

$$= 4\int_0^a \frac{b}{a}\sqrt{a^2 - x^2}\, dx$$

$$= \frac{4b}{a}\left[\frac{x}{2}\sqrt{a^2 - x^2} + \frac{a^2}{2}\sin^{-1}\frac{x}{a}\right]_0^a \quad \text{(Why?)}$$

$$= \frac{4b}{a}\left[\left(\frac{a}{2}\times 0 + \frac{a^2}{2}\sin^{-1}1\right) - 0\right]$$

$$= \frac{4b}{a}\frac{a^2}{2}\frac{\pi}{2} = \pi ab$$

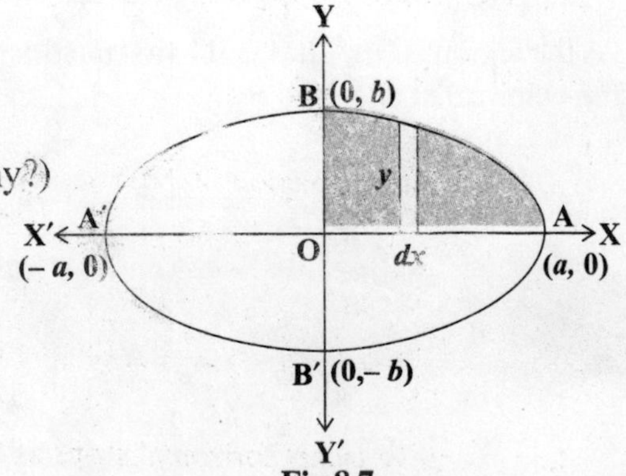

Fig 8.7

Alternatively, considering horizontal strips as shown in the Fig 8.8, the area of the ellipse is

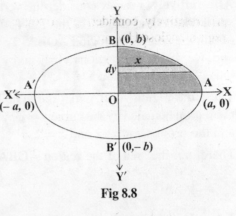

Fig 8.8

$$= 4\int_0^b xdy = 4\frac{a}{b}\int_0^b \sqrt{b^2 - y^2}\,dy \quad \text{(Why?)}$$

$$= \frac{4a}{b}\left[\frac{y}{2}\sqrt{b^2 - y^2} + \frac{b^2}{2}\sin^{-1}\frac{y}{b}\right]_0^b$$

$$= \frac{4a}{b}\left[\left(\frac{b}{2}\times 0 + \frac{b^2}{2}\sin^{-1}1\right) - 0\right]$$

$$= \frac{4a}{b}\frac{b^2}{2}\frac{\pi}{2} = \pi ab$$

8.2.1 *The area of the region bounded by a curve and a line*

In this subsection, we will find the area of the region bounded by a line and a circle, a line and a parabola, a line and an ellipse. Equations of above mentioned curves will be in their standard forms only as the cases in other forms go beyond the scope of this textbook.

Example 3 Find the area of the region bounded by the curve $y = x^2$ and the line $y = 4$.

Solution Since the given curve represented by the equation $y = x^2$ is a parabola symmetrical about y-axis only, therefore, from Fig 8.9, the required area of the region AOBA is given by

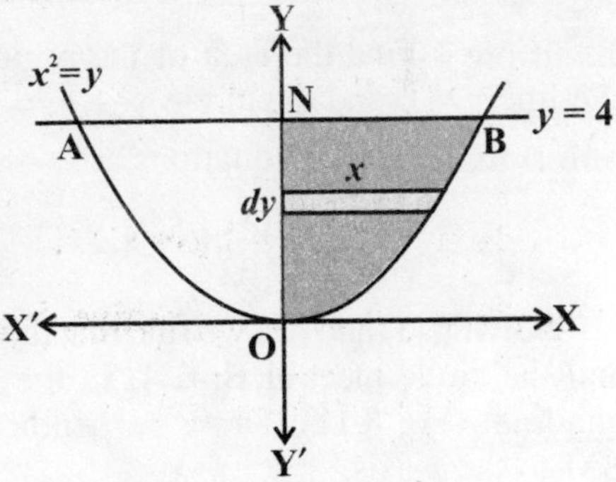

Fig 8.9

$$2\int_0^4 xdy =$$

$$2\left(\begin{array}{l}\text{area of the region BONB bounded by curve, } y - \text{axis}\\ \text{and the lines } y=0 \text{ and } y=4\end{array}\right)$$

$$= 2\int_0^4 \sqrt{y}\,dy = 2\times\frac{2}{3}\left[y^{\frac{3}{2}}\right]_0^4 = \frac{4}{3}\times 8 = \frac{32}{3} \quad \text{(Why?)}$$

Here, we have taken horizontal strips as indicated in the Fig 8.9.

Alternatively, we may consider the vertical strips like PQ as shown in the Fig 8.10 to obtain the area of the region AOBA. To this end, we solve the equations $x^2 = y$ and $y = 4$ which gives $x = -2$ and $x = 2$.

Thus, the region AOBA may be stated as the region bounded by the curve $y = x^2, y = 4$ and the ordinates $x = -2$ and $x = 2$.

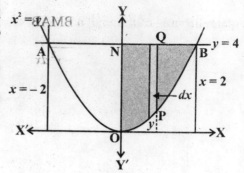

Fig 8.10

Therefore, the area of the region AOBA

$$= \int_{-2}^{2} y \, dx$$

$$[y = (y\text{-coordinate of Q}) - (y\text{-coordinate of P}) = 4 - x^2]$$

$$= 2 \int_{0}^{2} (4 - x^2) \, dx \quad \text{(Why?)}$$

$$= 2 \left[4x - \frac{x^3}{3} \right]_{0}^{2} = 2 \left[4 \times 2 - \frac{8}{3} \right] = \frac{32}{3}$$

Remark From the above examples, it is inferred that we can consider either vertical strips or horizontal strips for calculating the area of the region. Henceforth, we shall consider either of these two, most preferably vertical strips.

Example 4 Find the area of the region in the first quadrant enclosed by the x-axis, the line $y = x$, and the circle $x^2 + y^2 = 32$.

Solution The given equations are

$$y = x \qquad \ldots (1)$$

and $\qquad x^2 + y^2 = 32 \qquad \ldots (2)$

Solving (1) and (2), we find that the line and the circle meet at B(4, 4) in the first quadrant (Fig 8.11). Draw perpendicular BM to the x-axis.

Therefore, the required area = area of the region OBMO + area of the region BMAB.

Now, the area of the region OBMO

$$= \int_{0}^{4} y \, dx = \int_{0}^{4} x \, dx \qquad \ldots (3)$$

$$= \frac{1}{2} \left[x^2 \right]_{0}^{4} = 8$$

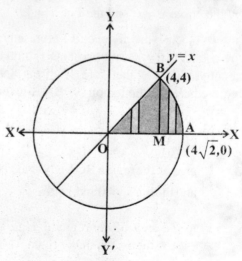

Fig 8.11

Again, the area of the region BMAB

$$= \int_4^{4\sqrt{2}} y\,dx = \int_4^{4\sqrt{2}} \sqrt{32 - x^2}\,dx$$

$$= \left[\frac{1}{2} x\sqrt{32 - x^2} + \frac{1}{2} \times 32 \times \sin^{-1} \frac{x}{4\sqrt{2}} \right]_4^{4\sqrt{2}}$$

$$= \left(\frac{1}{2} 4\sqrt{2} \times 0 + \frac{1}{2} \times 32 \times \sin^{-1} 1 \right) - \left(\frac{4}{2} \sqrt{32 - 16} + \frac{1}{2} \times 32 \times \sin^{-1} \frac{1}{\sqrt{2}} \right)$$

$$= 8\pi - (8 + 4\pi) = 4\pi - 8 \qquad \qquad \dots (4)$$

Adding (3) and (4), we get, the required area = 4π.

Example 5 Find the area bounded by the ellipse $\dfrac{x^2}{a^2} + \dfrac{y^2}{b^2} = 1$ and the ordinates $x = 0$

and $x = ae$, where, $b^2 = a^2 (1 - e^2)$ and $e < 1$.

Solution The required area (Fig 8.12) of the region BOB′RFSB is enclosed by the ellipse and the lines $x = 0$ and $x = ae$.

Note that the area of the region BOB′RFSB

$$= 2 \int_0^{ae} y\,dx = 2 \frac{b}{a} \int_0^{ae} \sqrt{a^2 - x^2}\,dx$$

$$= \frac{2b}{a} \left[\frac{x}{2} \sqrt{a^2 - x^2} + \frac{a^2}{2} \sin^{-1} \frac{x}{a} \right]_0^{ae}$$

$$= \frac{2b}{2a} \left[ae\sqrt{a^2 - a^2 e^2} + a^2 \sin^{-1} e \right]$$

$$= ab \left[e\sqrt{1 - e^2} + \sin^{-1} e \right]$$

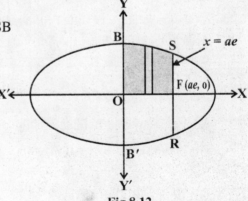

Fig 8.12

EXERCISE 8.1

1. Find the area of the region bounded by the curve $y^2 = x$ and the lines $x = 1$, $x = 4$ and the x-axis in the first quadrant.

2. Find the area of the region bounded by $y^2 = 9x$, $x = 2$, $x = 4$ and the x-axis in the first quadrant.

3. Find the area of the region bounded by $x^2 = 4y$, $y = 2$, $y = 4$ and the y-axis in the first quadrant.

4. Find the area of the region bounded by the ellipse $\dfrac{x^2}{16} + \dfrac{y^2}{9} = 1$.

5. Find the area of the region bounded by the ellipse $\dfrac{x^2}{4} + \dfrac{y^2}{9} = 1$.

6. Find the area of the region in the first quadrant enclosed by x-axis, line $x = \sqrt{3}\,y$ and the circle $x^2 + y^2 = 4$.

7. Find the area of the smaller part of the circle $x^2 + y^2 = a^2$ cut off by the line $x = \dfrac{a}{\sqrt{2}}$.

8. The area between $x = y^2$ and $x = 4$ is divided into two equal parts by the line $x = a$, find the value of a.

9. Find the area of the region bounded by the parabola $y = x^2$ and $y = |x|$.

10. Find the area bounded by the curve $x^2 = 4y$ and the line $x = 4y - 2$.

11. Find the area of the region bounded by the curve $y^2 = 4x$ and the line $x = 3$.

Choose the correct answer in the following Exercises 12 and 13.

12. Area lying in the first quadrant and bounded by the circle $x^2 + y^2 = 4$ and the lines $x = 0$ and $x = 2$ is

(A) π (B) $\dfrac{\pi}{2}$ (C) $\dfrac{\pi}{3}$ (D) $\dfrac{\pi}{4}$

13. Area of the region bounded by the curve $y^2 = 4x$, y-axis and the line $y = 3$ is

(A) 2 (B) $\dfrac{9}{4}$ (C) $\dfrac{9}{3}$ (D) $\dfrac{9}{2}$

3.3 Area between Two Curves

Intuitively, true in the sense of Leibnitz, integration is the act of calculating the area by cutting the region into a large number of small strips of elementary area and then adding up these elementary areas. Suppose we are given two curves represented by $y = f(x)$, $y = g(x)$, where $f(x) \geq g(x)$ in $[a, b]$ as shown in Fig 8.13. Here the points of intersection of these two curves are given by $x = a$ and $x = b$ obtained by taking common values of y from the given equation of two curves.

For setting up a formula for the integral, it is convenient to take elementary area in the form of vertical strips. As indicated in the Fig 8.13, elementary strip has height

$f(x) - g(x)$ and width dx so that the elementary area

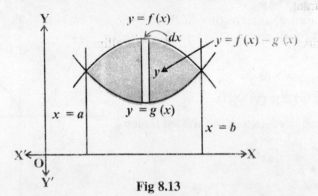

Fig 8.13

$dA = [f(x) - g(x)]\ dx$, and the total area A can be taken as

$$A = \int_a^b [f(x) - g(x)]\,dx$$

Alternatively,

A = [area bounded by $y = f(x)$, x-axis and the lines $x = a, x = b$]

   – [area bounded by $y = g(x)$, x-axis and the lines $x = a, x = b$]

$$= \int_a^b f(x)\,dx - \int_a^b g(x)\,dx\ = \int_a^b [f(x) - g(x)]\,dx, \text{ where } f(x) \geq g(x) \text{ in } [a, b]$$

If $f(x) \geq g(x)$ in $[a, c]$ and $f(x) \leq g(x)$ in $[c, b]$, where $a < c < b$ as shown in the Fig 8.14, then the area of the regions bounded by curves can be written as

Total Area = Area of the region ACBDA + Area of the region BPRQB

$$= \int_a^c [f(x) - g(x)]\,dx + \int_c^b [g(x) - f(x)]\,dx$$

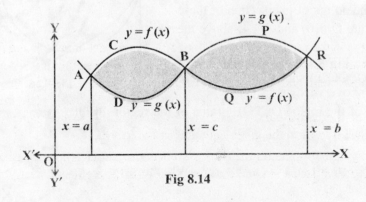

Fig 8.14

Example 6 Find the area of the region bounded by the two parabolas $y = x^2$ and $y^2 = x$.

Solution The point of intersection of these two parabolas are O (0, 0) and A (1, 1) as shown in the Fig 8.15.

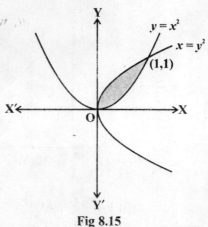

Here, we can set $y^2 = x$ or $y = \sqrt{x} = f(x)$ and $y = x^2$ = g(x), where, $f(x) \geq g(x)$ in [0, 1].

Therefore, the required area of the shaded region

$$= \int_0^1 \left[f(x) - g(x) \right] dx$$

$$= \int_0^1 \left[\sqrt{x} - x^2 \right] dx = \left[\frac{2}{3} x^{\frac{3}{2}} - \frac{x^3}{3} \right]_0^1$$

Fig 8.15

$$= \frac{2}{3} - \frac{1}{3} = \frac{1}{3}$$

Example 7 Find the area lying above x-axis and included between the circle $x^2 + y^2 = 8x$ and inside of the parabola $y^2 = 4x$.

Solution The given equation of the circle $x^2 + y^2 = 8x$ can be expressed as $(x - 4)^2 + y^2 = 16$. Thus, the centre of the circle is (4, 0) and radius is 4. Its intersection with the parabola $y^2 = 4x$ gives

$$x^2 + 4x = 8x$$

or $$x^2 - 4x = 0$$

or $$x (x - 4) = 0$$

or $$x = 0, x = 4$$

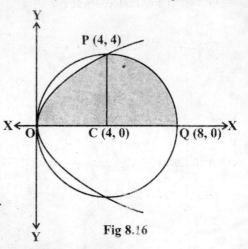

Thus, the points of intersection of these two curves are O(0, 0) and P(4, 4) above the x-axis.

From the Fig 8.16, the required area of the region OPQCO included between these two curves above x-axis is

Fig 8.16

= (area of the region OCPO) + (area of the region PCQP)

$$= \int_0^4 y \, dx + \int_4^8 y \, dx$$

$$= 2 \int_0^4 \sqrt{x} \, dx + \int_4^8 \sqrt{4^2 - (x-4)^2} \, dx \quad \text{(Why?)}$$

$$= 2 \times \frac{2}{3} \left[x^{\frac{3}{2}} \right]_0^4 + \int_0^4 \sqrt{4^2 - t^2}\, dt, \text{ where, } x - 4 = t \quad \text{(Why?)}$$

$$= \frac{32}{3} + \left[\frac{t}{2} \sqrt{4^2 - t^2} + \frac{1}{2} \times 4^2 \times \sin^{-1} \frac{t}{4} \right]_0^4$$

$$= \frac{32}{3} + \left[\frac{4}{2} \times 0 + \frac{1}{2} \times 4^2 \times \sin^{-1} 1 \right] = \frac{32}{3} + \left[0 + 8 \times \frac{\pi}{2} \right] = \frac{32}{3} + 4\pi = \frac{4}{3}(8 + 3\pi)$$

Example 8 In Fig 8.17, AOBA is the part of the ellipse $9x^2 + y^2 = 36$ in the first quadrant such that OA = 2 and OB = 6. Find the area between the arc AB and the chord AB.

Solution Given equation of the ellipse $9x^2 + y^2 = 36$ can be expressed as $\dfrac{x^2}{4} + \dfrac{y^2}{36} = 1$ or

$\dfrac{x^2}{2^2} + \dfrac{y^2}{6^2} = 1$ and hence, its shape is as given in Fig 8.17.

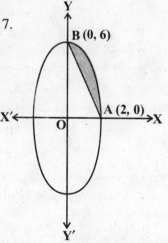

Accordingly, the equation of the chord AB is

$$y - 0 = \frac{6 - 0}{0 - 2}(x - 2)$$

or $\qquad y = -3(x - 2)$

or $\qquad y = -3x + 6$

Area of the shaded region as shown in the Fig 8.17.

$$= 3 \int_0^2 \sqrt{4 - x^2}\, dx - \int_0^2 (6 - 3x)\, dx \quad \text{(Why?)}$$

Fig 8.17

$$= 3 \left[\frac{x}{2} \sqrt{4 - x^2} + \frac{4}{2} \sin^{-1} \frac{x}{2} \right]_0^2 - \left[6x - \frac{3x^2}{2} \right]_0^2$$

$$= 3 \left[\frac{2}{2} \times 0 + 2 \sin^{-1}(1) \right] - \left[12 - \frac{12}{2} \right] = 3 \times 2 \times \frac{\pi}{2} - 6 = 3\pi - 6$$

Example 9 Using integration find the area of region bounded by the triangle whose vertices are (1, 0), (2, 2) and (3, 1).

Solution Let A(1, 0), B(2, 2) and C(3, 1) be the vertices of a triangle ABC (Fig 8.18).

Area of ΔABC

   = Area of ΔABD + Area of trapezium
      BDEC − Area of ΔAEC

Now equation of the sides AB, BC and CA are given by

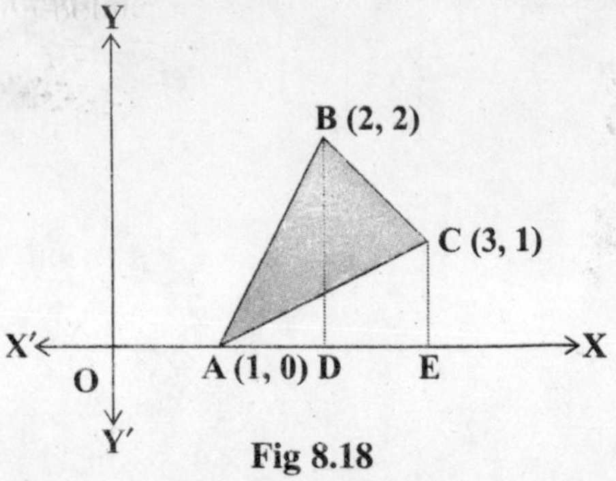

$$y = 2(x-1), \quad y = 4-x, \quad y = \frac{1}{2}(x-1), \text{ respectively.}$$

Hence, area of Δ ABC $= \int_1^2 2(x-1)\,dx + \int_2^3 (4-x)\,dx - \int_1^3 \frac{x-1}{2}\,dx$

$$= 2\left[\frac{x^2}{2} - x\right]_1^2 + \left[4x - \frac{x^2}{2}\right]_2^3 - \frac{1}{2}\left[\frac{x^2}{2} - x\right]_1^3$$

$$= 2\left[\left(\frac{2^2}{2} - 2\right) - \left(\frac{1}{2} - 1\right)\right] + \left[\left(4\times 3 - \frac{3^2}{2}\right) - \left(4\times 2 - \frac{2^2}{2}\right)\right] - \frac{1}{2}\left[\left(\frac{3^2}{2} - 3\right) - \left(\frac{1}{2} - 1\right)\right]$$

$$= \frac{3}{2}$$

Example 10 Find the area of the region enclosed between the two circles: $x^2 + y^2 = 4$ and $(x-2)^2 + y^2 = 4$.

Solution Equations of the given circles are

$$x^2 + y^2 = 4 \qquad \ldots (1)$$

and $(x-2)^2 + y^2 = 4 \qquad \ldots (2)$

Equation (1) is a circle with centre O at the origin and radius 2. Equation (2) is a circle with centre C (2, 0) and radius 2. Solving equations (1) and (2), we have

$$(x-2)^2 + y^2 = x^2 + y^2$$

or $x^2 - 4x + 4 + y^2 = x^2 + y^2$

or $x = 1$ which gives $y = \pm\sqrt{3}$

Thus, the points of intersection of the given circles are A(1, $\sqrt{3}$) and A'(1, $-\sqrt{3}$) as shown in the Fig 8.19.

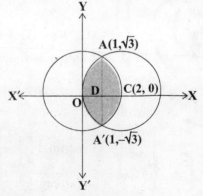

Fig 8.19

Fig 8.18

Required area of the enclosed region O ACA′O between circles

$$= 2 \text{ [area of the region ODCAO]} \qquad \text{(Why?)}$$

$$= 2 \text{ [area of the region ODAO + area of the region DCAD]}$$

$$= 2\left[\int_0^1 y\,dx + \int_1^2 y\,dx\right]$$

$$= 2\left[\int_0^1 \sqrt{4-(x-2)^2}\,dx + \int_1^2 \sqrt{4-x^2}\,dx\right] \qquad \text{(Why?)}$$

$$= 2\left[\frac{1}{2}(x-2)\sqrt{4-(x-2)^2} + \frac{1}{2}\times 4\sin^{-1}\left(\frac{x-2}{2}\right)\right]_0^1$$

$$+ 2\left[\frac{1}{2}x\sqrt{4-x^2} + \frac{1}{2}\times 4\sin^{-1}\frac{x}{2}\right]_1^2$$

$$= \left[(x-2)\sqrt{4-(x-2)^2} + 4\sin^{-1}\left(\frac{x-2}{2}\right)\right]_0^1 + \left[x\sqrt{4-x^2} + 4\sin^{-1}\frac{x}{2}\right]_1^2$$

$$= \left[\left(-\sqrt{3} + 4\sin^{-1}\left(\frac{-1}{2}\right)\right) - 4\sin^{-1}(-1)\right] + \left[4\sin^{-1}1 - \sqrt{3} - 4\sin^{-1}\frac{1}{2}\right]$$

$$= \left[\left(-\sqrt{3} - 4\times\frac{\pi}{6}\right) + 4\times\frac{\pi}{2}\right] + \left[4\times\frac{\pi}{2} - \sqrt{3} - 4\times\frac{\pi}{6}\right]$$

$$= \left(-\sqrt{3} - \frac{2\pi}{3} + 2\pi\right) + \left(2\pi - \sqrt{3} - \frac{2\pi}{3}\right)$$

$$= \frac{8\pi}{3} - 2\sqrt{3}$$

EXERCISE 8.2

1. Find the area of the circle $4x^2 + 4y^2 = 9$ which is interior to the parabola $x^2 = 4y$.

2. Find the area bounded by curves $(x-1)^2 + y^2 = 1$ and $x^2 + y^2 = 1$.

3. Find the area of the region bounded by the curves $y = x^2 + 2$, $y = x$, $x = 0$ and $x = 3$.

4. Using integration find the area of region bounded by the triangle whose vertices are $(-1, 0)$, $(1, 3)$ and $(3, 2)$.

5. Using integration find the area of the triangular region whose sides have the equations $y = 2x + 1$, $y = 3x + 1$ and $x = 4$.

Choose the correct answer in the following exercises 6 and 7.

6. Smaller area enclosed by the circle $x^2 + y^2 = 4$ and the line $x + y = 2$ is

　　(A) $2 (\pi - 2)$　　　(B) $\pi - 2$　　　(C) $2\pi - 1$　　　(D) $2 (\pi + 2)$

7. Area lying between the curves $y^2 = 4x$ and $y = 2x$ is

　　(A) $\dfrac{2}{3}$　　　(B) $\dfrac{1}{3}$　　　(C) $\dfrac{1}{4}$　　　(D) $\dfrac{3}{4}$

Miscellaneous Examples

Example 11 Find the area of the parabola $y^2 = 4ax$ bounded by its latus rectum.

Solution From Fig 8.20, the vertex of the parabola $y^2 = 4ax$ is at origin (0, 0). The equation of the latus rectum LSL′ is $x = a$. Also, parabola is symmetrical about the x-axis.

The required area of the region OLL′O
= 2 (area of the region OLSO)

$$= 2\int_0^a y\,dx = 2\int_0^a \sqrt{4ax}\ dx$$

$$= 2 \times 2\sqrt{a}\int_0^a \sqrt{x}\,dx$$

$$= 4\sqrt{a} \times \frac{2}{3}\left[x^{\frac{3}{2}}\right]_0^a$$

$$= \frac{8}{3}\sqrt{a}\left[a^{\frac{3}{2}}\right] = \frac{8}{3}a^2$$

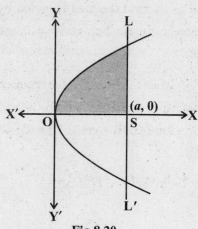

Fig 8.20

Example 12 Find the area of the region bounded by the line $y = 3x + 2$, the x-axis and the ordinates $x = -1$ and $x = 1$.

Solution As shown in the Fig 8.21, the line $y = 3x + 2$ meets x-axis at $x = \dfrac{-2}{3}$ and its graph lies below x-axis for $x \in \left(-1, \dfrac{-2}{3}\right)$ and above x-axis for $x \in \left(\dfrac{-2}{3}, 1\right)$.

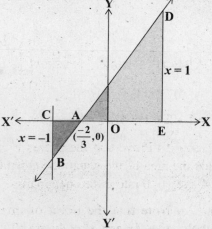

Fig 8.21

The required area = Area of the region ACBA + Area of the region ADEA

$$= \left| \int_{-1}^{\frac{-2}{3}} (3x+2)dx \right| + \int_{\frac{-2}{3}}^{1} (3x+2)dx$$

$$= \left| \left[\frac{3x^2}{2} + 2x \right]_{-1}^{\frac{-2}{3}} \right| + \left[\frac{3x^2}{2} + 2x \right]_{\frac{-2}{3}}^{1} = \frac{1}{6} + \frac{25}{6} = \frac{13}{3}$$

Example 13 Find the area bounded by the curve $y = \cos x$ between $x = 0$ and $x = 2\pi$.

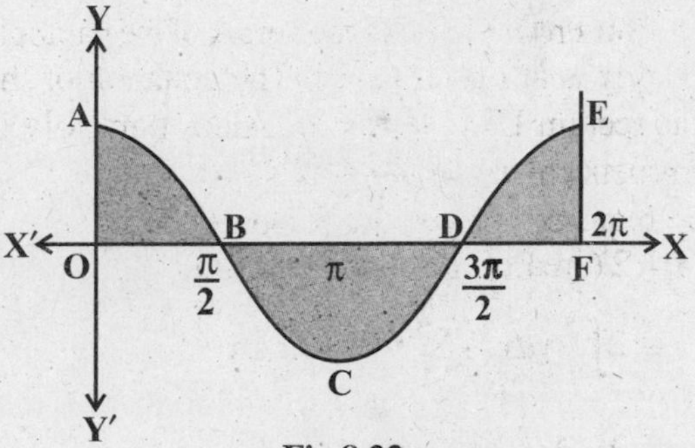

Solution From the Fig 8.22, the required area = area of the region OABO + area of the region BCDB + area of the region DEFD.

Thus, we have the required area

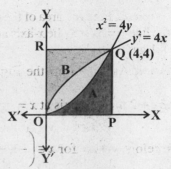

Fig 8.22

$$= \int_{0}^{\frac{\pi}{2}} \cos x \, dx + \left| \int_{\frac{\pi}{2}}^{\frac{3\pi}{2}} \cos x \, dx \right| + \int_{\frac{3\pi}{2}}^{2\pi} \cos x \, dx$$

$$= [\sin x]_{0}^{\frac{\pi}{2}} + \left| [\sin x]_{\frac{\pi}{2}}^{\frac{3\pi}{2}} \right| + [\sin x]_{\frac{3\pi}{2}}^{2\pi}$$

$$= 1 + 2 + 1 = 4$$

Example 13 Prove that the curves $y^2 = 4x$ and $x^2 = 4y$ divide the area of the square bounded by $x = 0$, $x = 4$, $y = 4$ and $y = 0$ into three equal parts.

Solution Note that the point of intersection of the parabolas $y^2 = 4x$ and $x^2 = 4y$ are (0, 0) and (4, 4) as

Fig 8.23

shown in the Fig 8.23.

Now, the area of the region OAQBO bounded by curves $y^2 = 4x$ and $x^2 = 4y$.

$$= \int_0^4 \left(2\sqrt{x} - \frac{x^2}{4} \right) dx = \left[2 \times \frac{2}{3} x^{\frac{3}{2}} - \frac{x^3}{12} \right]_0^4$$

$$= \frac{32}{3} - \frac{16}{3} = \frac{16}{3} \qquad \text{... (1)}$$

Again, the area of the region OPQAO bounded by the curves $x^2 = 4y$, $x = 0$, $x = 4$ and x-axis

$$= \int_0^4 \frac{x^2}{4} dx = \frac{1}{12} \left[x^3 \right]_0^4 = \frac{16}{3} \qquad \text{... (2)}$$

Similarly, the area of the region OBQRO bounded by the curve $y^2 = 4x$, y-axis, $y = 0$ and $y = 4$

$$= \int_0^4 x\, dy = \int_0^4 \frac{y^2}{4} dy = \frac{1}{12} \left[y^3 \right]_0^4 = \frac{16}{3} \qquad \text{... (3)}$$

From (1), (2) and (3), it is concluded that the area of the region OAQBO = area of the region OPQAO = area of the region OBQRO, i.e., area bounded by parabolas $y^2 = 4x$ and $x^2 = 4y$ divides the area of the square in three equal parts.

Example 14 Find the area of the region

$$\{(x, y) : 0 \le y \le x^2 + 1, 0 \le y \le x + 1, 0 \le x \le 2\}$$

Solution Let us first sketch the region whose area is to be found out. This region is the intersection of the following regions.

$$A_1 = \{(x, y) : 0 \le y \le x^2 + 1\},$$
$$A_2 = \{(x, y) : 0 \le y \le x + 1\}$$

and
$$A_3 = \{(x, y) : 0 \le x \le 2\}$$

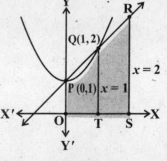

Fig 8.24

The points of intersection of $y = x^2 + 1$ and $y = x + 1$ are points P(0, 1) and Q(1, 2). From the Fig 8.24, the required region is the shaded region OPQRSTO whose area

= area of the region OTQPO + area of the region TSRQT

$$= \int_0^1 (x^2 + 1)\, dx + \int_1^2 (x + 1)\, dx \qquad \text{(Why?)}$$

$$= \left[\left(\frac{x^3}{3}+x\right)\right]_0^1 + \left[\left(\frac{x^2}{2}+x\right)\right]_1^2$$

$$= \left[\left(\frac{1}{3}+1\right)-0\right]+\left[(2+2)-\left(\frac{1}{2}+1\right)\right] = \frac{23}{6}$$

Miscellaneous Exercise on Chapter 8

1. Find the area under the given curves and given lines:

   (i) $y = x^2$, $x = 1$, $x = 2$ and x-axis

   (ii) $y = x^4$, $x = 1$, $x = 5$ and x-axis

2. Find the area between the curves $y = x$ and $y = x^2$.

3. Find the area of the region lying in the first quadrant and bounded by $y = 4x^2$, $x = 0$, $y = 1$ and $y = 4$.

4. Sketch the graph of $y = |x+3|$ and evaluate $\int_{-6}^{0}|x+3|\,dx$.

5. Find the area bounded by the curve $y = \sin x$ between $x = 0$ and $x = 2\pi$.

6. Find the area enclosed between the parabola $y^2 = 4ax$ and the line $y = mx$.

7. Find the area enclosed by the parabola $4y = 3x^2$ and the line $2y = 3x + 12$.

8. Find the area of the smaller region bounded by the ellipse $\frac{x^2}{9}+\frac{y^2}{4}=1$ and the line $\frac{x}{3}+\frac{y}{2}=1$.

9. Find the area of the smaller region bounded by the ellipse $\frac{x^2}{a^2}+\frac{y^2}{b^2}=1$ and the line $\frac{x}{a}+\frac{y}{b}=1$.

10. Find the area of the region enclosed by the parabola $x^2 = y$, the line $y = x + 2$ and the x-axis.

11. Using the method of integration find the area bounded by the curve $|x|+|y|=1$.

    [Hint: The required region is bounded by lines $x + y = 1$, $x - y = 1$, $-x + y = 1$ and $-x - y = 1$].

12. Find the area bounded by curves $\{(x, y) : y \geq x^2 \text{ and } y = |x|\}$.

13. Using the method of integration find the area of the triangle ABC, coordinates of whose vertices are A(2, 0), B (4, 5) and C (6, 3).

14. Using the method of integration find the area of the region bounded by lines:

$2x + y = 4, 3x - 2y = 6 \text{ and } x - 3y + 5 = 0$

15. Find the area of the region $\{(x, y) : y^2 \leq 4x, 4x^2 + 4y^2 \leq 9\}$

Choose the correct answer in the following Exercises from 16 to 20.

16. Area bounded by the curve $y = x^3$, the x-axis and the ordinates $x = -2$ and $x = 1$ is

(A) -9 (B) $\dfrac{-15}{4}$ (C) $\dfrac{15}{4}$ (D) $\dfrac{17}{4}$

17. The area bounded by the curve $y = x |x|$, x-axis and the ordinates $x = -1$ and $x = 1$ is given by

(A) 0   (B) $\dfrac{1}{3}$ (C) $\dfrac{2}{3}$ (D) $\dfrac{4}{3}$

[Hint : $y = x^2$ if $x > 0$ and $y = -x^2$ if $x < 0$].

18. The area of the circle $x^2 + y^2 = 16$ exterior to the parabola $y^2 = 6x$ is

(A) $\dfrac{4}{3}(4\pi - \sqrt{3})$ (B) $\dfrac{4}{3}(4\pi + \sqrt{3})$ (C) $\dfrac{4}{3}(8\pi - \sqrt{3})$ (D) $\dfrac{4}{3}(8\pi + \sqrt{3})$

19. The area bounded by the y-axis, $y = \cos x$ and $y = \sin x$ when $0 \leq x \leq \dfrac{\pi}{2}$ is

(A) $2(\sqrt{2}-1)$ (B) $\sqrt{2}-1$ (C) $\sqrt{2}+1$ (D) $\sqrt{2}$

Summary

◆ The area of the region bounded by the curve $y = f(x)$, x-axis and the lines $x = a$ and $x = b$ $(b > a)$ is given by the formula: $\text{Area} = \displaystyle\int_a^b y\,dx = \int_a^b f(x)dx$.

◆ The area of the region bounded by the curve $x = \phi(y)$, y-axis and the lines $y = c, y = d$ is given by the formula: $\text{Area} = \displaystyle\int_c^d x\,dy = \int_c^d \phi(y)dy$.

◆ The area of the region enclosed between two curves $y = f(x)$, $y = g(x)$ and the lines $x = a$, $x = b$ is given by the formula,

$$\text{Area} = \int_a^b \left[f(x) - g(x) \right] dx, \text{ where, } f(x) \geq g(x) \text{ in } [a, b]$$

◆ If $f(x) \geq g(x)$ in $[a, c]$ and $f(x) \leq g(x)$ in $[c, b]$, $a < c < b$, then

$$\text{Area} = \int_a^c \left[f(x) - g(x) \right] dx + \int_c^b \left[g(x) - f(x) \right] dx.$$

Historical Note

The origin of the Integral Calculus goes back to the early period of development of Mathematics and it is related to the method of exhaustion developed by the mathematicians of ancient Greece. This method arose in the solution of problems on calculating areas of plane figures, surface areas and volumes of solid bodies etc. In this sense, the method of exhaustion can be regarded as an early method of integration. The greatest development of method of exhaustion in the early period was obtained in the works of Eudoxus (440 B.C.) and Archimedes (300 B.C.)

Systematic approach to the theory of Calculus began in the 17th century. In 1665, Newton began his work on the Calculus described by him as the theory of fluxions and used his theory in finding the tangent and radius of curvature at any point on a curve. Newton introduced the basic notion of inverse function called the anti derivative (indefinite integral) or the inverse method of tangents.

During 1684-86, Leibnitz published an article in the *Acta Eruditorum* which he called *Calculas summatorius*, since it was connected with the summation of a number of infinitely small areas, whose sum, he indicated by the symbol '∫'. In 1696, he followed a suggestion made by J. Bernoulli and changed this article to Calculus integrali. This corresponded to Newton's inverse method of tangents.

Both Newton and Leibnitz adopted quite independent lines of approach which was radically different. However, respective theories accomplished results that were practically identical. Leibnitz used the notion of definite integral and what is quite certain is that he first clearly appreciated tie up between the antiderivative and the definite integral.

Conclusively, the fundamental concepts and theory of Integral Calculus and primarily its relationships with Differential Calculus were developed in the work of P.de Fermat, I. Newton and G. Leibnitz at the end of 17th century.

However, this justification by the concept of limit was only developed in the works of A.L. Cauchy in the early 19th century. Lastly, it is worth mentioning the following quotation by Lie Sophie's:

"It may be said that the conceptions of differential quotient and integral which in their origin certainly go back to Archimedes were introduced in Science by the investigations of Kepler, Descartes, Cavalieri, Fermat and Wallis .... The discovery that differentiation and integration are inverse operations belongs to Newton and Leibnitz".

Chapter 9

DIFFERENTIAL EQUATIONS

❖ *He who seeks for methods without having a definite problem in mind seeks for the most part in vain. – D. HILBERT* ❖

9.1 Introduction

In Class XI and in Chapter 5 of the present book, we discussed how to differentiate a given function f with respect to an independent variable, i.e., how to find $f'(x)$ for a given function f at each x in its domain of definition. Further, in the chapter on Integral Calculus, we discussed how to find a function f whose derivative is the function g, which may also be formulated as follows:

For a given function g, find a function f such that

$$\frac{dy}{dx} = g(x), \text{ where } y = f(x) \qquad \dots (1)$$

An equation of the form (1) is known as a *differential equation*. A formal definition will be given later.

Henri Poincare
(1854-1912)

These equations arise in a variety of applications, may it be in Physics, Chemistry, Biology, Anthropology, Geology, Economics etc. Hence, an indepth study of differential equations has assumed prime importance in all modern scientific investigations.

In this chapter, we will study some basic concepts related to differential equation, general and particular solutions of a differential equation, formation of differential equations, some methods to solve a first order - first degree differential equation and some applications of differential equations in different areas.

9.2 Basic Concepts

We are already familiar with the equations of the type:

$$x^2 - 3x + 3 = 0 \qquad \dots (1)$$
$$\sin x + \cos x = 0 \qquad \dots (2)$$
$$x + y = 7 \qquad \dots (3)$$

Let us consider the equation:

$$x\frac{dy}{dx} + y = 0 \tag{... (4)}$$

We see that equations (1), (2) and (3) involve independent and/or dependent variable (variables) only but equation (4) involves variables as well as derivative of the dependent variable y with respect to the independent variable x. Such an equation is called a *differential equation.*

In general, an equation involving derivative (derivatives) of the dependent variable with respect to independent variable (variables) is called a differential equation.

A differential equation involving derivatives of the dependent variable with respect to only one independent variable is called an ordinary differential equation, e.g.,

$$2\frac{d^2y}{dx^2} + \left(\frac{dy}{dx}\right)^3 = 0 \text{ is an ordinary differential equation} \tag{.... (5)}$$

Of course, there are differential equations involving derivatives with respect to more than one independent variables, called partial differential equations but at this stage we shall confine ourselves to the study of ordinary differential equations only. Now onward, we will use the term 'differential equation' for 'ordinary differential equation'.

☛ Note

1. We shall prefer to use the following notations for derivatives:

$$\frac{dy}{dx} = y', \frac{d^2y}{dx^2} = y'', \frac{d^3y}{dx^3} = y'''$$

2. For derivatives of higher order, it will be inconvenient to use so many dashes as supersuffix therefore, we use the notation y_n for nth order derivative $\dfrac{d^ny}{dx^n}$.

9.2.1. *Order of a differential equation*

Order of a differential equation is defined as the order of the highest order derivative of the dependent variable with respect to the independent variable involved in the given differential equation.

Consider the following differential equations:

$$\frac{dy}{dx} = e^x \tag{... (6)}$$

$$\frac{d^2y}{dx^2} + y = 0 \qquad\qquad \text{... (7)}$$

$$\left(\frac{d^3y}{dx^3}\right) + x^2 \left(\frac{d^2y}{dx^2}\right)^3 = 0 \qquad\qquad \text{... (8)}$$

The equations (6), (7) and (8) involve the highest derivative of first, second and third order respectively. Therefore, the order of these equations are 1, 2 and 3 respectively.

9.2.2 *Degree of a differential equation*

To study the degree of a differential equation, the key point is that the differential equation must be a polynomial equation in derivatives, i.e., y', y'', y''' etc. Consider the following differential equations:

$$\frac{d^3y}{dx^3} + 2\left(\frac{d^2y}{dx^2}\right)^2 - \frac{dy}{dx} + y = 0 \qquad\qquad \text{... (9)}$$

$$\left(\frac{dy}{dx}\right)^2 + \left(\frac{dy}{dx}\right) - \sin^2 y = 0 \qquad\qquad \text{... (10)}$$

$$\frac{dy}{dx} + \sin\left(\frac{dy}{dx}\right) = 0 \qquad\qquad \text{... (11)}$$

We observe that equation (9) is a polynomial equation in y''', y'' and y', equation (10) is a polynomial equation in y' (not a polynomial in y though). Degree of such differential equations can be defined. But equation (11) is not a polynomial equation in y' and degree of such a differential equation can not be defined.

By the degree of a differential equation, when it is a polynomial equation in derivatives, we mean the highest power (positive integral index) of the highest order derivative involved in the given differential equation.

In view of the above definition, one may observe that differential equations (6), (7), (8) and (9) each are of degree one, equation (10) is of degree two while the degree of differential equation (11) is not defined.

☞ Note Order and degree (if defined) of a differential equation are always positive integers.

Example 1 Find the order and degree, if defined, of each of the following differential equations:

(i) $\dfrac{dy}{dx} - \cos x = 0$

(ii) $xy\dfrac{d^2y}{dx^2} + x\left(\dfrac{dy}{dx}\right)^2 - y\dfrac{dy}{dx} = 0$

(iii) $y''' + y^2 + e^{y'} = 0$

Solution

(i) The highest order derivative present in the differential equation is $\dfrac{dy}{dx}$, so its order is one. It is a polynomial equation in y' and the highest power raised to $\dfrac{dy}{dx}$ is one, so its degree is one.

(ii) The highest order derivative present in the given differential equation is $\dfrac{d^2y}{dx^2}$, so its order is two. It is a polynomial equation in $\dfrac{d^2y}{dx^2}$ and $\dfrac{dy}{dx}$ and the highest power raised to $\dfrac{d^2y}{dx^2}$ is one, so its degree is one.

(iii) The highest order derivative present in the differential equation is y''', so its order is three. The given differential equation is not a polynomial equation in its derivatives and so its degree is not defined.

EXERCISE 9.1

Determine order and degree (if defined) of differential equations given in Exercises 1 to 10.

1. $\dfrac{d^4y}{dx^4} + \sin(y''') = 0$

2. $y' + 5y = 0$

3. $\left(\dfrac{ds}{dt}\right)^4 + 3s\dfrac{d^2s}{dt^2} = 0$

4. $\left(\dfrac{d^2y}{dx^2}\right)^2 + \cos\left(\dfrac{dy}{dx}\right) = 0$

5. $\dfrac{d^2y}{dx^2} = \cos 3x + \sin 3x$

6. $(y''')^2 + (y'')^3 + (y')^4 + y^5 = 0$

7. $y''' + 2y'' + y' = 0$

8. $y' + y = e^x$ **9.** $y'' + (y')^2 + 2y = 0$ **10.** $y'' + 2y' + \sin y = 0$

11. The degree of the differential equation

$$\left(\frac{d^2y}{dx^2}\right)^3 + \left(\frac{dy}{dx}\right)^2 + \sin\left(\frac{dy}{dx}\right) + 1 = 0 \text{ is}$$

(A) 3   (B) 2   (C) 1   (D) not defined

12. The order of the differential equation

$$2x^2\frac{d^2y}{dx^2} - 3\frac{dy}{dx} + y = 0 \text{ is}$$

(A) 2   (B) 1   (C) 0   (D) not defined

9.3. General and Particular Solutions of a Differential Equation

In earlier Classes, we have solved the equations of the type:

$$x^2 + 1 = 0 \qquad\qquad\qquad ... (1)$$

$$\sin^2 x - \cos x = 0 \qquad\qquad ... (2)$$

Solution of equations (1) and (2) are numbers, real or complex, that will satisfy the given equation i.e., when that number is substituted for the unknown x in the given equation, L.H.S. becomes equal to the R.H.S..

Now consider the differential equation $\dfrac{d^2y}{dx^2} + y = 0$ ... (3)

In contrast to the first two equations, the solution of this differential equation is a function ϕ that will satisfy it i.e., when the function ϕ is substituted for the unknown y (dependent variable) in the given differential equation, L.H.S. becomes equal to R.H.S..

The curve $y = \phi(x)$ is called the solution curve (integral curve) of the given differential equation. Consider the function given by

$$y = \phi(x) = a\sin(x + b), \qquad\qquad ... (4)$$

where $a, b \in \mathbf{R}$. When this function and its derivative are substituted in equation (3), L.H.S. = R.H.S.. So it is a solution of the differential equation (3).

Let a and b be given some particular values say $a = 2$ and $b = \dfrac{\pi}{4}$, then we get a

function $y = \phi_1(x) = 2\sin\left(x + \dfrac{\pi}{4}\right)$ ... (5)

When this function and its derivative are substituted in equation (3) again L.H.S. = R.H.S.. Therefore ϕ_1 is also a solution of equation (3).

Function ϕ consists of two arbitrary constants (parameters) a, b and it is called *general solution* of the given differential equation. Whereas function ϕ_1 contains no arbitrary constants but only the particular values of the parameters a and b and hence is called a *particular solution* of the given differential equation.

The solution which contains arbitrary constants is called the *general solution* (*primitive*) of the differential equation.

The solution free from arbitrary constants i.e., the solution obtained from the general solution by giving particular values to the arbitrary constants is called a *particular solution* of the differential equation.

Example 2 Verify that the function $y = e^{-3x}$ is a solution of the differential equation

$$\frac{d^2y}{dx^2} + \frac{dy}{dx} - 6y = 0$$

Solution Given function is $y = e^{-3x}$. Differentiating both sides of equation with respect to x, we get

$$\frac{dy}{dx} = -3e^{-3x} \qquad \text{... (1)}$$

Now, differentiating (1) with respect to x, we have

$$\frac{d^2y}{dx^2} = 9e^{-3x}$$

Substituting the values of $\frac{d^2y}{dx^2}, \frac{dy}{dx}$ and y in the given differential equation, we get

L.H.S. $= 9\ e^{-3x} + (-3e^{-3x}) - 6.e^{-3x} = 9\ e^{-3x} - 9\ e^{-3x} = 0 =$ R.H.S..

Therefore, the given function is a solution of the given differential equation.

Example 3 Verify that the function $y = a \cos x + b \sin x$, where, $a, b \in \mathbf{R}$ is a solution of the differential equation $\frac{d^2y}{dx^2} + y = 0$

Solution The given function is

$$y = a \cos x + b \sin x \qquad \text{... (1)}$$

Differentiating both sides of equation (1) with respect to x, successively, we get

$$\frac{dy}{dx} = -a \sin x + b \cos x$$

$$\frac{d^2y}{dx^2} = -a \cos x - b \sin x$$

Substituting the values of $\dfrac{d^2y}{dx^2}$ and y in the given differential equation, we get

L.H.S. = $(-a \cos x - b \sin x) + (a \cos x + b \sin x) = 0 =$ R.H.S..

Therefore, the given function is a solution of the given differential equation.

EXERCISE 9.2

In each of the Exercises 1 to 10 verify that the given functions (explicit or implicit) is a solution of the corresponding differential equation:

1. $y = e^x + 1$: $y'' - y' = 0$

2. $y = x^2 + 2x + C$: $y' - 2x - 2 = 0$

3. $y = \cos x + C$: $y' + \sin x = 0$

4. $y = \sqrt{1 + x^2}$: $y' = \dfrac{xy}{1 + x^2}$

5. $y = Ax$: $xy' = y \ (x \neq 0)$

6. $y = x \sin x$: $xy' = y + x \sqrt{x^2 - y^2} \ (x \neq 0 \text{ and } x > y \text{ or } x < -y)$

7. $xy = \log y + C$: $y' = \dfrac{y^2}{1 - xy} \ (xy \neq 1)$

8. $y - \cos y = x$: $(y \sin y + \cos y + x) \, y' = y$

9. $x + y = \tan^{-1}y$: $y^2 y' + y^2 + 1 = 0$

10. $y = \sqrt{a^2 - x^2} \ x \in (-a, a) :$ $x + y \, \dfrac{dy}{dx} = 0 \ (y \neq 0)$

11. The number of arbitrary constants in the general solution of a differential equation of fourth order are:

     (A) 0   (B) 2   (C) 3   (D) 4

12. The number of arbitrary constants in the particular solution of a differential equation of third order are:

     (A) 3   (B) 2   (C) 1   (D) 0

9.4. Formation of a Differential Equation whose General Solution is given

We know that the equation

$$x^2 + y^2 + 2x - 4y + 4 = 0 \quad\quad \text{... (1)}$$

represents a circle having centre at $(-1, 2)$ and radius 1 unit.

Differentiating equation (1) with respect to x, we get

$$\frac{dy}{dx} = \frac{x+1}{2-y} \quad (y \neq 2) \qquad \qquad \dots (2)$$

which is a differential equation. You will find later on [See (example 9 section 9.5.1.)] that this equation represents the family of circles and one member of the family is the circle given in equation (1).

Let us consider the equation

$$x^2 + y^2 = r^2 \qquad \qquad \dots (3)$$

By giving different values to r, we get different members of the family e.g. $x^2 + y^2 = 1$, $x^2 + y^2 = 4$, $x^2 + y^2 = 9$ etc. (see Fig 9.1). Thus, equation (3) represents a family of concentric circles centered at the origin and having different radii.

We are interested in finding a differential equation that is satisfied by each member of the family. The differential equation must be free from r because r is different for different members of the family. This equation is obtained by differentiating equation (3) with respect to x, i.e.,

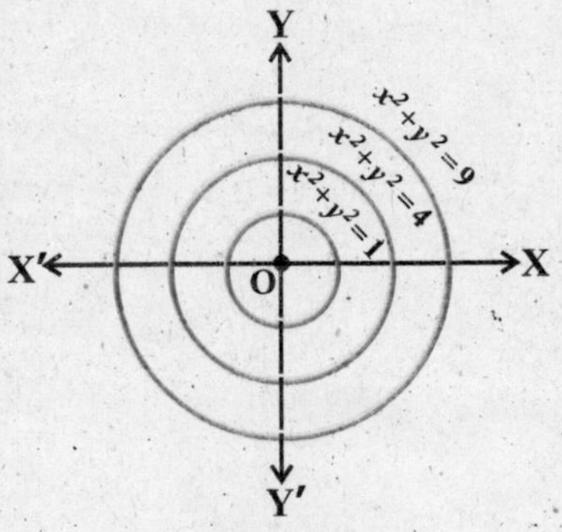

$$2x + 2y \frac{dy}{dx} = 0 \quad \text{or} \quad x + y \frac{dy}{dx} = 0 \qquad \dots (4)$$

Fig 9.1

which represents the family of concentric circles given by equation (3).

Again, let us consider the equation

$$y = mx + c \qquad \qquad \dots (5)$$

By giving different values to the parameters m and c, we get different members of the family, e.g.,

$$y = x \qquad \qquad (m = 1, \ c = 0)$$
$$y = \sqrt{3}\, x \qquad \qquad (m = \sqrt{3}, \ c = 0)$$
$$y = x + 1 \qquad \qquad (m = 1, \ c = 1)$$
$$y = -x \qquad \qquad (m = -1, \ c = 0)$$
$$y = -x - 1 \qquad \qquad (m = -1, \ c = -1) \text{ etc.} \qquad (\text{see Fig 9.2}).$$

Thus, equation (5) represents the family of straight lines, where m, c are parameters.

We are now interested in finding a differential equation that is satisfied by each member of the family. Further, the equation must be free from m and c because m and

c are different for different members of the family. This is obtained by differentiating equation (5) with respect to x, successively we get

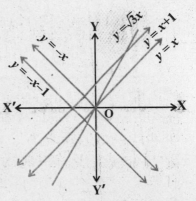

Fig 9.2

$$\frac{dy}{dx} = m, \text{ and } \frac{d^2y}{dx^2} = 0 \qquad \text{... (6)}$$

The equation (6) represents the family of straight lines given by equation (5).

Note that equations (3) and (5) are the general solutions of equations (4) and (6) respectively.

9.4.1 *Procedure to form a differential equation that will represent a given family of curves*

(a) If the given family F_1 of curves depends on only one parameter then it is represented by an equation of the form

$$F_1(x, y, a) = 0 \qquad \text{... (1)}$$

For example, the family of parabolas $y^2 = ax$ can be represented by an equation of the form $f(x, y, a) : y^2 = ax$.

Differentiating equation (1) with respect to x, we get an equation involving $y', y, x,$ and a, i.e.,

$$g(x, y, y', a) = 0 \qquad \text{... (2)}$$

The required differential equation is then obtained by eliminating a from equations (1) and (2) as

$$F(x, y, y') = 0 \qquad \text{... (3)}$$

(b) If the given family F_2 of curves depends on the parameters a, b (say) then it is represented by an equation of the from

$$F_2(x, y, a, b) = 0 \qquad \text{...(4)}$$

Differentiating equation (4) with respect to x, we get an equation involving y', x, y, a, b, i.e.,

$$g(x, y, y', a, b) = 0 \qquad \text{... (5)}$$

But it is not possible to eliminate two parameters a and b from the two equations and so, we need a third equation. This equation is obtained by differentiating equation (5), with respect to x, to obtain a relation of the form

$$h(x, y, y', y'', a, b) = 0 \qquad \text{... (6)}$$

The required differential equation is then obtained by eliminating a and b from equations (4), (5) and (6) as

$$F\ (x,\ y,\ y',\ y'') = 0 \qquad \qquad ... (7)$$

> **Note** The order of a differential equation representing a family of curves is same as the number of arbitrary constants present in the equation corresponding to the family of curves.

Example 4 Form the differential equation representing the family of curves $y = mx$, where, m is arbitrary constant.

Solution We have

$$y = mx \qquad \qquad ... (1)$$

Differentiating both sides of equation (1) with respect to x, we get

$$\frac{dy}{dx} = m$$

Substituting the value of m in equation (1) we get $y = \dfrac{dy}{dx} \cdot x$

or $$x\frac{dy}{dx} - y = 0$$

which is free from the parameter m and hence this is the required differential equation.

Example 5 Form the differential equation representing the family of curves $y = a \sin (x + b)$, where a, b are arbitrary constants.

Solution We have

$$y = a \sin (x + b) \qquad \qquad ... (1)$$

Differentiating both sides of equation (1) with respect to x, successively we get

$$\frac{dy}{dx} = a \cos (x + b) \qquad \qquad ... (2)$$

$$\frac{d^2 y}{dx^2} = -a \sin (x + b) \qquad \qquad ... (3)$$

Eliminating a and b from equations (1), (2) and (3), we get

$$\frac{d^2 y}{dx^2} + y = 0 \qquad \qquad ... (4)$$

which is free from the arbitrary constants a and b and hence this the required differential equation.

Example 6 Form the differential equation representing the family of ellipses having foci on x-axis and centre at the origin.

Solution We know that the equation of said family of ellipses (see Fig 9.3) is

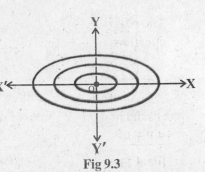

Fig 9.3

$$\frac{x^2}{a^2}+\frac{y^2}{b^2}=1 \qquad \ldots (1)$$

Differentiating equation (1) with respect to x, we get $\dfrac{2x}{a^2}+\dfrac{2y}{b^2}\cdot\dfrac{dy}{dx}=0$

or
$$\frac{y}{x}\left(\frac{dy}{dx}\right)=\frac{-b^2}{a^2} \qquad \ldots (2)$$

Differentiating both sides of equation (2) with respect to x, we get

$$\left(\frac{y}{x}\right)\left(\frac{d^2y}{dx^2}\right)+\left(\frac{x\dfrac{dy}{dx}-y}{x^2}\right)\frac{dy}{dx}=0$$

or
$$xy\frac{d^2y}{dx^2}+x\left(\frac{dy}{dx}\right)^2-y\frac{dy}{dx}=0 \qquad \ldots (3)$$

which is the required differential equation.

Example 7 Form the differential equation of the family of circles touching the x-axis at origin.

Solution Let C denote the family of circles touching x-axis at origin. Let (0, a) be the coordinates of the centre of any member of the family (see Fig 9.4). Therefore, equation of family C is

$$x^2+(y-a)^2=a^2 \text{ or } x^2+y^2=2ay \qquad \ldots (1)$$

where, a is an arbitrary constant. Differentiating both sides of equation (1) with respect to x, we get

$$2x+2y\frac{dy}{dx}=2a\frac{dy}{dx}$$

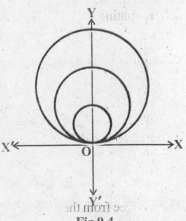

Fig 9.4

or $$x + y\frac{dy}{dx} = a\frac{dy}{dx} \quad \text{or} \quad a = \frac{x + y\dfrac{dy}{dx}}{\dfrac{dy}{dx}} \qquad \text{... (2)}$$

Substituting the value of a from equation (2) in equation (1), we get

$$x^2 + y^2 = 2y\frac{\left[x + y\dfrac{dy}{dx}\right]}{\dfrac{dy}{dx}}$$

or $$\frac{dy}{dx}(x^2 + y^2) = 2xy + 2y^2\frac{dy}{dx}$$

or $$\frac{dy}{dx} = \frac{2xy}{x^2 - y^2}$$

This is the required differential equation of the given family of circles.

Example 8 Form the differential equation representing the family of parabolas having vertex at origin and axis along positive direction of x-axis.

Solution Let P denote the family of above said parabolas (see Fig 9.5) and let $(a, 0)$ be the focus of a member of the given family, where a is an arbitrary constant. Therefore, equation of family P is

$$y^2 = 4ax \qquad \text{... (1)}$$

Differentiating both sides of equation (1) with respect to x, we get

$$2y\frac{dy}{dx} = 4a \qquad \text{... (2)}$$

Substituting the value of $4a$ from equation (2) in equation (1), we get

$$y^2 = \left(2y\frac{dy}{dx}\right)(x)$$

or $$y^2 - 2xy\frac{dy}{dx} = 0$$

which is the differential equation of the given family of parabolas.

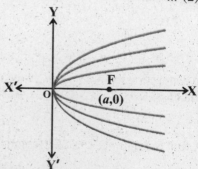

Fig 9.5

EXERCISE 9.3

In each of the Exercises 1 to 5, form a differential equation representing the given family of curves by eliminating arbitrary constants a and b.

1. $\dfrac{x}{a} + \dfrac{y}{b} = 1$ 2. $y^2 = a\,(b^2 - x^2)$ 3. $y = a\,e^{3x} + b\,e^{-2x}$

4. $y = e^{2x}\,(a + bx)$ 5. $y = e^x\,(a \cos x + b \sin x)$

6. Form the differential equation of the family of circles touching the y-axis at origin.

7. Form the differential equation of the family of parabolas having vertex at origin and axis along positive y-axis.

8. Form the differential equation of the family of ellipses having foci on y-axis and centre at origin.

9. Form the differential equation of the family of hyperbolas having foci on x-axis and centre at origin.

10. Form the differential equation of the family of circles having centre on y-axis and radius 3 units.

11. Which of the following differential equations has $y = c_1\,e^x + c_2\,e^{-x}$ as the general solution?

    (A) $\dfrac{d^2 y}{dx^2} + y = 0$ (B) $\dfrac{d^2 y}{dx^2} - y = 0$ (C) $\dfrac{d^2 y}{dx^2} + 1 = 0$ (D) $\dfrac{d^2 y}{dx^2} - 1 = 0$

12. Which of the following differential equations has $y = x$ as one of its particular solution?

    (A) $\dfrac{d^2 y}{dx^2} - x^2 \dfrac{dy}{dx} + xy = x$ (B) $\dfrac{d^2 y}{dx^2} + x \dfrac{dy}{dx} + xy = x$

    (C) $\dfrac{d^2 y}{dx^2} - x^2 \dfrac{dy}{dx} + xy = 0$ (D) $\dfrac{d^2 y}{dx^2} + x \dfrac{dy}{dx} + xy = 0$

9.5. Methods of Solving First Order, First Degree Differential Equations

In this section we shall discuss three methods of solving first order first degree differential equations.

9.5.1 Differential equations with variables separable

A first order-first degree differential equation is of the form

$$\frac{dy}{dx} = F(x,\, y) \qquad \qquad \dots (1)$$

If $F(x, y)$ can be expressed as a product $g(x) h(y)$, where, $g(x)$ is a function of x and $h(y)$ is a function of y, then the differential equation (1) is said to be of variable separable type. The differential equation (1) then has the form

$$\frac{dy}{dx} = h(y) \cdot g(x) \qquad \qquad \dots (2)$$

If $h(y) \neq 0$, separating the variables, (2) can be rewritten as

$$\frac{1}{h(y)} dy = g(x) \, dx \qquad \qquad \dots (3)$$

Integrating both sides of (3), we get

$$\int \frac{1}{h(y)} dy = \int g(x) \, dx \qquad \qquad \dots (4)$$

Thus, (4) provides the solutions of given differential equation in the form

$$H(y) = G(x) + C$$

Here, $H(y)$ and $G(x)$ are the anti derivatives of $\frac{1}{h(y)}$ and $g(x)$ respectively and C is the arbitrary constant.

Example 9 Find the general solution of the differential equation $\frac{dy}{dx} = \frac{x+1}{2-y}$, $(y \neq 2)$

Solution We have

$$\frac{dy}{dx} = \frac{x+1}{2-y} \qquad \qquad \dots (1)$$

Separating the variables in equation (1), we get

$$(2 - y) \, dy = (x + 1) \, dx \qquad \qquad \dots (2)$$

Integrating both sides of equation (2), we get

$$\int (2 - y) \, dy = \int (x + 1) \, dx$$

or

$$2y - \frac{y^2}{2} = \frac{x^2}{2} + x + C_1$$

or $x^2 + y^2 + 2x - 4y + 2 C_1 = 0$

or $x^2 + y^2 + 2x - 4y + C = 0$, where $C = 2C_1$

which is the general solution of equation (1).

Example 10 Find the general solution of the differential equation $\dfrac{dy}{dx} = \dfrac{1+y^2}{1+x^2}$.

Solution Since $1 + y^2 \neq 0$, therefore separating the variables, the given differential equation can be written as

$$\frac{dy}{1+y^2} = \frac{dx}{1+x^2} \qquad \text{... (1)}$$

Integrating both sides of equation (1), we get

$$\int \frac{dy}{1+y^2} = \int \frac{dx}{1+x^2}$$

or $\tan^{-1} y = \tan^{-1}x + C$

which is the general solution of equation (1).

Example 11 Find the particular solution of the differential equation $\dfrac{dy}{dx} = -4xy^2$ given

that $y = 1$, when $x = 0$.

Solution If $y \neq 0$, the given differential equation can be written as

$$\frac{dy}{y^2} = -4x\, dx \qquad \text{... (1)}$$

Integrating both sides of equation (1), we get

$$\int \frac{dy}{y^2} = -4\int x\, dx$$

or $-\dfrac{1}{y} = -2x^2 + C$

or $y = \dfrac{1}{2x^2 - C} \qquad \text{... (2)}$

Substituting $y = 1$ and $x = 0$ in equation (2), we get, $C = -1$.

Now substituting the value of C in equation (2), we get the particular solution of the

given differential equation as $y = \dfrac{1}{2x^2 + 1}$.

Example 12 Find the equation of the curve passing through the point (1, 1) whose differential equation is $x\, dy = (2x^2 + 1)\, dx\ (x \neq 0)$.

Solution The given differential equation can be expressed as

$$dy^* = \left(\frac{2x^2 + 1}{x}\right)dx^*$$

or

$$dy = \left(2x + \frac{1}{x}\right)dx \qquad \qquad \ldots (1)$$

Integrating both sides of equation (1), we get

$$\int dy = \int \left(2x + \frac{1}{x}\right)dx$$

or

$$y = x^2 + \log |x| + C \qquad \qquad \ldots (2)$$

Equation (2) represents the family of solution curves of the given differential equation but we are interested in finding the equation of a particular member of the family which passes through the point (1, 1). Therefore substituting $x = 1$, $y = 1$ in equation (2), we get $C = 0$.

Now substituting the value of C in equation (2) we get the equation of the required curve as $y = x^2 + \log |x|$.

Example 13 Find the equation of a curve passing through the point $(-2, 3)$, given that the slope of the tangent to the curve at any point (x, y) is $\dfrac{2x}{y^2}$.

Solution We know that the slope of the tangent to a curve is given by $\dfrac{dy}{dx}$.

so,

$$\frac{dy}{dx} = \frac{2x}{y^2} \qquad \qquad \ldots (1)$$

Separating the variables, equation (1) can be written as

$$y^2 \, dy = 2x \, dx \qquad \qquad \ldots (2)$$

Integrating both sides of equation (2), we get

$$\int y^2 dy = \int 2x \, dx$$

or

$$\frac{y^3}{3} = x^2 + C \qquad \qquad \ldots (3)$$

---

* The notation $\dfrac{dy}{dx}$ due to Leibnitz is extremely flexible and useful in many calculation and formal transformations, where we can deal with symbols dy and dx exactly as if they were ordinary numbers. By treating dx and dy like separate entities, we can give neater expressions to many calculations.

Refer: Introduction to Calculus and Analysis, volume-I page 172, By Richard Courant, Fritz John Spinger – Verlog New York.

Substituting $x = -2$, $y = 3$ in equation (3), we get $C = 5$.

Substituting the value of C in equation (3), we get the equation of the required curve as

$$\frac{y^3}{3} = x^2 + 5 \quad \text{or} \quad y = (3x^2 + 15)^{\frac{1}{3}}$$

Example 14 In a bank, principal increases continuously at the rate of 5% per year. In how many years Rs 1000 double itself?

Solution Let P be the principal at any time t. According to the given problem,

$$\frac{dp}{dt} = \left(\frac{5}{100}\right) \times P$$

or $$\frac{dp}{dt} = \frac{P}{20} \qquad \qquad \dots (1)$$

separating the variables in equation (1), we get

$$\frac{dp}{P} = \frac{dt}{20} \qquad \qquad \dots (2)$$

Integrating both sides of equation (2), we get

$$\log P = \frac{t}{20} + C_1$$

or $$P = e^{\frac{t}{20}} \cdot e^{C_1}$$

or $$P = C\, e^{\frac{t}{20}} \quad (\text{where } e^{C_1} = C) \qquad \dots (3)$$

Now $$P = 1000, \quad \text{when } t = 0$$

Substituting the values of P and t in (3), we get $C = 1000$. Therefore, equation (3), gives

$$P = 1000\, e^{\frac{t}{20}}$$

Let t years be the time required to double the principal. Then

$$2000 = 1000\, e^{\frac{t}{20}} \quad \Rightarrow \quad t = 20 \log_e 2$$

EXERCISE 9.4

For each of the differential equations in Exercises 1 to 10, find the general solution:

1. $\dfrac{dy}{dx} = \dfrac{1 - \cos x}{1 + \cos x}$

2. $\dfrac{dy}{dx} = \sqrt{4 - y^2} \quad (-2 < y < 2)$

3. $\dfrac{dy}{dx} + y = 1\,(y \neq 1)$

4. $\sec^2 x \tan y\,dx + \sec^2 y \tan x\,dy = 0$

5. $(e^x + e^{-x})\,dy - (e^x - e^{-x})\,dx = 0$

6. $\dfrac{dy}{dx} = (1 + x^2)(1 + y^2)$

7. $y \log y\,dx - x\,dy = 0$

8. $x^5 \dfrac{dy}{dx} = -y^5$

9. $\dfrac{dy}{dx} = \sin^{-1} x$

10. $e^x \tan y\,dx + (1 - e^x) \sec^2 y\,dy = 0$

For each of the differential equations in Exercises 11 to 14, find a particular solution satisfying the given condition:

11. $(x^3 + x^2 + x + 1)\dfrac{dy}{dx} = 2x^2 + x$; $y = 1$ when $x = 0$

12. $x(x^2 - 1)\dfrac{dy}{dx} = 1$; $y = 0$ when $x = 2$

13. $\cos\left(\dfrac{dy}{dx}\right) = a$ $(a \in \mathbf{R})$; $y = 1$ when $x = 0$

14. $\dfrac{dy}{dx} = y \tan x$; $y = 1$ when $x = 0$

15. Find the equation of a curve passing through the point $(0, 0)$ and whose differential equation is $y' = e^x \sin x$.

16. For the differential equation $xy\dfrac{dy}{dx} = (x + 2)(y + 2)$, find the solution curve passing through the point $(1, -1)$.

17. Find the equation of a curve passing through the point $(0, -2)$ given that at any point (x, y) on the curve, the product of the slope of its tangent and y coordinate of the point is equal to the x coordinate of the point.

18. At any point (x, y) of a curve, the slope of the tangent is twice the slope of the line segment joining the point of contact to the point $(-4, -3)$. Find the equation of the curve given that it passes through $(-2, 1)$.

19. The volume of spherical balloon being inflated changes at a constant rate. If initially its radius is 3 units and after 3 seconds it is 6 units. Find the radius of balloon after t seconds.

20. In a bank, principal increases continuously at the rate of r% per year. Find the value of r if Rs 100 double itself in 10 years ($\log_e 2 = 0.6931$).

21. In a bank, principal increases continuously at the rate of 5% per year. An amount of Rs 1000 is deposited with this bank, how much will it worth after 10 years ($e^{0.5} = 1.648$).

22. In a culture, the bacteria count is 1,00,000. The number is increased by 10% in 2 hours. In how many hours will the count reach 2,00,000, if the rate of growth of bacteria is proportional to the number present?

23. The general solution of the differential equation $\dfrac{dy}{dx} = e^{x+y}$ is

(A) $e^x + e^{-y} = C$ (B) $e^x + e^y = C$

(C) $e^{-x} + e^y = C$ (D) $e^{-x} + e^{-y} = C$

9.5.2 *Homogeneous differential equations*

Consider the following functions in x and y

$F_1(x, y) = y^2 + 2xy,$ $F_2(x, y) = 2x - 3y,$

$F_3(x, y) = \cos\left(\dfrac{y}{x}\right),$ $F_4(x, y) = \sin x + \cos y$

If we replace x and y by λx and λy respectively in the above functions, for any nonzero constant λ, we get

$F_1(\lambda x, \lambda y) = \lambda^2 (y^2 + 2xy) = \lambda^2 F_1(x, y)$

$F_2(\lambda x, \lambda y) = \lambda (2x - 3y) = \lambda F_2(x, y)$

$F_3(\lambda x, \lambda y) = \cos\left(\dfrac{\lambda y}{\lambda x}\right) = \cos\left(\dfrac{y}{x}\right) = \lambda^0 F_3(x, y)$

$F_4(\lambda x, \lambda y) = \sin \lambda x + \cos \lambda y \neq \lambda^n F_4(x, y)$, for any $n \in \mathbf{N}$

Here, we observe that the functions F_1, F_2, F_3 c n be written in the form $F(\lambda x, \lambda y) = \lambda^n F(x, y)$ but F_4 can not be written in this forn   This leads to the following definition:

A function $F(x, y)$ is said to be *homogeneous functi n of degree n* if

$F(\lambda x, \lambda y) = \lambda^n F(x, y)$ for any nonzero constant λ.

We note that in the above examples, F_1, F_2, F_3 are homogeneus functions of degree 2, 1, 0 respectively but F_4 is not a homogeneous function.

We also observe that

$$F_1(x, y) = x^2 \left(\frac{y^2}{x^2} + \frac{2y}{x} \right) = x^2 h_1 \left(\frac{y}{x} \right)$$

or

$$F_1(x, y) = y^2 \left(1 + \frac{2x}{y} \right) = y^2 h_2 \left(\frac{x}{y} \right)$$

$$F_2(x, y) = x^1 \left(2 - \frac{3y}{x} \right) = x^1 h_3 \left(\frac{y}{x} \right)$$

or

$$F_2(x, y) = y^1 \left(2\frac{x}{y} - 3 \right) = y^1 h_4 \left(\frac{x}{y} \right)$$

$$F_3(x, y) = x^0 \cos \left(\frac{y}{x} \right) = x^0 h_5 \left(\frac{y}{x} \right)$$

$$F_4(x, y) \neq x^n h_6 \left(\frac{y}{x} \right) , \text{ for any } n \in \mathbf{N}$$

or

$$F_4(x, y) \neq y^n h_7 \left(\frac{x}{y} \right), \text{ for any } n \in \mathbf{N}$$

Therefore, a function F (x, y) is a homogeneous function of degree n if

$$F(x, y) = x^n g \left(\frac{y}{x} \right) \quad \text{or} \quad y^n h \left(\frac{x}{y} \right)$$

A differential equation of the form $\frac{dy}{dx} = $ F (x, y) is said to be *homogenous* if F(x, y) is a homogenous function of degree zero.

To solve a homogeneous differential equation of the type

$$\frac{dy}{dx} = F(x, y) = g \left(\frac{y}{x} \right) \qquad \text{... (1)}$$

We make the substitution $y = v.x$ ... (2)

Differentiating equation (2) with respect to x, we get

$$\frac{dy}{dx} = v + x\frac{dv}{dx} \qquad \text{... (3)}$$

Substituting the value of $\frac{dy}{dx}$ from equation (3) in equation (1), we get

$$v + x\frac{dv}{dx} = g(v)$$

or $$x\frac{dv}{dx} = g(v) - v \qquad \text{... (4)}$$

Separating the variables in equation (4), we get

$$\frac{dv}{g(v) - v} = \frac{dx}{x} \qquad \text{... (5)}$$

Integrating both sides of equation (5), we get

$$\int \frac{dv}{g(v) - v} = \int \frac{1}{x}dx + C \qquad \text{... (6)}$$

Equation (6) gives general solution (primitive) of the differential equation (1) when we replace v by $\frac{y}{x}$.

> **☞ Note** If the homogeneous differential equation is in the form $\frac{dx}{dy} = F(x, y)$
> where, F(x, y) is homogenous function of degree zero, then we make substitution
> $\frac{x}{y} = v$ i.e., $x = vy$ and we proceed further to find the general solution as discussed
> above by writing $\frac{dx}{dy} = F(x, y) = h\left(\frac{x}{y}\right)$.

Example 15 Show that the differential equation $(x - y)\frac{dy}{dx} = x + 2y$ is homogeneous and solve it.

Solution The given differential equation can be expressed as

$$\frac{dy}{dx} = \frac{x + 2y}{x - y} \qquad \text{... (1)}$$

Let $$F(x, y) = \frac{x + 2y}{x - y}$$

Now $$F(\lambda x, \lambda y) = \frac{\lambda(x + 2y)}{\lambda(x - y)} = \lambda^0 \cdot f(x, y)$$

Therefore, $F(x, y)$ is a homogenous function of degree zero. So, the given differential equation is a homogenous differential equation.

Alternatively,

$$\frac{dy}{dx} = \left(\frac{1 + \dfrac{2y}{x}}{1 - \dfrac{y}{x}} \right) = g\left(\frac{y}{x} \right) \qquad \dots (2)$$

R.H.S. of differential equation (2) is of the form $g\left(\dfrac{y}{x} \right)$ and so it is a homogeneous

function of degree zero. Therefore, equation (1) is a homogeneous differential equation. To solve it we make the substitution

$$y = vx \qquad \dots (3)$$

Differentiating equation (3) with respect to, x we get

$$\frac{dy}{dx} = v + x\frac{dv}{dx} \qquad \dots (4)$$

Substituting the value of y and $\dfrac{dy}{dx}$ in equation (1) we get

$$v + x\frac{dv}{dx} = \frac{1 + 2v}{1 - v}$$

or
$$x\frac{dv}{dx} = \frac{1 + 2v}{1 - v} - v$$

or
$$x\frac{dv}{dx} = \frac{v^2 + v + 1}{1 - v}$$

or
$$\frac{v - 1}{v^2 + v + 1}dv = \frac{-dx}{x}$$

Integrating both sides of equation (5), we get

$$\int \frac{v - 1}{v^2 + v + 1}dv = -\int \frac{dx}{x}$$

or
$$\frac{1}{2}\int \frac{2v + 1 - 3}{v^2 + v + 1}dv = -\log |x| + C_1$$

or
$$\frac{1}{2}\int\frac{2v+1}{v^2+v+1}dv-\frac{3}{2}\int\frac{1}{v^2+v+1}dv=-\log|x|+C_1$$

or
$$\frac{1}{2}\log|v^2+v+1|-\frac{3}{2}\int\frac{1}{\left(v+\frac{1}{2}\right)^2+\left(\frac{\sqrt{3}}{2}\right)^2}dv=-\log|x|+C_1$$

or
$$\frac{1}{2}\log|v^2+v+1|-\frac{3}{2}\cdot\frac{2}{\sqrt{3}}\tan^{-1}\left(\frac{2v+1}{\sqrt{3}}\right)=-\log|x|+C_1$$

or
$$\frac{1}{2}\log|v^2+v+1|+\frac{1}{2}\log x^2=\sqrt{3}\tan^{-1}\left(\frac{2v+1}{\sqrt{3}}\right)+C_1 \qquad \text{(Why?)}$$

Replacing v by $\dfrac{y}{x}$, we get

or
$$\frac{1}{2}\log\left|\frac{y^2}{x^2}+\frac{y}{x}+1\right|+\frac{1}{2}\log x^2=\sqrt{3}\tan^{-1}\left(\frac{2y+x}{\sqrt{3}x}\right)+C_1$$

or
$$\frac{1}{2}\log\left|\left(\frac{y^2}{x^2}+\frac{y}{x}+1\right)x^2\right|=\sqrt{3}\tan^{-1}\left(\frac{2y+x}{\sqrt{3}x}\right)+C_1$$

or
$$\log|(y^2+xy+x^2)|=2\sqrt{3}\tan^{-1}\left(\frac{2y+x}{\sqrt{3}x}\right)+2C_1$$

or
$$\log|(x^2+xy+y^2)|=2\sqrt{3}\tan^{-1}\left(\frac{x+2y}{\sqrt{3}x}\right)+C$$

which is the general solution of the differential equation (1)

Example 16 Show that the differential equation $x\cos\left(\dfrac{y}{x}\right)\dfrac{dy}{dx}=y\cos\left(\dfrac{y}{x}\right)+x$ is homogeneous and solve it.

Solution The given differential equation can be written as

$$\frac{dy}{dx}=\frac{y\cos\left(\dfrac{y}{x}\right)+x}{x\cos\left(\dfrac{y}{x}\right)} \qquad \text{... (1)}$$

It is a differential equation of the form $\dfrac{dy}{dx} = F(x, y)$.

Here
$$F(x, y) = \frac{y \cos\left(\dfrac{y}{x}\right) + x}{x \cos\left(\dfrac{y}{x}\right)}$$

Replacing x by λx and y by λy, we get

$$F(\lambda x, \lambda y) = \frac{\lambda\left[y \cos\left(\dfrac{y}{x}\right) + x\right]}{\lambda\left(x \cos\dfrac{y}{x}\right)} = \lambda^0 [F(x, y)]$$

Thus, $F(x, y)$ is a homogeneous function of degree zero.

Therefore, the given differential equation is a homogeneous differential equation. To solve it we make the substitution

$$y = vx \qquad\qquad \ldots (2)$$

Differentiating equation (2) with respect to x, we get

$$\frac{dy}{dx} = v + x\frac{dv}{dx} \qquad\qquad \ldots (3)$$

Substituting the value of y and $\dfrac{dy}{dx}$ in equation (1), we get

$$v + x\frac{dv}{dx} = \frac{v \cos v + 1}{\cos v}$$

or
$$x\frac{dv}{dx} = \frac{v \cos v + 1}{\cos v} - v$$

or
$$x\frac{dv}{dx} = \frac{1}{\cos v}$$

or
$$\cos v \, dv = \frac{dx}{x}$$

Therefore
$$\int \cos v \, dv = \int \frac{1}{x} \, dx$$

or $\qquad\qquad\qquad$ $\sin v = \log |x| + \log |C|$

or $\qquad\qquad\qquad$ $\sin v = \log |Cx|$

Replacing v by $\dfrac{y}{x}$, we get

$$\sin\left(\frac{y}{x}\right) = \log |Cx|$$

which is the general solution of the differential equation (1).

Example 17 Show that the differential equation $2y\, e^{\frac{x}{y}} dx + \left(y - 2x\, e^{\frac{x}{y}}\right) dy = 0$ is homogeneous and find its particular solution, given that, $x = 0$ when $y = 1$.

Solution The given differential equation can be written as

$$\frac{dx}{dy} = \frac{2x\, e^{\frac{x}{y}} - y}{2y\, e^{\frac{x}{y}}} \qquad \dots (1)$$

Let $\qquad\qquad$ $F(x, y) = \dfrac{2xe^{\frac{x}{y}} - y}{2ye^{\frac{x}{y}}}$

Then $\qquad\qquad$ $F(\lambda x, \lambda y) = \dfrac{\lambda\left(2xe^{\frac{x}{y}} - y\right)}{\lambda\left(2ye^{\frac{x}{y}}\right)} = \lambda^{0}\,[F(x, y)]$

Thus, $F(x, y)$ is a homogeneous function of degree zero. Therefore, the given differential equation is a homogeneous differential equation.

To solve it, we make the substitution

$$x = vy \qquad \dots (2)$$

Differentiating equation (2) with respect to y, we get

$$\frac{dx}{dy} = v + y\frac{dv}{dy}$$

Substituting the value of x and $\dfrac{dx}{dy}$ in equation (1), we get

$$v + y\frac{dv}{dy} = \frac{2v\,e^v - 1}{2e^v}$$

or $\qquad\qquad\qquad y\dfrac{dv}{dy} = \dfrac{2v\,e^v - 1}{2e^v} - v$

or $\qquad\qquad\qquad y\dfrac{dv}{dy} = -\dfrac{1}{2e^v}$

or $\qquad\qquad\qquad 2e^v\,dv = \dfrac{-dy}{y}$

or $\qquad\qquad\qquad \displaystyle\int 2e^v \cdot dv = -\int \frac{dy}{y}$

or $\qquad\qquad\qquad 2\,e^v = -\log|y| + C$

and replacing v by $\dfrac{x}{y}$, we get

$$2\,e^{\frac{x}{y}} + \log|y| = C \qquad\qquad\qquad\qquad \dots (3)$$

Substituting $x = 0$ and $y = 1$ in equation (3), we get

$$2\,e^0 + \log|1| = C \Rightarrow C = 2$$

Substituting the value of C in equation (3), we get

$$2\,e^{\frac{x}{y}} + \log|y| = 2$$

which is the particular solution of the given differential equation.

Example 18 Show that the family of curves for which the slope of the tangent at any

point (x, y) on it is $\dfrac{x^2 + y^2}{2xy}$, is given by $x^2 - y^2 = cx$.

Solution We know that the slope of the tangent at any point on a curve is $\dfrac{dy}{dx}$.

Therefore, $\qquad\qquad\qquad \dfrac{dy}{dx} = \dfrac{x^2 + y^2}{2xy}$

or
$$\frac{dy}{dx} = \frac{1 + \dfrac{y^2}{x^2}}{\dfrac{2y}{x}} \qquad \qquad \text{... (1)}$$

Clearly, (1) is a homogenous differential equation. To solve it we make substitution

$$y = vx$$

Differentiating $y = vx$ with respect to x, we get

$$\frac{dy}{dx} = v + x\frac{dv}{dx}$$

or
$$v + x\frac{dv}{dx} = \frac{1 + v^2}{2v}$$

or
$$x\frac{dv}{dx} = \frac{1 - v^2}{2v}$$

$$\frac{2v}{1 - v^2}dv = \frac{dx}{x}$$

or
$$\frac{2v}{v^2 - 1}dv = -\frac{dx}{x}$$

Therefore
$$\int \frac{2v}{v^2 - 1}dv = -\int \frac{1}{x}dx$$

or
$$\log|v^2 - 1| = -\log|x| + \log|C_1|$$

or
$$\log|(v^2 - 1)(x)| = \log|C_1|$$

or
$$(v^2 - 1)x = \pm C_1$$

Replacing v by $\dfrac{y}{x}$, we get

$$\left(\frac{y^2}{x^2} - 1\right)x = \pm C_1$$

or
$$(y^2 - x^2) = \pm C_1 x \text{ or } x^2 - y^2 = Cx$$

EXERCISE 9.5

In each of the Exercises 1 to 10, show that the given differential equation is homogeneous and solve each of them.

1. $(x^2 + xy)\, dy = (x^2 + y^2)\, dx$

2. $y' = \dfrac{x+y}{x}$

3. $(x - y)\, dy - (x + y)\, dx = 0$

4. $(x^2 - y^2)\, dx + 2xy\, dy = 0$

5. $x^2 \dfrac{dy}{dx} = x^2 - 2y^2 + xy$

6. $x\, dy - y\, dx = \sqrt{x^2 + y^2}\, dx$

7. $\left\{ x\cos\left(\dfrac{y}{x}\right) + y\sin\left(\dfrac{y}{x}\right) \right\} y\, dx = \left\{ y\sin\left(\dfrac{y}{x}\right) - x\cos\left(\dfrac{y}{x}\right) \right\} x\, dy$

8. $x\dfrac{dy}{dx} - y + x\sin\left(\dfrac{y}{x}\right) = 0$

9. $y\, dx + x\log\left(\dfrac{y}{x}\right) dy - 2x\, dy = 0$

10. $\left(1 + e^{\frac{x}{y}}\right) dx + e^{\frac{x}{y}}\left(1 - \dfrac{x}{y}\right) dy = 0$

For each of the differential equations in Exercises from 11 to 15, find the particular solution satisfying the given condition:

11. $(x + y)\, dy + (x - y)\, dx = 0;\ y = 1$ when $x = 1$

12. $x^2\, dy + (xy + y^2)\, dx = 0;\ y = 1$ when $x = 1$

13. $\left[x\sin^2\left(\dfrac{y}{x}\right) - y \right] dx + x\, dy = 0;\ y = \dfrac{\pi}{4}$ when $x = 1$

14. $\dfrac{dy}{dx} - \dfrac{y}{x} + \operatorname{cosec}\left(\dfrac{y}{x}\right) = 0;\ y = 0$ when $x = 1$

15. $2xy + y^2 - 2x^2 \dfrac{dy}{dx} = 0;\ y = 2$ when $x = 1$

16. A homogeneous differential equation of the from $\dfrac{dx}{dy} = h\left(\dfrac{x}{y}\right)$ can be solved by making the substitution.

 (A) $y = vx$ (B) $v = yx$ (C) $x = vy$ (D) $x = v$

17. Which of the following is a homogeneous differential equation?

(A) $(4x + 6y + 5)\, dy - (3y + 2x + 4)\, dx = 0$

(B) $(xy)\, dx - (x^3 + y^3)\, dy = 0$

(C) $(x^3 + 2y^2)\, dx + 2xy\, dy = 0$

(D) $y^2\, dx + (x^2 - xy - y^2)\, dy = 0$

9.5.3 Linear differential equations

A differential equation of the from

$$\frac{dy}{dx} + Py = Q$$

where, P and Q are constants or functions of x only, is known as a first order linear differential equation. Some examples of the first order linear differential equation are

$$\frac{dy}{dx} + y = \sin x$$

$$\frac{dy}{dx} + \left(\frac{1}{x}\right) y = e^x$$

$$\frac{dy}{dx} + \left(\frac{y}{x \log x}\right) = \frac{1}{x}$$

Another form of first order linear differential equation is

$$\frac{dx}{dy} + P_1 x = Q_1$$

where, P_1 and Q_1 are constants or functions of y only. Some examples of this type of differential equation are

$$\frac{dx}{dy} + x = \cos y$$

$$\frac{dx}{dy} + \frac{-2x}{y} = y^2 e^{-y}$$

To solve the first order linear differential equation of the type

$$\frac{dy}{dx} + Py = Q \qquad \qquad \dots (1)$$

Multiply both sides of the equation by a function of x say $g(x)$ to get

$$g(x)\, \frac{dy}{dx} + P.(g(x))\, y = Q . g(x) \qquad \dots (2)$$

Choose $g(x)$ in such a way that R.H.S. becomes a derivative of $y \cdot g(x)$.

i.e.
$$g(x) \frac{dy}{dx} + P.g(x) y = \frac{d}{dx} [y \cdot g(x)]$$

or
$$g(x) \frac{dy}{dx} + P.g(x) y = g(x) \frac{dy}{dx} + y g'(x)$$

$$\Rightarrow \qquad P.g(x) = g'(x)$$

or
$$P = \frac{g'(x)}{g(x)}$$

Integrating both sides with respect to x, we get

$$\int P dx = \int \frac{g'(x)}{g(x)} dx$$

or
$$\int P \cdot dx = \log(g(x))$$

or
$$g(x) = e^{\int P \, dx}$$

On multiplying the equation (1) by $g(x) = e^{\int P \, dx}$, the L.H.S. becomes the derivative of some function of x and y. This function $g(x) = e^{\int P \, dx}$ is called *Integrating Factor* (I.F.) of the given differential equation.

Substituting the value of $g(x)$ in equation (2), we get

$$e^{\int P \, dx} \frac{dy}{dx} + P e^{\int P \, dx} y = Q \cdot e^{\int P \, dx}$$

or
$$\frac{d}{dx} \left(y \, e^{\int P dx} \right) = Q e^{\int P dx}$$

Integrating both sides with respect to x, we get

$$y \cdot e^{\int P dx} = \int \left(Q \cdot e^{\int P dx} \right) dx$$

or
$$y = e^{-\int P dx} \cdot \int \left(Q \cdot e^{\int P dx} \right) dx + C$$

which is the general solution of the differential equation.

Steps involved to solve first order linear differential equation:

(i) Write the given differential equation in the form $\dfrac{dy}{dx} + Py = Q$ where P, Q are constants or functions of x only.

(ii) Find the Integrating Factor (I.F) $= e^{\int P\,dx}$

(iii) Write the solution of the given differential equation as

$$y\,(I.F) = \int (Q \times I.F)\,dx + C$$

In case, the first order linear differential equation is in the form $\dfrac{dx}{dy} + P_1 x = Q_1$,

where, P_1 and Q_1 are constants or functions of y only. Then I.F $= e^{P_1\,dy}$ and the solution of the differential equation is given by

$$x\,.\,(I.F) = \int (Q_1 \times I.F)\,dy + C$$

Example 19 Find the general solution of the differential equation $\dfrac{dy}{dx} - y = \cos x$.

Solution Given differential equation is of the form

$$\frac{dy}{dx} + Py = Q,\ \text{where}\ P = -1\ \text{and}\ Q = \cos x$$

Therefore   I.F $= e^{\int -1\,dx} = e^{-x}$

Multiplying both sides of equation by I.F, we get

$$e^{-x}\frac{dy}{dx} - e^{-x}y = e^{-x}\cos x$$

or $\dfrac{d}{dx}\left(ye^{-x}\right) = e^{-x}\cos x$

On integrating both sides with respect to x, we get

$$ye^{-x} = \int e^{-x}\cos x\,dx + C \qquad \qquad ...\,(1)$$

Let $I = \int e^{-x}\cos x\,dx$

$$= \cos x\left(\frac{e^{-x}}{-1}\right) - \int (-\sin x)\,(-e^{-x})\,dx$$

$$= -\cos x\, e^{-x} - \int \sin x\, e^{-x}\, dx$$

$$= -\cos x\, e^{-x} - \left[\sin x(-e^{-x}) - \int \cos x\, (-e^{-x})\, dx \right]$$

$$= -\cos x\, e^{-x} + \sin x\, e^{-x} - \int \cos x\, e^{-x}\, dx$$

or $$I = -e^{-x} \cos x + \sin x\, e^{-x} - I$$

or $$2I = (\sin x - \cos x)\, e^{-x}$$

or $$I = \frac{(\sin x - \cos x)e^{-x}}{2}$$

Substituting the value of I in equation (1), we get

$$ye^{-x} = \left(\frac{\sin x - \cos x}{2} \right) e^{-x} + C$$

or $$y = \left(\frac{\sin x - \cos x}{2} \right) + C e^{x}$$

which is the general solution of the given differential equation.

Example 20 Find the general solution of the differential equation $x\dfrac{dy}{dx} + 2y = x^2 \ (x \neq 0)$.

Solution The given differential equation is

$$x\frac{dy}{dx} + 2y = x^2 \qquad\qquad ... (1)$$

Dividing both sides of equation (1) by x, we get

$$\frac{dy}{dx} + \frac{2}{x} y = x$$

which is a linear differential equation of the type $\dfrac{dy}{dx} + Py = Q$, where $P = \dfrac{2}{x}$ and $Q = x$.

So $$I.F = e^{\int \frac{2}{x} dx} = e^{2\log x} = e^{\log x^2} = x^2 \ [as \ e^{\log f(x)} = f(x)]$$

Therefore, solution of the given equation is given by

$$y \cdot x^2 = \int (x)(x^2)\, dx + C = \int x^3 dx + C$$

or $$y = \frac{x^2}{4} + C x^{-2}$$

which is the general solution of the given differential equation.

Example 21 Find the general solution of the differential equation $y\, dx - (x + 2y^2)\, dy = 0$.

Solution The given differential equation can be written as

$$\frac{dx}{dy} - \frac{x}{y} = 2y$$

This is a linear differential equation of the type $\dfrac{dx}{dy} + P_1 x = Q_1$, where $P_1 = -\dfrac{1}{y}$ and

$Q_1 = 2y$. Therefore $\text{I.F} = e^{\int -\frac{1}{y}\, dy} = e^{-\log y} = e^{\log (y)^{-1}} = \dfrac{1}{y}$

Hence, the solution of the given differential equation is

$$x\frac{1}{y} = \int (2y)\left(\frac{1}{y}\right) dy + C$$

or

$$\frac{x}{y} = \int (2dy) + C$$

or

$$\frac{x}{y} = 2y + C$$

or

$$x = 2y^2 + Cy$$

which is a general solution of the given differential equation.

Example 22 Find the particular solution of the differential equation

$$\frac{dy}{dx} + y \cot x = 2x + x^2 \cot x \quad (x \neq 0)$$

given that $y = 0$ when $x = \dfrac{\pi}{2}$.

Solution The given equation is a linear differential equation of the type $\dfrac{dy}{dx} + Py = Q$,

where $P = \cot x$ and $Q = 2x + x^2 \cot x$. Therefore

$$\text{I.F} = e^{\int \cot x\, dx} = e^{\log \sin x} = \sin x$$

Hence, the solution of the differential equation is given by

$$y \cdot \sin x = \int (2x + x^2 \cot x) \sin x\, dx + C$$

or
$$y \sin x = \int 2x \sin x \, dx + \int x^2 \cos x \, dx + C$$

or
$$y \sin x = \sin x \left(\frac{2x^2}{2} \right) - \int \cos x \left(\frac{2x^2}{2} \right) dx + \int x^2 \cos x \, dx + C$$

or
$$y \sin x = x^2 \sin x - \int x^2 \cos x \, dx + \int x^2 \cos x \, dx + C$$

or
$$y \sin x = x^2 \sin x + C \qquad \qquad \dots (1)$$

Substituting $y = 0$ and $x = \dfrac{\pi}{2}$ in equation (1), we get

$$0 = \left(\frac{\pi}{2} \right)^2 \sin \left(\frac{\pi}{2} \right) + C$$

or
$$C = \frac{-\pi^2}{4}$$

Substituting the value of C in equation (1), we get

$$y \sin x = x^2 \sin x - \frac{\pi^2}{4}$$

or
$$y = x^2 - \frac{\pi^2}{4 \sin x} \ (\sin x \neq 0)$$

which is the particular solution of the given differential equation.

Example 23 Find the equation of a curve passing through the point (0, 1). If the slope of the tangent to the curve at any point (x, y) is equal to the sum of the x coordinate (abscissa) and the product of the x coordinate and y coordinate (ordinate) of that point.

Solution We know that the slope of the tangent to the curve is $\dfrac{dy}{dx}$.

Therefore,
$$\frac{dy}{dx} = x + xy$$

or
$$\frac{dy}{dx} - xy = x \qquad \qquad \dots (1)$$

This is a linear differential equation of the type $\dfrac{dy}{dx} + Py = Q$, where $P = -x$ and $Q = x$.

Therefore,
$$\text{I.F} = e^{\int -x \, dx} = e^{\frac{-x^2}{2}}$$

Hence, the solution of equation is given by

$$y \cdot e^{\frac{-x^2}{2}} = \int (x) \left(e^{\frac{-x^2}{2}} \right) dx + C \qquad \ldots (2)$$

Let

$$I = \int (x) \, e^{\frac{-x^2}{2}} \, dx$$

Let $\dfrac{-x^2}{2} = t$, then $-x \, dx = dt$ or $x \, dx = -dt$.

Therefore, $I = -\int e^t \, dt = -e^t = -e^{\frac{-x^2}{2}}$

Substituting the value of I in equation (2), we get

$$y \, e^{\frac{-x^2}{2}} = -e^{\frac{-x^2}{2}} + C$$

or

$$y = -1 + C \, e^{\frac{x^2}{2}} \qquad \ldots (3)$$

Now (3) represents the equation of family of curves. But we are interested in finding a particular member of the family passing through (0, 1). Substituting $x = 0$ and $y = 1$ in equation (3) we get

$$1 = -1 + C \cdot e^0 \quad \text{or} \quad C = 2$$

Substituting the value of C in equation (3), we get

$$y = -1 + 2 \, e^{\frac{x^2}{2}}$$

which is the equation of the required curve.

EXERCISE 9.6

For each of the differential equations given in Exercises 1 to 12, find the general solution:

1. $\dfrac{dy}{dx} + 2y = \sin x$ 2. $\dfrac{dy}{dx} + 3y = e^{-2x}$ 3. $\dfrac{dy}{dx} + \dfrac{y}{x} = x^2$

4. $\dfrac{dy}{dx} + (\sec x) \, y = \tan x \left(0 \leq x < \dfrac{\pi}{2} \right)$ 5. $\cos^2 x \dfrac{dy}{dx} + y = \tan x \left(0 \leq x < \dfrac{\pi}{2} \right)$

6. $x \dfrac{dy}{dx} + 2y = x^2 \log x$ 7. $x \log x \dfrac{dy}{dx} + y = \dfrac{2}{x} \log x$

8. $(1 + x^2) \, dy + 2xy \, dx = \cot x \, dx \ (x \neq 0)$

9. $x\dfrac{dy}{dx}+y-x+xy\cot x=0 \ (x\neq 0)$ 10. $(x+y)\dfrac{dy}{dx}=1$

11. $y\,dx+(x-y^2)\,dy=0$ 12. $(x+3y^2)\dfrac{dy}{dx}=y \ (y>0)$.

For each of the differential equations given in Exercises 13 to 15, find a particular solution satisfying the given condition:

13. $\dfrac{dy}{dx}+2y\tan x=\sin x; \ y=0$ when $x=\dfrac{\pi}{3}$

14. $(1+x^2)\dfrac{dy}{dx}+2xy=\dfrac{1}{1+x^2}; \ y=0$ when $x=1$

15. $\dfrac{dy}{dx}-3y\cot x=\sin 2x; \ y=2$ when $x=\dfrac{\pi}{2}$

16. Find the equation of a curve passing through the origin given that the slope of the tangent to the curve at any point (x, y) is equal to the sum of the coordinates of the point.

17. Find the equation of a curve passing through the point $(0, 2)$ given that the sum of the coordinates of any point on the curve exceeds the magnitude of the slope of the tangent to the curve at that point by 5.

18. The Integrating Factor of the differential equation $x\dfrac{dy}{dx}-y=2x^2$ is

(A) e^{-x} (B) e^{-y} (C) $\dfrac{1}{x}$ (D) x

19. The Integrating Factor of the differential equation

$(1-y^2)\dfrac{dx}{dy}+yx=ay(-1<y<1)$ is

(A) $\dfrac{1}{y^2-1}$ (B) $\dfrac{1}{\sqrt{y^2-1}}$ (C) $\dfrac{1}{1-y^2}$ (D) $\dfrac{1}{\sqrt{1-y^2}}$

Miscellaneous Examples

Example 24 Verify that the function $y=c_1\,e^{ax}\cos bx+c_2\,e^{ax}\sin bx$, where c_1, c_2 are arbitrary constants is a solution of the differential equation

$$\dfrac{d^2y}{dx^2}-2a\dfrac{dy}{dx}+(a^2+b^2)y=0$$

Solution The given function is

$$y = e^{ax} [c_1 \cos bx + c_2 \sin bx] \qquad ... (1)$$

Differentiating both sides of equation (1) with respect to x, we get

$$\frac{dy}{dx} = e^{ax}[-bc_1 \sin bx + bc_2 \cos bx] + [c_1 \cos bx + c_2 \sin bx] e^{ax} \cdot a$$

or

$$\frac{dy}{dx} = e^{ax}[(bc_2 + ac_1) \cos bx + (ac_2 - bc_1) \sin bx] \qquad ... (2)$$

Differentiating both sides of equation (2) with respect to x, we get

$$\frac{d^2 y}{dx^2} = e^{ax}[(bc_2 + ac_1)(-b \sin bx) + (ac_2 - bc_1)(b \cos bx)]$$

$$+ [(bc_2 + ac_1) \cos bx + (ac_2 - bc_1) \sin bx] e^{ax} \cdot a$$

$$= e^{ax}[(a^2 c_2 - 2abc_1 - b^2 c_2) \sin bx + (a^2 c_1 + 2abc_2 - b^2 c_1) \cos bx]$$

Substituting the values of $\frac{d^2 y}{dx^2}, \frac{dy}{dx}$ and y in the given differential equation, we get

L.H.S. $= e^{ax}[a^2 c_2 - 2abc_1 - b^2 c_2) \sin bx + (a^2 c_1 + 2abc_2 - b^2 c_1) \cos bx]$

$$- 2ae^{ax}[(bc_2 + ac_1) \cos bx + (ac_2 - bc_1) \sin bx]$$

$$+ (a^2 + b^2) e^{ax}[c_1 \cos bx + c_2 \sin bx]$$

$$= e^{ax} \left[\begin{array}{l} (a^2 c_2 - 2abc_1 - b^2 c_2 - 2a^2 c_2 + 2abc_1 + a^2 c_2 + b^2 c_2) \sin bx \\ + (a^2 c_1 + 2abc_2 - b^2 c_1 - 2abc_2 - 2a^2 c_1 + a^2 c_1 + b^2 c_1) \cos bx \end{array} \right]$$

$$= e^{ax}[0 \times \sin bx + 0 \cos bx] = e^{ax} \times 0 = 0 = \text{R.H.S.}$$

Hence, the given function is a solution of the given differential equation.

Example 25 Form the differential equation of the family of circles in the second quadrant and touching the coordinate axes.

Solution Let C denote the family of circles in the second quadrant and touching the coordinate axes. Let $(-a, a)$ be the coordinate of the centre of any member of this family (see Fig 9.6).

Equation representing the family C is

$$(x + a)^2 + (y - a)^2 = a^2 \qquad \text{... (1)}$$

or $x^2 + y^2 + 2ax - 2ay + a^2 = 0 \qquad \text{... (2)}$

Differentiating equation (2) with respect to x, we get

$$2x + 2y\frac{dy}{dx} + 2a - 2a\frac{dy}{dx} = 0$$

or

$$x + y\frac{dy}{dx} = a\left(\frac{dy}{dx} - 1\right)$$

or

$$a = \frac{x + y\,y'}{y' - 1}$$

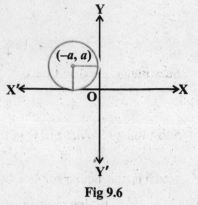

Fig 9.6

Substituting the value of a in equation (1), we get

$$\left[x + \frac{x + y\,y'}{y' - 1}\right]^2 + \left[y - \frac{x + y\,y'}{y' - 1}\right]^2 = \left[\frac{x + y\,y'}{y' - 1}\right]^2$$

or $[xy' - x + x + y\,y']^2 + [y\,y' - y - x - y\,y']^2 = [x + y\,y']^2$

or $(x + y)^2\,y'^2 + [x + y]^2 = [x + y\,y']^2$

or $(x + y)^2\,[(y')^2 + 1] = [x + y\,y']^2$

which is the differential equation representing the given family of circles.

Example 26 Find the particular solution of the differential equation $\log\left(\dfrac{dy}{dx}\right) = 3x + 4y$

given that $y = 0$ when $x = 0$.

Solution The given differential equation can be written as

$$\frac{dy}{dx} = e^{(3x + 4y)}$$

or

$$\frac{dy}{dx} = e^{3x} \cdot e^{4y} \qquad \text{... (1)}$$

Separating the variables, we get

$$\frac{dy}{e^{4y}} = e^{3x}\, dx$$

Therefore

$$\int e^{-4y}\, dy = \int e^{3x}\, dx$$

or
$$\frac{e^{-4y}}{-4} = \frac{e^{3x}}{3} + C$$

or $\qquad 4\,e^{3x} + 3\,e^{-4y} + 12\,C = 0$ ... (2)

Substituting $x = 0$ and $y = 0$ in (2), we get

$$4 + 3 + 12\,C = 0 \text{ or } C = \frac{-7}{12}$$

Substituting the value of C in equation (2), we get

$$4\,e^{3x} + 3\,e^{-4y} - 7 = 0,$$

which is a particular solution of the given differential equation.

Example 27 Solve the differential equation

$$(x\,dy - y\,dx)\,y\,\sin\left(\frac{y}{x}\right) = (y\,dx + x\,dy)\,x\,\cos\left(\frac{y}{x}\right).$$

Solution The given differential equation can be written as

$$\left[x\,y\sin\left(\frac{y}{x}\right) - x^2\cos\left(\frac{y}{x}\right)\right]dy = \left[xy\cos\left(\frac{y}{x}\right) + y^2\sin\left(\frac{y}{x}\right)\right]dx$$

or $\qquad \dfrac{dy}{dx} = \dfrac{xy\cos\left(\dfrac{y}{x}\right) + y^2\sin\left(\dfrac{y}{x}\right)}{xy\sin\left(\dfrac{y}{x}\right) - x^2\cos\left(\dfrac{y}{x}\right)}$

Dividing numerator and denominator on RHS by x^2, we get

$$\frac{dy}{dx} = \frac{\dfrac{y}{x}\cos\left(\dfrac{y}{x}\right) + \left(\dfrac{y^2}{x^2}\right)\sin\left(\dfrac{y}{x}\right)}{\dfrac{y}{x}\sin\left(\dfrac{y}{x}\right) - \cos\left(\dfrac{y}{x}\right)} \qquad \text{... (1)}$$

Clearly, equation (1) is a homogeneous differential equation of the form $\dfrac{dy}{dx} = g\left(\dfrac{y}{x}\right)$.

To solve it, we make the substitution

$$y = vx \qquad \text{... (2)}$$

or
$$\frac{dy}{dx} = v + x\frac{dv}{dx}$$

or $$v + x \frac{dv}{dx} = \frac{v \cos v + v^2 \sin v}{v \sin v - \cos v} \qquad \text{(using (1) and (2))}$$

or $$x \frac{dv}{dx} = \frac{2v \cos v}{v \sin v - \cos v}$$

or $$\left(\frac{v \sin v - \cos v}{v \cos v} \right) dv = \frac{2 \, dx}{x}$$

Therefore $$\int \left(\frac{v \sin v - \cos v}{v \cos v} \right) dv = 2 \int \frac{1}{x} \, dx$$

or $$\int \tan v \, dv - \int \frac{1}{v} \, dv = 2 \int \frac{1}{x} \, dx$$

or $$\log |\sec v| - \log |v| = 2 \log |x| + \log |C_1|$$

or $$\log \left| \frac{\sec v}{v \, x^2} \right| = \log |C_1|$$

or $$\frac{\sec v}{v \, x^2} = \pm \, C_1 \qquad \qquad \dots (3)$$

Replacing v by $\dfrac{y}{x}$ in equation (3), we get

$$\frac{\sec \left(\dfrac{y}{x} \right)}{\left(\dfrac{y}{x} \right)(x^2)} = C \text{ where, } C = \pm \, C_1$$

or $$\sec \left(\frac{y}{x} \right) = C \, xy$$

which is the general solution of the given differential equation.

Example 28 Solve the differential equation

$$(\tan^{-1} y - x) \, dy = (1 + y^2) \, dx.$$

Solution The given differential equation can be written as

$$\frac{dx}{dy} + \frac{x}{1 + y^2} = \frac{\tan^{-1} y}{1 + y^2} \qquad \qquad \dots (1)$$

Now (1) is a linear differential equation of the form $\dfrac{dx}{dy} + P_1\, x = Q_1,$

where, $P_1 = \dfrac{1}{1+y^2}$ and $Q_1 = \dfrac{\tan^{-1}y}{1+y^2}.$

Therefore, $I.F = e^{\int \frac{1}{1+y^2}\,dy} = e^{\tan^{-1}y}$

Thus, the solution of the given differential equation is

$$x\,e^{\tan^{-1}y} = \int \left(\dfrac{\tan^{-1}y}{1+y^2}\right) e^{\tan^{-1}y}\,dy + C \qquad \qquad \text{... (2)}$$

Let $I = \int \left(\dfrac{\tan^{-1}y}{1+y^2}\right) e^{\tan^{-1}y}\,dy$

Substituting $\tan^{-1}y = t$ so that $\left(\dfrac{1}{1+y^2}\right)dy = dt$, we get

$$I = \int t\, e^t\,dt = t\, e^t - \int 1 \cdot e^t\,dt = t\, e^t - e^t = e^t\,(t-1)$$

or, $I = e^{\tan^{-1}y}\,(\tan^{-1}y - 1)$

Substituting the value of I in equation (2), we get

$$x \cdot e^{\tan^{-1}y} = e^{\tan^{-1}y}\,(\tan^{-1}y - 1) + C$$

or $x = (\tan^{-1}y - 1) + C\, e^{-\tan^{-1}y}.$

which is the general solution of the given differential equation.

Miscellaneous Exercise on Chapter 9

1. For each of the differential equations given below, indicate its order and degree (if defined).

(i) $\dfrac{d^2y}{dx^2} + 5x\left(\dfrac{dy}{dx}\right)^2 - 6y = \log x$ (ii) $\left(\dfrac{dy}{dx}\right)^3 - 4\left(\dfrac{dy}{dx}\right)^2 + 7y = \sin x$

(iii) $\dfrac{d^4y}{dx^4} - \sin\left(\dfrac{d^3y}{dx^3}\right) = 0$

2. For each of the exercises given below, verify that the given function (implicit or explicit) is a solution of the corresponding differential equation.

   (i) $y = a\,e^x + b\,e^{-x} + x^2$: $x\dfrac{d^2 y}{dx^2} + 2\dfrac{dy}{dx} - xy + x^2 - 2 = 0$

   (ii) $y = e^x\,(a\cos x + b\sin x)$: $\dfrac{d^2 y}{dx^2} - 2\dfrac{dy}{dx} + 2y = 0$

   (iii) $y = x\sin 3x$: $\dfrac{d^2 y}{dx^2} + 9y - 6\cos 3x = 0$

   (iv) $x^2 = 2y^2 \log y$: $(x^2 + y^2)\dfrac{dy}{dx} - xy = 0$

3. Form the differential equation representing the family of curves given by $(x - a)^2 + 2y^2 = a^2$, where a is an arbitrary constant.

4. Prove that $x^2 - y^2 = c\,(x^2 + y^2)^2$ is the general solution of differential equation $(x^3 - 3x\,y^2)\,dx = (y^3 - 3x^2 y)\,dy$, where c is a parameter.

5. Form the differential equation of the family of circles in the first quadrant which touch the coordinate axes.

6. Find the general solution of the differential equation $\dfrac{dy}{dx} + \sqrt{\dfrac{1 - y^2}{1 - x^2}} = 0$.

7. Show that the general solution of the differential equation $\dfrac{dy}{dx} + \dfrac{y^2 + y + 1}{x^2 + x + 1} = 0$ is given by $(x + y + 1) = A\,(1 - x - y - 2xy)$, where A is parameter.

8. Find the equation of the curve passing through the point $\left(0, \dfrac{\pi}{4}\right)$ whose differential equation is $\sin x \cos y\, dx + \cos x \sin y\, dy = 0$.

9. Find the particular solution of the differential equation $(1 + e^{2x})\,dy + (1 + y^2)\,e^x\, dx = 0$, given that $y = 1$ when $x = 0$.

10. Solve the differential equation $y\,e^{\frac{x}{y}}\,dx = \left(x\,e^{\frac{x}{y}} + y^2\right)dy\;(y \neq 0)$.

11. Find a particular solution of the differential equation $(x - y)\,(dx + dy) = dx - dy$, given that $y = -1$, when $x = 0$. (Hint: put $x - y = t$)

12. Solve the differential equation $\left[\dfrac{e^{-2\sqrt{x}}}{\sqrt{x}} - \dfrac{y}{\sqrt{x}}\right]\dfrac{dx}{dy} = 1\,(x \neq 0)$.

13. Find a particular solution of the differential equation $\dfrac{dy}{dx} + y\cot x = 4x\,\mathrm{cosec}\,x$

   $(x \neq 0)$, given that $y = 0$ when $x = \dfrac{\pi}{2}$.

14. Find a particular solution of the differential equation $(x + 1)\dfrac{dy}{dx} = 2e^{-y} - 1$, given

   that $y = 0$ when $x = 0$.

15. The population of a village increases continuously at the rate proportional to the number of its inhabitants present at any time. If the population of the village was 20, 000 in 1999 and 25000 in the year 2004, what will be the population of the village in 2009?

16. The general solution of the differential equation $\dfrac{y\,dx - x\,dy}{y} = 0$ is

   (A) $xy = C$ (B) $x = Cy^2$ (C) $y = Cx$ (D) $y = Cx^2$

17. The general solution of a differential equation of the type $\dfrac{dx}{dy} + P_1 x = Q_1$ is

   (A) $y\,e^{\int P_1\,dy} = \int \left(Q_1 e^{\int P_1\,dy}\right) dy + C$

   (B) $y \cdot e^{\int P_1\,dx} = \int \left(Q_1 e^{\int P_1\,dx}\right) dx + C$

   (C) $x\,e^{\int P_1\,dy} = \int \left(Q_1 e^{\int P_1\,dy}\right) dy + C$

   (D) $x\,e^{\int P_1\,dx} = \int \left(Q_1 e^{\int P_1\,dx}\right) dx + C$

18. The general solution of the differential equation $e^x\,dy + (y\,e^x + 2x)\,dx = 0$ is
   (A) $x\,e^y + x^2 = C$ (B) $x\,e^y + y^2 = C$
   (C) $y\,e^x + x^2 = C$ (D) $y\,e^x + x^2 = C$

Summary

◆ An equation involving derivatives of the dependent variable with respect to independent variable (variables) is known as a differential equation.

◆ Order of a differential equation is the order of the highest order derivative occurring in the differential equation.

◆ Degree of a differential equation is defined if it is a polynomial equation in its derivatives.

◆ Degree (when defined) of a differential equation is the highest power (positive integer only) of the highest order derivative in it.

◆ A function which satisfies the given differential equation is called its solution. The solution which contains as many arbitrary constants as the order of the differential equation is called a general solution and the solution free from arbitrary constants is called particular solution.

◆ To form a differential equation from a given function we differentiate the function successively as many times as the number of arbitrary constants in the given function and then eliminate the arbitrary constants.

◆ Variable separable method is used to solve such an equation in which variables can be separated completely i.e. terms containing y should remain with dy and terms containing x should remain with dx.

◆ A differential equation which can be expressed in the form $\dfrac{dy}{dx} = f(x, y)$ or $\dfrac{dx}{dy} = g(x, y)$ where, $f(x, y)$ and $g(x, y)$ are homogenous functions of degree zero is called a homogeneous differential equation.

◆ A differential equation of the form $\dfrac{dy}{dx} + Py = Q$, where P and Q are constants or functions of x only is called a first order linear differential equation.

Historical Note

One of the principal languages of Science is that of differential equations. Interestingly, the date of birth of differential equations is taken to be November, 11,1675, when Gottfried Wilhelm Freiherr Leibnitz (1646 - 1716) first put in black and white the identity $\int y \, dy = \dfrac{1}{2} y^2$, thereby introducing both the symbols $\int$ and dy.

Leibnitz was actually interested in the problem of finding a curve whose tangents were prescribed. This led him to discover the *'method of separation of variables'* 1691. A year later he formulated the *'method of solving the homogeneous differential equations of the first order'*. He went further in a very short time to the discovery of the *'method of solving a linear differential equation of the first-order'*. How surprising is it that all these methods came from a single man and that too within 25 years of the birth of differential equations!

In the old days, what we now call the 'solution' of a differential equation, was used to be referred to as 'integral' of the differential equation, the word being coined by James Bernoulli (1654 - 1705) in 1690. The word 'solution was first used by Joseph Louis Lagrange (1736 - 1813) in 1774, which was almost hundred years since the birth of differential equations. It was Jules Henri Poincare (1854 - 1912) who strongly advocated the use of the word 'solution' and thus the word 'solution' has found its deserved place in modern terminology. The name of the *'method of separation of variables'* is due to John Bernoulli (1667 - 1748), a younger brother of James Bernoulli.

Application to geometric problems were also considered. It was again John Bernoulli who first brought into light the intricate nature of differential equations. In a letter to Leibnitz, dated May 20, 1715, he revealed the solutions of the differential equation

$$x^2 \, y'' = 2y,$$

which led to three types of curves, viz., parabolas, hyperbolas and a class of cubic curves. This shows how varied the solutions of such innocent looking differential equation can be. From the second half of the twentieth century attention has been drawn to the investigation of this complicated nature of the solutions of differential equations, under the heading *'qualitative analysis of differential equations'*. Now-a-days, this has acquired prime importance being absolutely necessary in almost all investigations.

Chapter 10

❨ VECTOR ALGEBRA ❩

❖ *In most sciences one generation tears down what another has built and what one has established another undoes. In Mathematics alone each generation builds a new story to the old structure. – HERMAN HANKEL* ❖

10.1 Introduction

In our day to day life, we come across many queries such as – What is your height? How should a football player hit the ball to give a pass to another player of his team? Observe that a possible answer to the first query may be 1.6 meters, a quantity that involves only one value (magnitude) which is a real number. Such quantities are called *scalars*. However, an answer to the second query is a quantity (called force) which involves muscular strength (magnitude) and direction (in which another player is positioned). Such quantities are called *vectors*. In mathematics, physics and engineering, we frequently come across with both types of quantities, namely, scalar quantities such as length, mass, time, distance, speed, area, volume, temperature, work,

W.R. Hamilton
(1805-1865)

money, voltage, density, resistance etc. and vector quantities like displacement, velocity, acceleration, force, weight, momentum, electric field intensity etc.

In this chapter, we will study some of the basic concepts about vectors, various operations on vectors, and their algebraic and geometric properties. These two type of properties, when considered together give a full realisation to the concept of vectors, and lead to their vital applicability in various areas as mentioned above.

10.2 Some Basic Concepts

Let 'l' be any straight line in plane or three dimensional space. This line can be given two directions by means of arrowheads. A line with one of these directions prescribed is called a *directed line* (Fig 10.1 (i), (ii)).

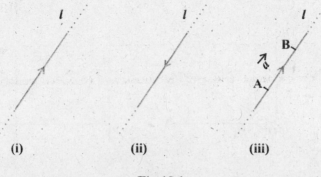

Fig 10.1

Now observe that if we restrict the line *l* to the line segment AB, then a magnitude is prescribed on the line *l* with one of the two directions, so that we obtain a *directed line segment* (Fig 10.1(iii)). Thus, a directed line segment has magnitude as well as direction.

Definition 1 A quantity that has magnitude as well as direction is called a vector.

Notice that a directed line segment is a vector (Fig 10.1(iii)), denoted as $\overrightarrow{AB}$ or simply as $\vec{a}$, and read as 'vector $\overrightarrow{AB}$' or 'vector $\vec{a}$'.

The point A from where the vector $\overrightarrow{AB}$ starts is called its *initial point*, and the point B where it ends is called its *terminal point*. The distance between initial and terminal points of a vector is called the *magnitude* (or length) of the vector, denoted as. $|\overrightarrow{AB}|$, or $|\vec{a}|$, or a. The arrow indicates the direction of the vector.

> **Note** Since the length is never negative, the notation $|\vec{a}| < 0$ has no meaning.

Position Vector

From Class XI, recall the three dimensional right handed rectangular coordinate system (Fig 10.2(i)). Consider a point P in space, having coordinates (x, y, z) with respect to the origin O $(0, 0, 0)$. Then, the vector $\overrightarrow{OP}$ having O and P as its initial and terminal points, respectively, is called the *position vector* of the point P with respect to O. Using distance formula (from Class XI), the magnitude of $\overrightarrow{OP}$ (or $\vec{r}$) is given by

$$|\overrightarrow{OP}| = \sqrt{x^2 + y^2 + z^2}$$

In practice, the position vectors of points A, B, C, etc., with respect to the origin O are denoted by $\vec{a}$, $\vec{b}, \vec{c}$, etc., respectively (Fig 10.2 (ii)).

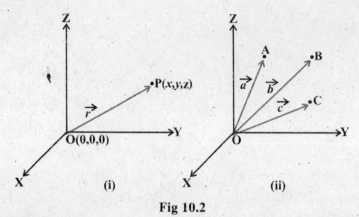

Fig 10.2

Direction Cosines

Consider the position vector $\overrightarrow{OP}$ (or $\vec{r}$) of a point P(x, y, z) as in Fig 10.3. The angles α, β, γ made by the vector $\vec{r}$ with the positive directions of x, y and z-axes respectively, are called its *direction angles*. The cosine values of these angles, i.e., $\cos\alpha$, $\cos\beta$ and $\cos\gamma$ are called *direction cosines* of the vector $\vec{r}$, and usually denoted by l, m and n, respectively.

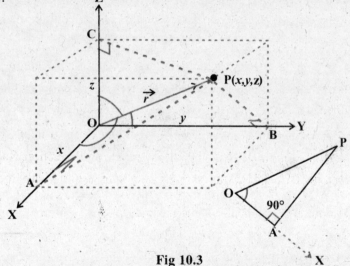

Fig 10.3

From Fig 10.3, one may note that the triangle OAP is right angled, and in it, we have $\cos\alpha = \dfrac{x}{r}$ (r stands for $|\vec{r}|$). Similarly, from the right angled triangles OBP and OCP, we may write $\cos\beta = \dfrac{y}{r}$ and $\cos\gamma = \dfrac{z}{r}$. Thus, the coordinates of the point P may also be expressed as (lr, mr, nr). The numbers lr, mr and nr, proportional to the direction cosines are called as *direction ratios* of vector $\vec{r}$, and denoted as a, b and c, respectively.

> **Note** One may note that $l^2 + m^2 + n^2 = 1$ but $a^2 + b^2 + c^2 \neq 1$, in general.

10.3 Types of Vectors

Zero Vector A vector whose initial and terminal points coincide, is called a zero vector (or null vector), and denoted as $\vec{0}$. Zero vector can not be assigned a definite direction as it has zero magnitude. Or, alternatively otherwise, it may be regarded as having any direction. The vectors $\overrightarrow{AA}$, $\overrightarrow{BB}$ represent the zero vector,

Unit Vector A vector whose magnitude is unity (i.e., 1 unit) is called a unit vector. The unit vector in the direction of a given vector $\vec{a}$ is denoted by $\hat{a}$.

Coinitial Vectors Two or more vectors having the same initial point are called coinitial vectors.

Collinear Vectors Two or more vectors are said to be collinear if they are parallel to the same line, irrespective of their magnitudes and directions.

Equal Vectors Two vectors $\vec{a}$ and $\vec{b}$ are said to be equal, if they have the same magnitude and direction regardless of the positions of their initial points, and written as $\vec{a} = \vec{b}$.

Negative of a Vector A vector whose magnitude is the same as that of a given vector (say, $\overrightarrow{AB}$), but direction is opposite to that of it, is called *negative* of the given vector. For example, vector $\overrightarrow{BA}$ is negative of the vector $\overrightarrow{AB}$, and written as $\overrightarrow{BA} = -\overrightarrow{AB}$.

Remark The vectors defined above are such that any of them may be subject to its parallel displacement without changing its magnitude and direction. Such vectors are called *free vectors*. Throughout this chapter, we will be dealing with free vectors only.

Example 1 Represent graphically a displacement of 40 km, 30° west of south.

Solution The vector $\overrightarrow{OP}$ represents the required displacement (Fig 10.4).

Example 2 Classify the following measures as scalars and vectors.

     (i) 5 seconds

     (ii) 1000 cm³

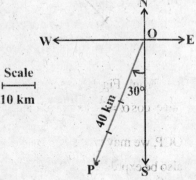

Scale
|————|
10 km

Fig 10.4

(iii) 10 Newton   (iv) 30 km/hr   (v) 10 g/cm³

(vi) 20 m/s towards north

Solution

(i) Time-scalar   (ii) Volume-scalar   (iii) Force-vector

(iv) Speed-scalar   (v) Density-scalar   (vi) Velocity-vector

Example 3 In Fig 10.5, which of the vectors are:

(i) Collinear   (ii) Equal   (iii) Coinitial

Solution

(i) Collinear vectors : $\vec{a}$, $\vec{c}$ and $\vec{d}$.

(ii) Equal vectors : $\vec{a}$ and $\vec{c}$.

(iii) Coinitial vectors : $\vec{b}$, $\vec{c}$ and $\vec{d}$.

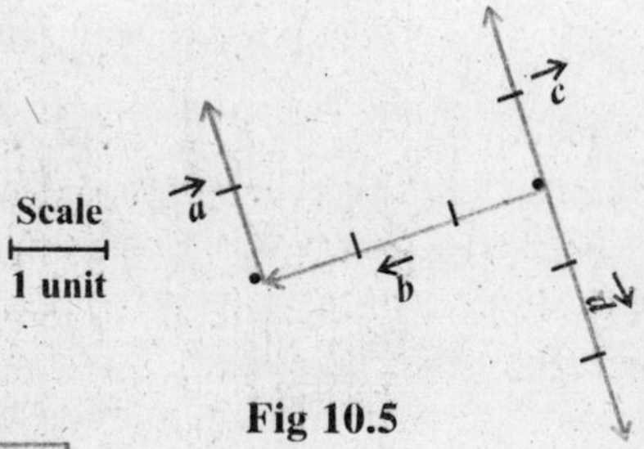

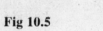

Scale
├────┤
1 unit

Fig 10.5

EXERCISE 10.1

1. Represent graphically a displacement of 40 km, 30° east of north.

2. Classify the following measures as scalars and vectors.

   (i) 10 kg   (ii) 2 meters north-west   (iii) 40°

   (iv) 40 watt   (v) 10⁻¹⁹ coulomb   (vi) 20 m/s²

3. Classify the following as scalar and vector quantities.

   (i) time period   (ii) distance   (iii) force

   (iv) velocity   (v) work done

4. In Fig 10.6 (a square), identify the following vectors.

   (i) Coinitial   (ii) Equal

   (iii) Collinear but not equal

5. Answer the following as true or false.

   (i) $\vec{a}$ and $-\vec{a}$ are collinear.

   (ii) Two collinear vectors are always equal in magnitude.

   (iii) Two vectors having same magnitude are collinear.

   (iv) Two collinear vectors having the same magnitude are equal.

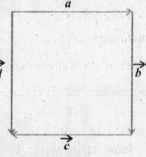

Fig 10.6

10.4 Addition of Vectors

A vector $\overline{AB}$ simply means the displacement from a point A to the point B. Now consider a situation that a girl moves from A to B and then from B to C (Fig 10.7). The net displacement made by the girl from point A to the point C, is given by the vector $\overline{AC}$ and expressed as

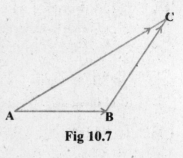

Fig 10.7

$$\overline{AC} = \overline{AB} + \overline{BC}$$

This is known as the *triangle law of vector addition.*

In general, if we have two vectors $\vec{a}$ and $\vec{b}$ (Fig 10.8 (i)), then to add them, they are positioned so that the initial point of one coincides with the terminal point of the other (Fig 10.8(ii)).

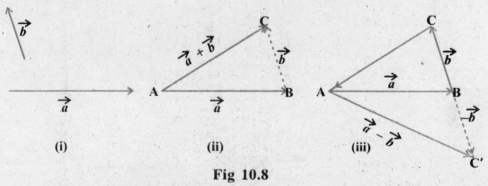

(i)   (ii)   (iii)

Fig 10.8

For example, in Fig 10.8 (ii), we have shifted vector $\vec{b}$ without changing its magnitude and direction, so that it's initial point coincides with the terminal point of $\vec{a}$. Then, the vector $\vec{a} + \vec{b}$, represented by the third side AC of the triangle ABC, gives us the sum (or resultant) of the vectors $\vec{a}$ and $\vec{b}$ i.e., in triangle ABC (Fig 10.8 (ii)), we have

$$\overline{AB} + \overline{BC} = \overline{AC}$$

Now again, since $\overline{AC} = -\overline{CA}$, from the above equation, we have

$$\overline{AB} + \overline{BC} + \overline{CA} = \overline{AA} = \vec{0}$$

This means that when the sides of a triangle are taken in order, it leads to zero resultant as the initial and terminal points get coincided (Fig 10.8(iii)).

Now, construct a vector $\overrightarrow{BC'}$ so that its magnitude is same as the vector $\overrightarrow{BC}$, but the direction opposite to that of it (Fig 10.8 (iii)), i.e.,

$$\overrightarrow{BC'} = -\overrightarrow{BC}$$

Then, on applying triangle law from the Fig 10.8 (iii), we have

$$\overrightarrow{AC'} = \overrightarrow{AB} + \overrightarrow{BC'} = \overrightarrow{AB} + (-\overrightarrow{BC}) = \vec{a} - \vec{b}$$

The vector $\overrightarrow{AC'}$ is said to represent the *difference of* $\vec{a}$ *and* $\vec{b}$.

Now, consider a boat in a river going from one bank of the river to the other in a direction perpendicular to the flow of the river. Then, it is acted upon by two velocity vectors–one is the velocity imparted to the boat by its engine and other one is the velocity of the flow of river water. Under the simultaneous influence of these two velocities, the boat in actual starts travelling with a different velocity. To have a precise idea about the effective speed and direction (i.e., the resultant velocity) of the boat, we have the following law of vector addition.

If we have two vectors $\vec{a}$ and $\vec{b}$ represented by the two adjacent sides of a parallelogram in magnitude and direction (Fig 10.9), then their sum $\vec{a} + \vec{b}$ is represented in magnitude and direction by the diagonal of the parallelogram through their common point. This is known as the *parallelogram law of vector addition.*

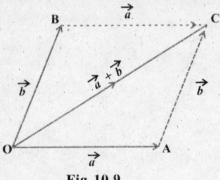

Fig 10.9

Note From Fig 10.9, using the triangle law, one may note that

$$\overrightarrow{OA} + \overrightarrow{AC} = \overrightarrow{OC}$$

or $\qquad\qquad \overrightarrow{OA} + \overrightarrow{OB} = \overrightarrow{OC} \qquad\qquad$ (since $\overrightarrow{AC} = \overrightarrow{OB}$)

which is parallelogram law. Thus, we may say that the two laws of vector addition are equivalent to each other.

Properties of vector addition

Property 1 For any two vectors $\vec{a}$ and $\vec{b}$,

$$\vec{a} + \vec{b} = \vec{b} + \vec{a} \qquad\qquad \text{(Commutative property)}$$

Proof Consider the parallelogram ABCD (Fig 10.10). Let $\overrightarrow{AB} = \vec{a}$ and $\overrightarrow{BC} = \vec{b}$, then using the triangle law, from triangle ABC, we have

$$\overrightarrow{AC} = \vec{a} + \vec{b}$$

Now, since the opposite sides of a parallelogram are equal and parallel, from Fig 10.10, we have, $\overrightarrow{AD} = \overrightarrow{BC} = \vec{b}$ and $\overrightarrow{DC} = \overrightarrow{AB} = \vec{a}$. Again using triangle law, from triangle ADC, we have

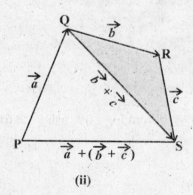

Fig 10.10

$$\overrightarrow{AC} = \overrightarrow{AD} + \overrightarrow{DC} = \vec{b} + \vec{a}$$

Hence $\vec{a} + \vec{b} = \vec{b} + \vec{a}$

Property 2 For any three vectors $\vec{a}, \vec{b}$ and $\vec{c}$

$$(\vec{a} + \vec{b}) + \vec{c} = \vec{a} + (\vec{b} + \vec{c}) \qquad \text{(Associative property)}$$

Proof Let the vectors $\vec{a}, \vec{b}$ and $\vec{c}$ be represented by $\overrightarrow{PQ}$, $\overrightarrow{QR}$ and $\overrightarrow{RS}$, respectively, as shown in Fig 10.11(i) and (ii).

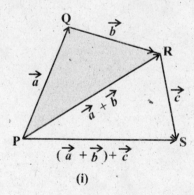

(i)

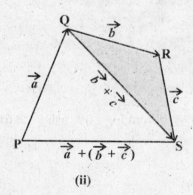

(ii)

Fig 10.11

Then $$\vec{a} + \vec{b} = \overrightarrow{PQ} + \overrightarrow{QR} = \overrightarrow{PR}$$

and $$\vec{b} + \vec{c} = \overrightarrow{QR} + \overrightarrow{RS} = \overrightarrow{QS}$$

So $$(\vec{a} + \vec{b}) + \vec{c} = \overrightarrow{PR} + \overrightarrow{RS} = \overrightarrow{PS}$$

and $\vec{a} + (\vec{b} + \vec{c}) = \overrightarrow{PQ} + \overrightarrow{QS} = \overrightarrow{PS}$

Hence $(\vec{a} + \vec{b}) + \vec{c} = \vec{a} + (\vec{b} + \vec{c})$

Remark The associative property of vector addition enables us to write the sum of three vectors $\vec{a}$, $\vec{b}$, $\vec{c}$ as $\vec{a} + \vec{b} + \vec{c}$ without using brackets.

Note that for any vector $\vec{a}$, we have

$$\vec{a} + \vec{0} = \vec{0} + \vec{a} = \vec{a}$$

Here, the zero vector $\vec{0}$ is called the *additive identity* for the vector addition.

10.5 Multiplication of a Vector by a Scalar

Let $\vec{a}$ be a given vector and λ a scalar. Then the product of the vector $\vec{a}$ by the scalar λ, denoted as $\lambda \vec{a}$, is called the multiplication of vector $\vec{a}$ by the scalar λ. Note that, $\lambda \vec{a}$ is also a vector, collinear to the vector $\vec{a}$. The vector $\lambda \vec{a}$ has the direction same (or opposite) to that of vector $\vec{a}$ according as the value of λ is positive (or negative). Also, the magnitude of vector $\lambda \vec{a}$ is $|\lambda|$ times the magnitude of the vector $\vec{a}$, i.e.,

$$|\lambda \vec{a}| = |\lambda| |\vec{a}|$$

A geometric visualisation of multiplication of a vector by a scalar is given in Fig 10.12.

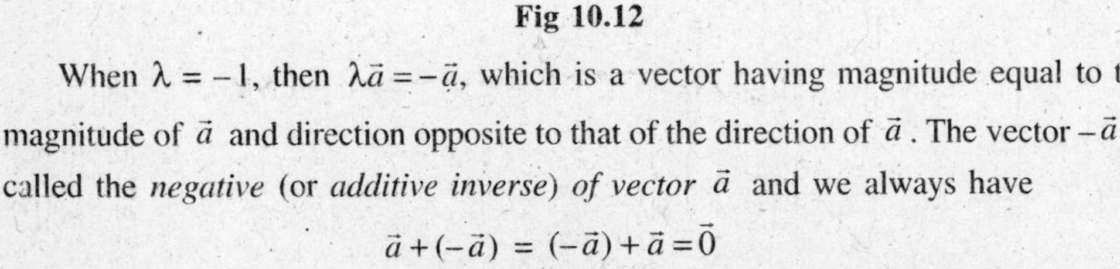

Fig 10.12

When $\lambda = -1$, then $\lambda \vec{a} = -\vec{a}$, which is a vector having magnitude equal to the magnitude of $\vec{a}$ and direction opposite to that of the direction of $\vec{a}$. The vector $-\vec{a}$ is called the *negative* (or *additive inverse*) *of vector* $\vec{a}$ and we always have

$$\vec{a} + (-\vec{a}) = (-\vec{a}) + \vec{a} = \vec{0}$$

Also, if $\lambda = \dfrac{1}{|\vec{a}|}$, provided $\vec{a} \neq 0$, i.e. $\vec{a}$ is not a null vector, then

$$|\lambda \vec{a}| = |\lambda| |\vec{a}| = \dfrac{1}{|\vec{a}|} |\vec{a}| = 1$$

So, $\lambda \vec{a}$ *represents the unit vector in the direction of* $\vec{a}$. We write it as

$$\hat{a} = \frac{1}{|\vec{a}|}\vec{a}$$

> **Note** For any scalar k, $k\vec{0} = \vec{0}$.

10.5.1 *Components of a vector*

Let us take the points A(1, 0, 0), B(0, 1, 0) and C(0, 0, 1) on the x-axis, y-axis and z-axis, respectively. Then, clearly

$$|\overrightarrow{OA}| = 1, |\overrightarrow{OB}| = 1 \text{ and } |\overrightarrow{OC}| = 1$$

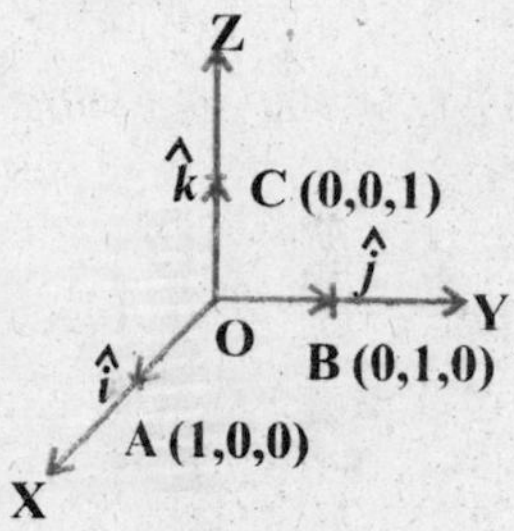

The vectors $\overrightarrow{OA}$, $\overrightarrow{OB}$ and $\overrightarrow{OC}$, each having magnitude 1, are called *unit vectors along the axes* OX, OY and OZ, respectively, and denoted by $\hat{i}, \hat{j}$ and $\hat{k}$, respectively (Fig 10.13).

Fig 10.13

Now, consider the position vector $\overrightarrow{OP}$ of a point P(x, y, z) as in Fig 10.14. Let P₁ be the foot of the perpendicular from P on the plane XOY. We, thus, see that P₁P is

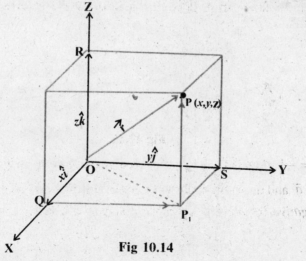

Fig 10.14

parallel to z-axis. As $\hat{i}, \hat{j}$ and $\hat{k}$ are the unit vectors along the x, y and z-axes, respectively, and by the definition of the coordinates of P, we have $\overrightarrow{P_1P} = \overrightarrow{OR} = z\hat{k}$.

Similarly, $\overrightarrow{QP_1} = \overrightarrow{OS} = y\hat{j}$ and $\overrightarrow{OQ} = x\hat{i}$.

Therefore, it follows that $\qquad \overrightarrow{OP_1} = \overrightarrow{OQ} + \overrightarrow{QP_1} = x\hat{i} + y\hat{j}$

and $\qquad\qquad\qquad\qquad \overrightarrow{OP} = \overrightarrow{OP_1} + \overrightarrow{P_1P} = x\hat{i} + y\hat{j} + z\hat{k}$

Hence, the position vector of P with reference to O is given by

$$\overrightarrow{OP} \text{ (or } \vec{r}) = x\hat{i} + y\hat{j} + z\hat{k}$$

This form of any vector is called its *component form*. Here, x, y and z are called as the *scalar components* of $\vec{r}$, and $x\hat{i}$, $y\hat{j}$ and $z\hat{k}$ are called the *vector components* of $\vec{r}$ along the respective axes. Sometimes x, y and z are also termed as *rectangular components*.

The length of any vector $\vec{r} = x\hat{i} + y\hat{j} + z\hat{k}$, is readily determined by applying the Pythagoras theorem twice. We note that in the right angle triangle OQP_1 (Fig 10.14)

$$|\overrightarrow{OP_1}| = \sqrt{|\overrightarrow{OQ}|^2 + |\overrightarrow{QP_1}|^2} = \sqrt{x^2 + y^2} ,$$

and in the right angle triangle OP_1P, we have

$$|\overrightarrow{OP}| = \sqrt{|\overrightarrow{OP_1}|^2 + |\overrightarrow{P_1P}|^2} = \sqrt{(x^2 + y^2) + z^2}$$

Hence, the length of any vector $\vec{r} = x\hat{i} + y\hat{j} + z\hat{k}$ is given by

$$|\vec{r}| = |x\hat{i} + y\hat{j} + z\hat{k}| = \sqrt{x^2 + y^2 + z^2}$$

If $\vec{a}$ and $\vec{b}$ are any two vectors given in the component form $a_1\hat{i} + a_2\hat{j} + a_3\hat{k}$ and $b_1\hat{i} + b_2\hat{j} + b_3\hat{k}$, respectively, then

(i)   the sum (or resultant) of the vectors $\vec{a}$ and $\vec{b}$ is given by

$$\vec{a} + \vec{b} = (a_1 + b_1)\hat{i} + (a_2 + b_2)\hat{j} + (a_3 + b_3)\hat{k}$$

(ii) the difference of the vector $\vec{a}$ and $\vec{b}$ is given by

$$\vec{a} - \vec{b} = (a_1 - b_1)\hat{i} + (a_2 - b_2)\hat{j} + (a_3 - b_3)\hat{k}$$

(iii) the vectors $\vec{a}$ and $\vec{b}$ are equal if and only if

$$a_1 = b_1, a_2 = b_2 \text{ and } a_3 = b_3$$

(iv) the multiplication of vector $\vec{a}$ by any scalar λ is given by

$$\lambda\vec{a} = (\lambda a_1)\hat{i} + (\lambda a_2)\hat{j} + (\lambda a_3)\hat{k}$$

The addition of vectors and the multiplication of a vector by a scalar together give the following distributive laws:

Let $\vec{a}$ and $\vec{b}$ be any two vectors, and k and m be any scalars. Then

(i) $k\vec{a} + m\vec{a} = (k + m)\vec{a}$

(ii) $k(m\vec{a}) = (km)\vec{a}$

(iii) $k(\vec{a} + \vec{b}) = k\vec{a} + k\vec{b}$

Remarks

(i)   One may observe that whatever be the value of λ, the vector $\lambda\vec{a}$ is always collinear to the vector $\vec{a}$. In fact, two vectors $\vec{a}$ and $\vec{b}$ are collinear if and only if there exists a nonzero scalar λ such that $\vec{b} = \lambda\vec{a}$. If the vectors $\vec{a}$ and $\vec{b}$ are given in the component form, i.e. $\vec{a} = a_1\hat{i} + a_2\hat{j} + a_3\hat{k}$ and $\vec{b} = b_1\hat{i} + b_2\hat{j} + b_3\hat{k}$, then the two vectors are collinear if and only if

$$b_1\hat{i} + b_2\hat{j} + b_3\hat{k} = \lambda(a_1\hat{i} + a_2\hat{j} + a_3\hat{k})$$

$$\Leftrightarrow \qquad b_1\hat{i} + b_2\hat{j} + b_3\hat{k} = (\lambda a_1)\hat{i} + (\lambda a_2)\hat{j} + (\lambda a_3)\hat{k}$$

$$\Leftrightarrow \qquad b_1 = \lambda a_1, \ b_2 = \lambda a_2, \ b_3 = \lambda a_3$$

$$\Leftrightarrow \qquad \frac{b_1}{a_1} = \frac{b_2}{a_2} = \frac{b_3}{a_3} = \lambda$$

(ii) If $\vec{a} = a_1\hat{i} + a_2\hat{j} + a_3\hat{k}$, then a_1, a_2, a_3 are also called direction ratios of $\vec{a}$.

(iii) In case if it is given that l, m, n are direction cosines of a vector, then $l\hat{i} + m\hat{j} + n\hat{k}$

$= (\cos\alpha)\hat{i} + (\cos\beta)\hat{j} + (\cos\gamma)\hat{k}$ is the unit vector in the direction of that vector, where α, β and γ are the angles which the vector makes with x, y and z axes respectively.

Example 4 Find the values of x, y and z so that the vectors $\vec{a} = x\hat{i} + 2\hat{j} + z\hat{k}$ and $\vec{b} = 2\hat{i} + y\hat{j} + \hat{k}$ are equal.

Solution Note that two vectors are equal if and only if their corresponding components are equal. Thus, the given vectors $\vec{a}$ and $\vec{b}$ will be equal if and only if

$$x = 2, \ y = 2, \ z = 1$$

Example 5 Let $\vec{a} = \hat{i} + 2\hat{j}$ and $\vec{b} = 2\hat{i} + \hat{j}$. Is $|\vec{a}| = |\vec{b}|$? Are the vectors $\vec{a}$ and $\vec{b}$ equal?

Solution We have $|\vec{a}| = \sqrt{1^2 + 2^2} = \sqrt{5}$ and $|\vec{b}| = \sqrt{2^2 + 1^2} = \sqrt{5}$

So, $|\vec{a}| = |\vec{b}|$. But, the two vectors are not equal since their corresponding components are distinct.

Example 6 Find unit vector in the direction of vector $\vec{a} = 2\hat{i} + 3\hat{j} + \hat{k}$

Solution The unit vector in the direction of a vector $\vec{a}$ is given by $\hat{a} = \dfrac{1}{|\vec{a}|}\vec{a}$.

Now
$$|\vec{a}| = \sqrt{2^2 + 3^2 + 1^2} = \sqrt{14}$$

Therefore $\hat{a} = \dfrac{1}{\sqrt{14}}(2\hat{i} + 3\hat{j} + \hat{k}) = \dfrac{2}{\sqrt{14}}\hat{i} + \dfrac{3}{\sqrt{14}}\hat{j} + \dfrac{1}{\sqrt{14}}\hat{k}$

Example 7 Find a vector in the direction of vector $\vec{a} = \hat{i} - 2\hat{j}$ that has magnitude 7 units.

Solution The unit vector in the direction of the given vector $\vec{a}$ is

$$\hat{a} = \dfrac{1}{|\vec{a}|}\vec{a} = \dfrac{1}{\sqrt{5}}(\hat{i} - 2\hat{j}) = \dfrac{1}{\sqrt{5}}\hat{i} - \dfrac{2}{\sqrt{5}}\hat{j}$$

Therefore, the vector having magnitude equal to 7 and in the direction of $\vec{a}$ is

$$7\hat{a} = 7\left(\dfrac{1}{\sqrt{5}}\hat{i} - \dfrac{2}{\sqrt{5}}\hat{j}\right) = \dfrac{7}{\sqrt{5}}\hat{i} - \dfrac{14}{\sqrt{5}}\hat{j}$$

Example 8 Find the unit vector in the direction of the sum of the vectors, $\vec{a} = 2\hat{i} + 2\hat{j} - 5\hat{k}$ and $\vec{b} = 2\hat{i} + \hat{j} + 3\hat{k}$.

Solution The sum of the given vectors is

$$\vec{a} + \vec{b} \, (= \vec{c}, \text{say}) = 4\hat{i} + 3\hat{j} - 2\hat{k}$$

and
$$|\vec{c}| = \sqrt{4^2 + 3^2 + (-2)^2} = \sqrt{29}$$

Thus, the required unit vector is

$$\hat{c} = \frac{1}{|\vec{c}|}\vec{c} = \frac{1}{\sqrt{29}}(4\hat{i} + 3\hat{j} - 2\hat{k}) = \frac{4}{\sqrt{29}}\hat{i} + \frac{3}{\sqrt{29}}\hat{j} - \frac{2}{\sqrt{29}}\hat{k}$$

Example 9 Write the direction ratios of the vector $\vec{a} = \hat{i} + \hat{j} - 2\hat{k}$ and hence calculate its direction cosines.

Solution Note that the direction ratios a, b, c of a vector $\vec{r} = x\hat{i} + y\hat{j} + z\hat{k}$ are just the respective components x, y and z of the vector. So, for the given vector, we have $a = 1$, $b = 1$ and $c = -2$. Further, if l, m and n are the direction cosines of the given vector, then

$$l = \frac{a}{|\vec{r}|} = \frac{1}{\sqrt{6}}, \quad m = \frac{b}{|\vec{r}|} = \frac{1}{\sqrt{6}}, \quad n = \frac{c}{|\vec{r}|} = \frac{-2}{\sqrt{6}} \quad \text{as } |\vec{r}| = \sqrt{6}$$

Thus, the direction cosines are $\left(\frac{1}{\sqrt{6}}, \frac{1}{\sqrt{6}}, -\frac{2}{\sqrt{6}}\right)$.

10.5.2 Vector joining two points

If $P_1(x_1, y_1, z_1)$ and $P_2(x_2, y_2, z_2)$ are any two points, then the vector joining P_1 and P_2 is the vector $\overrightarrow{P_1P_2}$ (Fig 10.15).

Joining the points P_1 and P_2 with the origin O, and applying triangle law, from the triangle OP_1P_2, we have

$$\overrightarrow{OP_1} + \overrightarrow{P_1P_2} = \overrightarrow{OP_2}.$$

Using the properties of vector addition, the above equation becomes

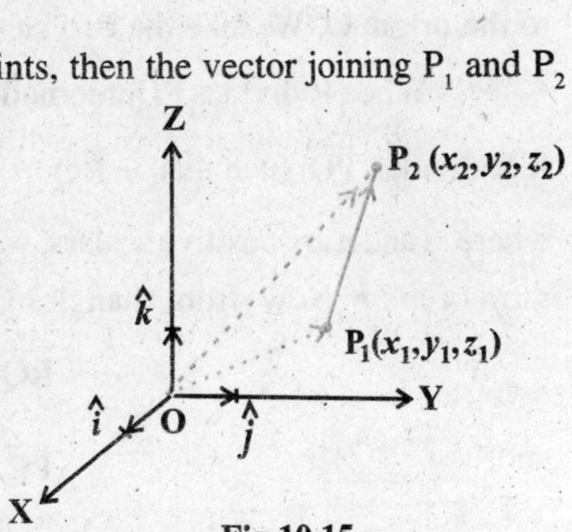

$$\overrightarrow{P_1P_2} = \overrightarrow{OP_2} - \overrightarrow{OP_1}$$

i.e.

$$\overrightarrow{P_1P_2} = (x_2\hat{i} + y_2\hat{j} + z_2\hat{k}) - (x_1\hat{i} + y_1\hat{j} + z_1\hat{k})$$

$$= (x_2 - x_1)\hat{i} + (y_2 - y_1)\hat{j} + (z_2 - z_1)\hat{k}$$

Fig 10.15

The magnitude of vector $\overrightarrow{P_1P_2}$ is given by

$$|\overrightarrow{P_1P_2}| = \sqrt{(x_2 - x_1)^2 + (y_2 - y_1)^2 + (z_2 - z_1)^2}$$

Example 10 Find the vector joining the points P(2, 3, 0) and Q(– 1, – 2, – 4) directed from P to Q.

Solution Since the vector is to be directed from P to Q, clearly P is the initial point and Q is the terminal point. So, the required vector joining P and Q is the vector $\overrightarrow{PQ}$, given by

$$\overrightarrow{PQ} = (-1-2)\hat{i} + (-2-3)\hat{j} + (-4-0)\hat{k}$$

i.e. $$\overrightarrow{PQ} = -3\hat{i} - 5\hat{j} - 4\hat{k}.$$

10.5.3 Section formula

Let P and Q be two points represented by the position vectors $\overrightarrow{OP}$ and $\overrightarrow{OQ}$, respectively, with respect to the origin O. Then the line segment joining the points P and Q may be divided by a third point, say R, in two ways – internally (Fig 10.16) and externally (Fig 10.17). Here, we intend to find the position vector $\overrightarrow{OR}$ for the point R with respect to the origin O. We take the two cases one by one.

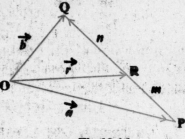

Fig 10.16

Case I When R divides PQ internally (Fig 10.16).

- If R divides $\overrightarrow{PQ}$ such that $m\,\overrightarrow{RQ} = n\,\overrightarrow{PR}$,

where *m* and *n* are positive scalars, we say that the point R divides $\overrightarrow{PQ}$ internally in the ratio of *m* : *n*. Now from triangles ORQ and OPR, we have

$$\overrightarrow{RQ} = \overrightarrow{OQ} - \overrightarrow{OR} = \vec{b} - \vec{r}$$

and $$\overrightarrow{PR} = \overrightarrow{OR} - \overrightarrow{OP} = \vec{r} - \vec{a},$$

Therefore, we have $m(\vec{b} - \vec{r}) = n(\vec{r} - \vec{a})$ **(Why?)**

or $$\vec{r} = \frac{m\vec{b} + n\vec{a}}{m+n}$$ (on simplification)

Hence, the position vector of the point R which divides P and Q internally in the ratio *m* : *n* is given by

$$\overrightarrow{OR} = \frac{m\vec{b} + n\vec{a}}{m+n}$$

Case II When R divides PQ externally (Fig 10.17). We leave it to the reader as an exercise to verify that the position vector of the point R which divides the line segment PQ externally in the ratio

$m : n$ $\left(\text{i.e. } \dfrac{PR}{QR} = \dfrac{m}{n}\right)$ is given by

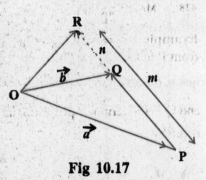

$$\overline{OR} = \frac{m\vec{b} - n\vec{a}}{m - n}$$

Fig 10.17

Remark If R is the midpoint of PQ , then $m = n$. And therefore, from Case I, the midpoint R of $\overline{PQ}$, will have its position vector as

$$\overline{OR} = \frac{\vec{a} + \vec{b}}{2}$$

Example 11 Consider two points P and Q with position vectors $\overrightarrow{OP} = 3\vec{a} - 2\vec{b}$ and $\overrightarrow{OQ} = \vec{a} + \vec{b}$. Find the position vector of a point R which divides the line segment joining P and Q in the ratio 2:1, (i) internally, and (ii) externally.

Solution

(i) The position vector of the point R dividing the join of P and Q internally in the ratio 2:1 is

$$\overline{OR} = \frac{2(\vec{a} + \vec{b}) + (3\vec{a} - 2\vec{b})}{2 + 1} = \frac{5\vec{a}}{3}$$

(ii) The position vector of the point R dividing the join of P and Q externally in the ratio 2:1 is

$$\overline{OR} = \frac{2(\vec{a} + \vec{b}) - (3\vec{a} - 2\vec{b})}{2 - 1} = 4\vec{b} - \vec{a}$$

Example 12 Show that the points $A(2\hat{i} - \hat{j} + \hat{k})$, $B(\hat{i} - 3\hat{j} - 5\hat{k})$, $C(3\hat{i} - 4\hat{j} - 4\hat{k})$ are the vertices of a right angled triangle.

Solution We have

$$\overrightarrow{AB} = (1 - 2)\hat{i} + (-3 + 1)\hat{j} + (-5 - 1)\hat{k} = -\hat{i} - 2\hat{j} - 6\hat{k}$$

$$\overrightarrow{BC} = (3 - 1)\hat{i} + (-4 + 3)\hat{j} + (-4 + 5)\hat{k} = 2\hat{i} - \hat{j} + \hat{k}$$

and

$$\overrightarrow{CA} = (2 - 3)\hat{i} + (-1 + 4)\hat{j} + (1 + 4)\hat{k} = -\hat{i} + 3\hat{j} + 5\hat{k}$$

Further, note that

$$|\overline{AB}|^2 = 41 = 6 + 35 = |\overline{BC}|^2 + |\overline{CA}|^2$$

Hence, the triangle is a right angled triangle.

EXERCISE 10.2

1. Compute the magnitude of the following vectors:

$$\vec{a} = \hat{i} + \hat{j} + \hat{k}; \quad \vec{b} = 2\hat{i} - 7\hat{j} - 3\hat{k}; \quad \vec{c} = \frac{1}{\sqrt{3}}\hat{i} + \frac{1}{\sqrt{3}}\hat{j} - \frac{1}{\sqrt{3}}\hat{k}$$

2. Write two different vectors having same magnitude.

3. Write two different vectors having same direction.

4. Find the values of x and y so that the vectors $2\hat{i} + 3\hat{j}$ and $x\hat{i} + y\hat{j}$ are equal.

5. Find the scalar and vector components of the vector with initial point $(2, 1)$ and terminal point $(-5, 7)$.

6. Find the sum of the vectors $\vec{a} = \hat{i} - 2\hat{j} + \hat{k}$, $\vec{b} = -2\hat{i} + 4\hat{j} + 5\hat{k}$ and $\vec{c} = \hat{i} - 6\hat{j} - 7\hat{k}$.

7. Find the unit vector in the direction of the vector $\vec{a} = \hat{i} + \hat{j} + 2\hat{k}$.

8. Find the unit vector in the direction of vector $\overline{PQ}$, where P and Q are the points $(1, 2, 3)$ and $(4, 5, 6)$, respectively.

9. For given vectors, $\vec{a} = 2\hat{i} - \hat{j} + 2\hat{k}$ and $\vec{b} = -\hat{i} + \hat{j} - \hat{k}$, find the unit vector in the direction of the vector $\vec{a} + \vec{b}$.

10. Find a vector in the direction of vector $5\hat{i} - \hat{j} + 2\hat{k}$ which has magnitude 8 units.

11. Show that the vectors $2\hat{i} - 3\hat{j} + 4\hat{k}$ and $-4\hat{i} + 6\hat{j} - 8\hat{k}$ are collinear.

12. Find the direction cosines of the vector $\hat{i} + 2\hat{j} + 3\hat{k}$.

13. Find the direction cosines of the vector joining the points A $(1, 2, -3)$ and B$(-1, -2, 1)$, directed from A to B.

14. Show that the vector $\hat{i} + \hat{j} + \hat{k}$ is equally inclined to the axes OX, OY and OZ.

15. Find the position vector of a point R which divides the line joining two points P and Q whose position vectors are $\hat{i} + 2\hat{j} - \hat{k}$ and $-\hat{i} + \hat{j} + \hat{k}$ respectively, in the ratio $2 : 1$

    (i) internally   (ii) externally

16. Find the position vector of the mid point of the vector joining the points P(2, 3, 4) and Q(4, 1, –2).

17. Show that the points A, B and C with position vectors, $\vec{a} = 3\hat{i} - 4\hat{j} - 4\hat{k}$, $\vec{b} = 2\hat{i} - \hat{j} + \hat{k}$ and $\vec{c} = \hat{i} - 3\hat{j} - 5\hat{k}$, respectively form the vertices of a right angled triangle.

18. In triangle ABC (Fig 10.18), which of the following is not true:

(A) $\overrightarrow{AB} + \overrightarrow{BC} + \overrightarrow{CA} = \vec{0}$

(B) $\overrightarrow{AB} + \overrightarrow{BC} - \overrightarrow{AC} = \vec{0}$

(C) $\overrightarrow{AB} + \overrightarrow{BC} - \overrightarrow{CA} = \vec{0}$

(D) $\overrightarrow{AB} - \overrightarrow{CB} + \overrightarrow{CA} = \vec{0}$

Fig 10.18

19. If $\vec{a}$ and $\vec{b}$ are two collinear vectors, then which of the following are incorrect:

(A) $\vec{b} = \lambda\vec{a}$, for some scalar λ

(B) $\vec{a} = \pm\vec{b}$

(C) the respective components of $\vec{a}$ and $\vec{b}$ are not proportional

(D) both the vectors $\vec{a}$ and $\vec{b}$ have same direction, but different magnitudes.

10.6 Product of Two Vectors

So far we have studied about addition and subtraction of vectors. An other algebraic operation which we intend to discuss regarding vectors is their product. We may recall that product of two numbers is a number, product of two matrices is again a matrix. But in case of functions, we may multiply them in two ways, namely, multiplication of two functions pointwise and composition of two functions. Similarly, multiplication of two vectors is also defined in two ways, namely, scalar (or dot) product where the result is a scalar, and vector (or cross) product where the result is a vector. Based upon these two types of products for vectors, we have found various applications in geometry, mechanics and engineering. In this section, we will discuss these two types of products.

10.6.1 Scalar (or dot) product of two vectors

Definition 2 The scalar product of two nonzero vectors $\vec{a}$ and $\vec{b}$, denoted by $\vec{a} \cdot \vec{b}$, is defined as $\qquad \vec{a} \cdot \vec{b} = |\vec{a}||\vec{b}|\cos\theta,$

where, θ is the angle between $\vec{a}$ and $\vec{b}, 0 \le \theta \le \pi$ (Fig 10.19).

If either $\vec{a} = \vec{0}$ or $\vec{b} = \vec{0}$, then θ is not defined, and in this case,

we define $\vec{a} \cdot \vec{b} = 0$

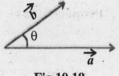

Fig 10.19

Observations

1. $\vec{a} \cdot \vec{b}$ is a real number.

2. Let $\vec{a}$ and $\vec{b}$ be two nonzero vectors, then $\vec{a} \cdot \vec{b} = 0$ if and only if $\vec{a}$ and $\vec{b}$ are perpendicular to each other. i.e.

   $\vec{a} \cdot \vec{b} = 0 \Leftrightarrow \vec{a} \perp \vec{b}$

3. If $\theta = 0$, then $\vec{a} \cdot \vec{b} = |\vec{a}||\vec{b}|$

   In particular, $\vec{a} \cdot \vec{a} = |\vec{a}|^2$, as θ in this case is 0.

4. If $\theta = \pi$, then $\vec{a} \cdot \vec{b} = -|\vec{a}||\vec{b}|$

   In particular, $\vec{a} \cdot (-\vec{a}) = -|\vec{a}|^2$, as θ in this case is π.

5. In view of the Observations 2 and 3, for mutually perpendicular unit vectors $\hat{i}, \hat{j}$ and $\hat{k}$, we have

$$\hat{i} \cdot \hat{i} = \hat{j} \cdot \hat{j} = \hat{k} \cdot \hat{k} = 1,$$
$$\hat{i} \cdot \hat{j} = \hat{j} \cdot \hat{k} = \hat{k} \cdot \hat{i} = 0$$

6. The angle between two nonzero vectors $\vec{a}$ and $\vec{b}$ is given by

$$\cos\theta = \frac{\vec{a} \cdot \vec{b}}{|\vec{a}||\vec{b}|}, \text{ or } \theta = \cos^{-1}\left(\frac{\vec{a}.\vec{b}}{|\vec{a}||\vec{b}|}\right)$$

7. The scalar product is commutative. i.e.

$$\vec{a} \cdot \vec{b} = \vec{b} \cdot \vec{a} \qquad \text{(Why?)}$$

Two important properties of scalar product

Property 1 (Distributivity of scalar product over addition) Let $\vec{a}, \vec{b}$ and $\vec{c}$ be any three vectors, then

$$\vec{a} \cdot (\vec{b} + \vec{c}) = \vec{a} \cdot \vec{b} + \vec{a} \cdot \vec{c}$$

Property 2 Let $\vec{a}$ and $\vec{b}$ be any two vectors, and λ be any scalar. Then

$$(\lambda\vec{a})\cdot\vec{b} = \lambda(\vec{a}\cdot\vec{b}) = \vec{a}\cdot(\lambda\vec{b})$$

If two vectors $\vec{a}$ and $\vec{b}$ are given in component form as $a_1\hat{i}+a_2\hat{j}+a_3\hat{k}$ and $b_1\hat{i}+b_2\hat{j}+b_3\hat{k}$, then their scalar product is given as

$$
\begin{aligned}
\vec{a}\cdot\vec{b} &= (a_1\hat{i}+a_2\hat{j}+a_3\hat{k})\cdot(b_1\hat{i}+b_2\hat{j}+b_3\hat{k}) \\
&= a_1\hat{i}\cdot(b_1\hat{i}+b_2\hat{j}+b_3\hat{k})+a_2\hat{j}\cdot(b_1\hat{i}+b_2\hat{j}+b_3\hat{k})+a_3\hat{k}\cdot(b_1\hat{i}+b_2\hat{j}+b_3\hat{k}) \\
&= a_1b_1(\hat{i}\cdot\hat{i})+a_1b_2(\hat{i}\cdot\hat{j})+a_1b_3(\hat{i}\cdot\hat{k})+a_2b_1(\hat{j}\cdot\hat{i})+a_2b_2(\hat{j}\cdot\hat{j})+a_2b_3(\hat{j}\cdot\hat{k}) \\
&\quad + a_3b_1(\hat{k}\cdot\hat{i})+a_3b_2(\hat{k}\cdot\hat{j})+a_3b_3(\hat{k}\cdot\hat{k}) \text{ (Using the above Properties 1 and 2)} \\
&= a_1b_1 + a_2b_2 + a_3b_3 \qquad\qquad\qquad\qquad \text{(Using Observation 5)}
\end{aligned}
$$

Thus $\qquad \vec{a}\cdot\vec{b} = a_1b_1 + a_2b_2 + a_3b_3$

10.6.2 *Projection of a vector on a line*

Suppose a vector $\overrightarrow{AB}$ makes an angle θ with a given directed line l (say), in the *anticlockwise direction* (Fig 10.20). Then the projection of $\overrightarrow{AB}$ on l is a vector $\vec{p}$ (say) with magnitude $|\overrightarrow{AB}|\cos\theta$, and the direction of $\vec{p}$ being the same (or opposite) to that of the line l, depending upon whether $\cos\theta$ is positive or negative. The vector $\vec{p}$

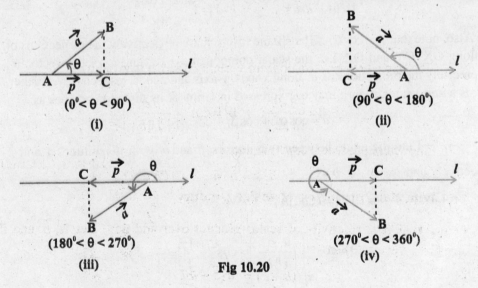

$(0°<\theta<90°)$ (i)

$(90°<\theta<180°)$ (ii)

$(180°<\theta<270°)$ (iii)

$(270°<\theta<360°)$ (iv)

Fig 10.20

is called the *projection vector*, and its magnitude $|\vec{p}|$ is simply called as the *projection* of the vector $\overrightarrow{AB}$ on the directed line l.

For example, in each of the following figures (Fig 10.20 (i) to (iv)), projection vector of $\overrightarrow{AB}$ along the line l is vector $\overrightarrow{AC}$.

Observations

1. If $\hat{p}$ is the unit vector along a line l, then the projection of a vector $\vec{a}$ on the line l is given by $\vec{a} \cdot \hat{p}$.

2. Projection of a vector $\vec{a}$ on other vector $\vec{b}$, is given by

$$\vec{a} \cdot \vec{b}, \quad \text{or} \quad \vec{a} \cdot \left(\frac{\vec{b}}{|\vec{b}|}\right), \quad \text{or} \quad \frac{1}{|\vec{b}|}(\vec{a} \cdot \vec{b})$$

3. If $\theta = 0$, then the projection vector of $\overrightarrow{AB}$ will be $\overrightarrow{AB}$ itself and if $\theta = \pi$, then the projection vector of $\overrightarrow{AB}$ will be $\overrightarrow{BA}$.

4. If $\theta = \dfrac{\pi}{2}$ or $\theta = \dfrac{3\pi}{2}$, then the projection vector of $\overrightarrow{AB}$ will be zero vector.

Remark If α, β and γ are the direction angles of vector $\vec{a} = a_1\hat{i} + a_2\hat{j} + a_3\hat{k}$, then its direction cosines may be given as

$$\cos\alpha = \frac{\vec{a} \cdot \hat{i}}{|\vec{a}||\hat{i}|} = \frac{a_1}{|\vec{a}|}, \quad \cos\beta = \frac{a_2}{|\vec{a}|}, \quad \text{and} \quad \cos\gamma = \frac{a_3}{|\vec{a}|}$$

Also, note that $|\vec{a}|\cos\alpha$, $|\vec{a}|\cos\beta$ and $|\vec{a}|\cos\gamma$ are respectively the projections of $\vec{a}$ along OX, OY and OZ. i.e., the scalar components a_1, a_2 and a_3 of the vector $\vec{a}$, are precisely the projections of $\vec{a}$ along x-axis, y-axis and z-axis, respectively. Further, if $\vec{a}$ is a unit vector, then it may be expressed in terms of its direction cosines as

$$\vec{a} = \cos\alpha\hat{i} + \cos\beta\hat{j} + \cos\gamma\hat{k}$$

Example 13 Find the angle between two vectors $\vec{a}$ and $\vec{b}$ with magnitudes 1 and 2 respectively and when $\vec{a} \cdot \vec{b} = 1$.

Solution Given $\vec{a} \cdot \vec{b} = 1, |\vec{a}| = 1$ and $|\vec{b}| = 2$. We have

$$\theta = \cos^{-1}\left(\frac{\vec{a} \cdot \vec{b}}{|\vec{a}||\vec{b}|}\right) = \cos^{-1}\left(\frac{1}{2}\right) = \frac{\pi}{3}$$

Example 14 Find angle 'θ' between the vectors $\vec{a} = \hat{i} + \hat{j} - \hat{k}$ and $\vec{b} = \hat{i} - \hat{j} + \hat{k}$.

Solution The angle θ between two vectors $\vec{a}$ and $\vec{b}$ is given by

$$\cos\theta = \frac{\vec{a} \cdot \vec{b}}{|\vec{a}||\vec{b}|}$$

Now

$$\vec{a} \cdot \vec{b} = (\hat{i} + \hat{j} - \hat{k}) \cdot (\hat{i} - \hat{j} + \hat{k}) = 1 - 1 - 1 = -1.$$

Therefore, we have

$$\cos\theta = \frac{-1}{3}$$

hence the required angle is

$$\theta = \cos^{-1}\left(-\frac{1}{3}\right)$$

Example 15 If $\vec{a} = 5\hat{i} - \hat{j} - 3\hat{k}$ and $\vec{b} = \hat{i} + 3\hat{j} - 5\hat{k}$, then show that the vectors $\vec{a} + \vec{b}$ and $\vec{a} - \vec{b}$ are perpendicular.

Solution We know that two nonzero vectors are perpendicular if their scalar product is zero.

Here

$$\vec{a} + \vec{b} = (5\hat{i} - \hat{j} - 3\hat{k}) + (\hat{i} + 3\hat{j} - 5\hat{k}) = 6\hat{i} + 2\hat{j} - 8\hat{k}$$

and

$$\vec{a} - \vec{b} = (5\hat{i} - \hat{j} - 3\hat{k}) - (\hat{i} + 3\hat{j} - 5\hat{k}) = 4\hat{i} - 4\hat{j} + 2\hat{k}$$

So

$$(\vec{a} + \vec{b}) \cdot (\vec{a} - \vec{b}) = (6\hat{i} + 2\hat{j} - 8\hat{k}) \cdot (4\hat{i} - 4\hat{j} + 2\hat{k}) = 24 - 8 - 16 = 0.$$

Hence $\vec{a} + \vec{b}$ and $\vec{a} - \vec{b}$ are perpendicular vectors.

Example 16 Find the projection of the vector $\vec{a} = 2\hat{i} + 3\hat{j} + 2\hat{k}$ on the vector $\vec{b} = \hat{i} + 2\hat{j} + \hat{k}$.

Solution The projection of vector $\vec{a}$ on the vector $\vec{b}$ is given by

$$\frac{1}{|\vec{b}|}(\vec{a} \cdot \vec{b}) = \frac{(2 \times 1 + 3 \times 2 + 2 \times 1)}{\sqrt{(1)^2 + (2)^2 + (1)^2}} = \frac{10}{\sqrt{6}} = \frac{5}{3}\sqrt{6}$$

Example 17 Find $|\vec{a} - \vec{b}|$, if two vectors $\vec{a}$ and $\vec{b}$ are such that $|\vec{a}| = 2$, $|\vec{b}| = 3$ and $\vec{a} \cdot \vec{b} = 4$.

Solution We have

$$|\vec{a} - \vec{b}|^2 = (\vec{a} - \vec{b}) \cdot (\vec{a} - \vec{b})$$

$$= \vec{a}.\vec{a} - \vec{a} \cdot \vec{b} - \vec{b} \cdot \vec{a} + \vec{b}.\vec{b}$$

$$= |\vec{a}|^2 - 2(\vec{a} \cdot \vec{b}) + |\vec{b}|^2$$

$$= (2)^2 - 2(4) + (3)^2$$

Therefore $\qquad |\vec{a} - \vec{b}| = \sqrt{5}$

Example 18 If $\vec{a}$ is a unit vector and $(\vec{x} - \vec{a}) \cdot (\vec{x} + \vec{a}) = 8$, then find $|\vec{x}|$.

Solution Since $\vec{a}$ is a unit vector, $|\vec{a}| = 1$. Also,

$$(\vec{x} - \vec{a}) \cdot (\vec{x} + \vec{a}) = 8$$

or $\qquad \vec{x} \cdot \vec{x} + \vec{x} \cdot \vec{a} - \vec{a} \cdot \vec{x} - \vec{a} \cdot \vec{a} = 8$

or $\qquad |\vec{x}|^2 - 1 = 8$ i.e. $|\vec{x}|^2 = 9$

Therefore $\qquad |\vec{x}| = 3$ (as magnitude of a vector is non negative).

Example 19 For any two vectors $\vec{a}$ and $\vec{b}$, we always have $|\vec{a} \cdot \vec{b}| \le |\vec{a}||\vec{b}|$ (Cauchy-Schwartz inequality).

Solution The inequality holds trivially when either $\vec{a} = \vec{0}$ or $\vec{b} = \vec{0}$. Actually, in such a situation we have $|\vec{a} \cdot \vec{b}| = 0 = |\vec{a}||\vec{b}|$. So, let us assume that $|\vec{a}| \ne 0 \ne |\vec{b}|$. Then, we have

$$\frac{|\vec{a} \cdot \vec{b}|}{|\vec{a}||\vec{b}|} = |\cos\theta| \le 1$$

Therefore $\qquad |\vec{a} \cdot \vec{b}| \le |\vec{a}||\vec{b}|$

Example 20 For any two vectors $\vec{a}$ and $\vec{b}$, we always have $|\vec{a} + \vec{b}| \le |\vec{a}| + |\vec{b}|$ (triangle inequality).

Solution The inequality holds trivially in case either $\vec{a} = \vec{0}$ or $\vec{b} = \vec{0}$ (How?). So, let $|\vec{a}| \ne \vec{0} \ne |\vec{b}|$. Then,

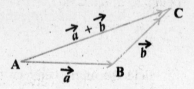

$$|\vec{a} + \vec{b}|^2 = (\vec{a} + \vec{b})^2 = (\vec{a} + \vec{b}) \cdot (\vec{a} + \vec{b})$$

Fig 10.21

$$= \vec{a} \cdot \vec{a} + \vec{a} \cdot \vec{b} + \vec{b} \cdot \vec{a} + \vec{b} \cdot \vec{b}$$

$$= |\vec{a}|^2 + 2\vec{a} \cdot \vec{b} + |\vec{b}|^2 \qquad \text{(scalar product is commutative)}$$

$$\le |\vec{a}|^2 + 2|\vec{a} \cdot \vec{b}| + |\vec{b}|^2 \qquad \text{(since } x \le |x| \; \forall x \in \mathbf{R})$$

$$\le |\vec{a}|^2 + 2|\vec{a}||\vec{b}| + |\vec{b}|^2 \qquad \text{(from Example 19)}$$

$$= (|\vec{a}| + |\vec{b}|)^2$$

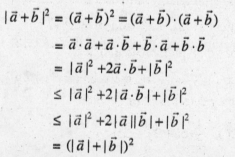

Hence $\qquad\qquad |\vec{a}+\vec{b}| \leq |\vec{a}|+|\vec{b}|$

Remark If the equality holds in triangle inequality (in the above Example 20), i.e.

$$|\vec{a}+\vec{b}| = |\vec{a}|+|\vec{b}|,$$

then $\qquad\qquad |\overrightarrow{AC}| = |\overrightarrow{AB}|+|\overrightarrow{BC}|$

showing that the points A, B and C are collinear.

Example 21 Show that the points $A(-2\hat{i}+3\hat{j}+5\hat{k})$, $B(\hat{i}+2\hat{j}+3\hat{k})$ and $C(7\hat{i}-\hat{k})$ are collinear.

Solution We have

$$\overrightarrow{AB} = (1+2)\hat{i}+(2-3)\hat{j}+(3-5)\hat{k} = 3\hat{i}-\hat{j}-2\hat{k},$$

$$\overrightarrow{BC} = (7-1)\hat{i}+(0-2)\hat{j}+(-1-3)\hat{k} = 6\hat{i}-2\hat{j}-4\hat{k},$$

$$\overrightarrow{AC} = (7+2)\hat{i}+(0-3)\hat{j}+(-1-5)\hat{k} = 9\hat{i}-3\hat{j}-6\hat{k}$$

$$|\overrightarrow{AB}| = \sqrt{14}, |\overrightarrow{BC}| = 2\sqrt{14} \text{ and } |\overrightarrow{AC}| = 3\sqrt{14}$$

Therefore $\qquad\qquad \left|\overrightarrow{AC}\right| = |\overrightarrow{AB}|+|\overrightarrow{BC}|$

Hence the points A, B and C are collinear.

> **Note** In Example 21, one may note that although $\overrightarrow{AB}+\overrightarrow{BC}+\overrightarrow{CA}=\vec{0}$ but the points A, B and C do not form the vertices of a triangle.

EXERCISE 10.3

1. Find the angle between two vectors $\vec{a}$ and $\vec{b}$ with magnitudes $\sqrt{3}$ and 2, respectively having $\vec{a}\cdot\vec{b}=\sqrt{6}$.

2. Find the angle between the vectors $\hat{i}-2\hat{j}+3\hat{k}$ and $3\hat{i}-2\hat{j}+\hat{k}$

3. Find the projection of the vector $\hat{i}-\hat{j}$ on the vector $\hat{i}+\hat{j}$.

4. Find the projection of the vector $\hat{i}+3\hat{j}+7\hat{k}$ on the vector $7\hat{i}-\hat{j}+8\hat{k}$.

5. Show that each of the given three vectors is a unit vector:

$$\frac{1}{7}(2\hat{i}+3\hat{j}+6\hat{k}), \frac{1}{7}(3\hat{i}-6\hat{j}+2\hat{k}), \frac{1}{7}(6\hat{i}+2\hat{j}-3\hat{k})$$

Also, show that they are mutually perpendicular to each other.

6.   Find $|\vec{a}|$ and $|\vec{b}|$, if $(\vec{a}+\vec{b})\cdot(\vec{a}-\vec{b})=8$ and $|\vec{a}|=8|\vec{b}|$.

7.   Evaluate the product $(3\vec{a}-5\vec{b})\cdot(2\vec{a}+7\vec{b})$.

8.   Find the magnitude of two vectors $\vec{a}$ and $\vec{b}$, having the same magnitude and such that the angle between them is 60° and their scalar product is $\dfrac{1}{2}$.

9.   Find $|\vec{x}|$, if for a unit vector $\vec{a}$, $(\vec{x}-\vec{a})\cdot(\vec{x}+\vec{a})=12$.

10. If $\vec{a}=2\hat{i}+2\hat{j}+3\hat{k}$, $\vec{b}=-\hat{i}+2\hat{j}+\hat{k}$ and $\vec{c}=3\hat{i}+\hat{j}$ are such that $\vec{a}+\lambda\vec{b}$ is perpendicular to $\vec{c}$, then find the value of λ.

11. Show that $|\vec{a}|\vec{b}+|\vec{b}|\vec{a}$ is perpendicular to $|\vec{a}|\vec{b}-|\vec{b}|\vec{a}$, for any two nonzero vectors $\vec{a}$ and $\vec{b}$.

12. If $\vec{a}\cdot\vec{a}=0$ and $\vec{a}\cdot\vec{b}=0$, then what can be concluded about the vector $\vec{b}$?

13. If $\vec{a},\vec{b},\vec{c}$ are unit vectors such that $\vec{a}+\vec{b}+\vec{c}=\vec{0}$, find the value of $\vec{a}\cdot\vec{b}+\vec{b}\cdot\vec{c}+\vec{c}\cdot\vec{a}$.

14. If either vector $\vec{a}=\vec{0}$ or $\vec{b}=\vec{0}$, then $\vec{a}\cdot\vec{b}=0$. But the converse need not be true. Justify your answer with an example.

15. If the vertices A, B, C of a triangle ABC are (1, 2, 3), (–1, 0, 0), (0, 1, 2), respectively, then find ∠ABC. [∠ABC is the angle between the vectors $\overrightarrow{BA}$ and $\overrightarrow{BC}$].

16. Show that the points A(1, 2, 7), B(2, 6, 3) and C(3, 10, –1) are collinear.

17. Show that the vectors $2\hat{i}-\hat{j}+\hat{k}$, $\hat{i}-3\hat{j}-5\hat{k}$ and $3\hat{i}-4\hat{j}-4\hat{k}$ form the vertices of a right angled triangle.

18. If $\vec{a}$ is a nonzero vector of magnitude 'a' and λ a nonzero scalar, then $\lambda\vec{a}$ is unit vector if
     (A) $\lambda=1$ (B) $\lambda=-1$ (C) $a=|\lambda|$ (D) $a=1/|\lambda|$

10.6.3 *Vector (or cross) product of two vectors*

In Section 10.2, we have discussed on the three dimensional right handed rectangular coordinate system. In this system, when the positive x-axis is rotated counterclockwise into the positive y-axis, a right handed (standard) screw would advance in the direction of the positive z-axis (Fig 10.22(i)).

In a right handed coordinate system, the thumb of the right hand points in the direction of the positive z-axis when the fingers are curled in the direction away from the positive x-axis toward the positive y-axis (Fig 10.22(ii)).

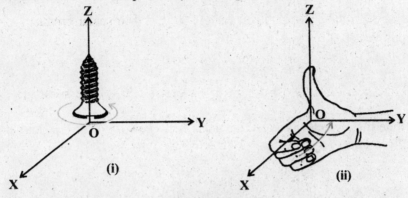

Fig 10.22 (i), (ii)

Definition 3 The vector product of two nonzero vectors $\vec{a}$ and $\vec{b}$, is denoted by $\vec{a} \times \vec{b}$ and defined as

$$\vec{a} \times \vec{b} = |\vec{a}||\vec{b}|\sin\theta\,\hat{n},$$

where, θ is the angle between $\vec{a}$ and $\vec{b}$, $0 \le \theta \le \pi$ and $\hat{n}$ is

a unit vector perpendicular to both $\vec{a}$ and $\vec{b}$, such that

$\vec{a}, \vec{b}$ and $\hat{n}$ form a right handed system (Fig 10.23). i.e., the

right handed system rotated from $\vec{a}$ to $\vec{b}$ moves in the

direction of $\hat{n}$.

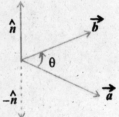

Fig 10.23

If either $\vec{a} = \vec{0}$ or $\vec{b} = \vec{0}$, then θ is not defined and in this case, we define $\vec{a} \times \vec{b} = \vec{0}$.

Observations

1. $\vec{a} \times \vec{b}$ is a vector.

2. Let $\vec{a}$ and $\vec{b}$ be two nonzero vectors. Then $\vec{a} \times \vec{b} = \vec{0}$ if and only if $\vec{a}$ and $\vec{b}$ are parallel (or collinear) to each other, i.e.,

$$\vec{a} \times \vec{b} = \vec{0} \Leftrightarrow \vec{a} \| \vec{b}$$

In particular, $\vec{a} \times \vec{a} = \vec{0}$ and $\vec{a} \times (-\vec{a}) = \vec{0}$, since in the first situation, $\theta = 0$ and in the second one, $\theta = \pi$, making the value of $\sin \theta$ to be 0.

3. If $\theta = \dfrac{\pi}{2}$ then $\vec{a} \times \vec{b} = |\vec{a}||\vec{b}|$.

4. In view of the Observations 2 and 3, for mutually perpendicular unit vectors $\hat{i}$, $\hat{j}$ and $\hat{k}$ (Fig 10.24), we have

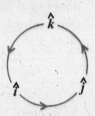

$$\hat{i} \times \hat{i} = \hat{j} \times \hat{j} = \hat{k} \times \hat{k} = \vec{0}$$

$$\hat{i} \times \hat{j} = \hat{k}, \quad \hat{j} \times \hat{k} = \hat{i}, \quad \hat{k} \times \hat{i} = \hat{j}$$

Fig 10.24

5. In terms of vector product, the angle between two vectors $\vec{a}$ and $\vec{b}$ may be given as

$$\sin \theta = \frac{|\vec{a} \times \vec{b}|}{|\vec{a}||\vec{b}|}$$

6. It is always true that the vector product is not commutative, as $\vec{a} \times \vec{b} = -\vec{b} \times \vec{a}$.

Indeed, $\vec{a} \times \vec{b} = |\vec{a}||\vec{b}|\sin \theta \hat{n}$, where $\vec{a}, \vec{b}$ and $\hat{n}$ form a right handed system, i.e., θ is traversed from $\vec{a}$ to $\vec{b}$, Fig 10.25 (i). While, $\vec{b} \times \vec{a} = |\vec{a}||\vec{b}|\sin \theta \hat{n}_1$, where $\vec{b}, \vec{a}$ and $\hat{n}_1$ form a right handed system i.e. θ is traversed from $\vec{b}$ to $\vec{a}$, Fig 10.25(ii).

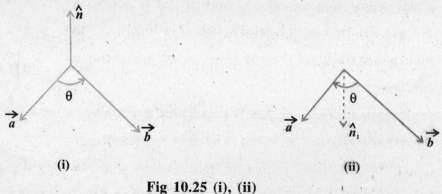

(i)   (ii)

Fig 10.25 (i), (ii)

Thus, if we assume $\vec{a}$ and $\vec{b}$ to lie in the plane of the paper, then $\hat{n}$ and $\hat{n}_1$ both will be perpendicular to the plane of the paper. But, $\hat{n}$ being directed above the paper while $\hat{n}_1$ directed below, the paper. i.e. $\hat{n}_1 = -\hat{n}$.

Hence $\qquad \vec{a} \times \vec{b} = |\vec{a}||\vec{b}|\sin\theta\,\hat{n}$

$$= -|\vec{a}||\vec{b}|\sin\theta\hat{n}_1 = -\vec{b} \times \vec{a}$$

7. In view of the Observations 4 and 6, we have

$$\hat{j} \times \hat{i} = -\hat{k}, \quad \hat{k} \times \hat{j} = -\hat{i} \text{ and } \hat{i} \times \hat{k} = -\hat{j}.$$

8. If $\vec{a}$ and $\vec{b}$ represent the adjacent sides of a triangle then its area is given as

$\dfrac{1}{2}|\vec{a} \times \vec{b}|$.

By definition of the area of a triangle, we have from Fig 10.26,

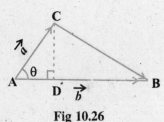

Area of triangle ABC = $\dfrac{1}{2}$ AB·CD.

Fig 10.26

But AB = $|\vec{b}|$ (as given), and CD = $|\vec{a}|\sin\theta$.

Thus, Area of triangle ABC = $\dfrac{1}{2}|\vec{b}||\vec{a}|\sin\theta$ = $\dfrac{1}{2}|\vec{a} \times \vec{b}|$.

9. If $\vec{a}$ and $\vec{b}$ represent the adjacent sides of a parallelogram, then its area is given by $|\vec{a} \times \vec{b}|$.

From Fig 10.27, we have

Area of parallelogram ABCD = AB. DE.

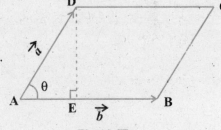

But AB = $|\vec{b}|$ (as given), and

DE = $|\vec{a}|\sin\theta$.

Thus,

Fig 10.27

Area of parallelogram ABCD = $|\vec{b}||\vec{a}|\sin\theta$ = $|\vec{a} \times \vec{b}|$.

We now state two important properties of vector product.

Property 3 (Distributivity of vector product over addition): If $\vec{a}, \vec{b}$ and $\vec{c}$ are any three vectors and λ be a scalar, then

(i) $\vec{a} \times (\vec{b} + \vec{c}) = \vec{a} \times \vec{b} + \vec{a} \times \vec{c}$

(ii) $\lambda(\vec{a} \times \vec{b}) = (\lambda\vec{a}) \times \vec{b} = \vec{a} \times (\lambda\vec{b})$

Let $\vec{a}$ and $\vec{b}$ be two vectors given in component form as $a_1\hat{i} + a_2\hat{j} + a_3\hat{k}$ and $b_1\hat{i} + b_2\hat{j} + b_3\hat{k}$, respectively. Then their cross product may be given by

$$\vec{a} \times \vec{b} = \begin{vmatrix} \hat{i} & \hat{j} & \hat{k} \\ a_1 & a_2 & a_3 \\ b_1 & b_2 & b_3 \end{vmatrix}$$

Explanation We have

$$\vec{a} \times \vec{b} = (a_1\hat{i} + a_2\hat{j} + a_3\hat{k}) \times (b_1\hat{i} + b_2\hat{j} + b_3\hat{k})$$

$$= a_1b_1(\hat{i} \times \hat{i}) + a_1b_2(\hat{i} \times \hat{j}) + a_1b_3(\hat{i} \times \hat{k}) + a_2b_1(\hat{j} \times \hat{i})$$

$$\quad + a_2b_2(\hat{j} \times \hat{j}) + a_2b_3(\hat{j} \times \hat{k})$$

$$\quad + a_3b_1(\hat{k} \times \hat{i}) + a_3b_2(\hat{k} \times \hat{j}) + a_3b_3(\hat{k} \times \hat{k}) \qquad \text{(by Property 1)}$$

$$= a_1b_2(\hat{i} \times \hat{j}) - a_1b_3(\hat{k} \times \hat{i}) - a_2b_1(\hat{i} \times \hat{j})$$

$$\quad + a_2b_3(\hat{j} \times \hat{k}) + a_3b_1(\hat{k} \times \hat{i}) - a_3b_2(\hat{j} \times \hat{k})$$

(as $\hat{i} \times \hat{i} = \hat{j} \times \hat{j} = \hat{k} \times \hat{k} = 0$ and $\hat{i} \times \hat{k} = -\hat{k} \times \hat{i}, \ \hat{j} \times \hat{i} = -\hat{i} \times \hat{j}$ and $\hat{k} \times \hat{j} = -\hat{j} \times \hat{k}$)

$$= a_1b_2\hat{k} - a_1b_3\hat{j} - a_2b_1\hat{k} + a_2b_3\hat{i} + a_3b_1\hat{j} - a_3b_2\hat{i}$$

(as $\hat{i} \times \hat{j} = \hat{k}, \ \hat{j} \times \hat{k} = \hat{i}$ and $\hat{k} \times \hat{i} = \hat{j}$)

$$= (a_2b_3 - a_3b_2)\hat{i} - (a_1b_3 - a_3b_1)\hat{j} + (a_1b_2 - a_2b_1)\hat{k}$$

$$= \begin{vmatrix} \hat{i} & \hat{j} & \hat{k} \\ a_1 & a_2 & a_3 \\ b_1 & b_2 & b_3 \end{vmatrix}$$

Example 22 Find $|\vec{a} \times \vec{b}|$, if $\vec{a} = 2\hat{i} + \hat{j} + 3\hat{k}$ and $\vec{b} = 3\hat{i} + 5\hat{j} - 2\hat{k}$

Solution We have

$$\vec{a} \times \vec{b} = \begin{vmatrix} \hat{i} & \hat{j} & \hat{k} \\ 2 & 1 & 3 \\ 3 & 5 & -2 \end{vmatrix}$$

$$= \hat{i}(-2-15) - (-4-9)\hat{j} + (10-3)\hat{k} = -17\hat{i} + 13\hat{j} + 7\hat{k}$$

Hence $|\vec{a} \times \vec{b}| = \sqrt{(-17)^2 + (13)^2 + (7)^2} = \sqrt{507}$

Example 23 Find a unit vector perpendicular to each of the vectors $(\vec{a}+\vec{b})$ and $(\vec{a}-\vec{b})$, where $\vec{a}=\hat{i}+\hat{j}+\hat{k}, \ \vec{b}=\hat{i}+2\hat{j}+3\hat{k}$.

Solution We have $\vec{a}+\vec{b}=2\hat{i}+3\hat{j}+4\hat{k}$ and $\vec{a}-\vec{b}=-\hat{j}-2\hat{k}$

A vector which is perpendicular to both $\vec{a}+\vec{b}$ and $\vec{a}-\vec{b}$ is given by

$$(\vec{a}+\vec{b})\times(\vec{a}-\vec{b}) = \begin{vmatrix} \hat{i} & \hat{j} & \hat{k} \\ 2 & 3 & 4 \\ 0 & -1 & -2 \end{vmatrix} = -2\hat{i}+4\hat{j}-2\hat{k} \ (=\vec{c}, \text{ say})$$

Now $$|\vec{c}| = \sqrt{4+16+4} = \sqrt{24} = 2\sqrt{6}$$

Therefore, the required unit vector is

$$\frac{\vec{c}}{|\vec{c}|} = \frac{-1}{\sqrt{6}}\hat{i}+\frac{2}{\sqrt{6}}\hat{j}-\frac{1}{\sqrt{6}}\hat{k}$$

> **☞ Note** There are two perpendicular directions to any plane. Thus, another unit vector perpendicular to $\vec{a}+\vec{b}$ and $\vec{a}-\vec{b}$ will be $\frac{1}{\sqrt{6}}\hat{i}-\frac{2}{\sqrt{6}}\hat{j}+\frac{1}{\sqrt{6}}\hat{k}$. But that will be a consequence of $(\vec{a}-\vec{b})\times(\vec{a}+\vec{b})$.

Example 24 Find the area of a triangle having the points A(1, 1, 1), B(1, 2, 3) and C(2, 3, 1) as its vertices.

Solution We have $\overrightarrow{AB}=\hat{j}+2\hat{k}$ and $\overrightarrow{AC}=\hat{i}+2\hat{j}$. The area of the given triangle is $\frac{1}{2}|\overrightarrow{AB}\times\overrightarrow{AC}|$.

Now, $$\overrightarrow{AB}\times\overrightarrow{AC} = \begin{vmatrix} \hat{i} & \hat{j} & \hat{k} \\ 0 & 1 & 2 \\ 1 & 2 & 0 \end{vmatrix} = -4\hat{i}+2\hat{j}-\hat{k}$$

Therefore $$|\overrightarrow{AB}\times\overrightarrow{AC}| = \sqrt{16+4+1} = \sqrt{21}$$

Thus, the required area is $\frac{1}{2}\sqrt{21}$

Example 25 Find the area of a parallelogram whose adjacent sides are given by the vectors $\vec{a} = 3\hat{i} + \hat{j} + 4\hat{k}$ and $\vec{b} = \hat{i} - \hat{j} + \hat{k}$

Solution The area of a parallelogram with $\vec{a}$ and $\vec{b}$ as its adjacent sides is given by $|\vec{a} \times \vec{b}|$.

Now
$$\vec{a} \times \vec{b} = \begin{vmatrix} \hat{i} & \hat{j} & \hat{k} \\ 3 & 1 & 4 \\ 1 & -1 & 1 \end{vmatrix} = 5\hat{i} + \hat{j} - 4\hat{k}$$

Therefore
$$|\vec{a} \times \vec{b}| = \sqrt{25 + 1 + 16} = \sqrt{42}$$

and hence, the required area is $\sqrt{42}$.

EXERCISE 10.4

1. Find $|\vec{a} \times \vec{b}|$, if $\vec{a} = \hat{i} - 7\hat{j} + 7\hat{k}$ and $\vec{b} = 3\hat{i} - 2\hat{j} + 2\hat{k}$.

2. Find a unit vector perpendicular to each of the vector $\vec{a} + \vec{b}$ and $\vec{a} - \vec{b}$, where $\vec{a} = 3\hat{i} + 2\hat{j} + 2\hat{k}$ and $\vec{b} = \hat{i} + 2\hat{j} - 2\hat{k}$.

3. If a unit vector $\vec{a}$ makes angles $\dfrac{\pi}{3}$ with $\hat{i}$, $\dfrac{\pi}{4}$ with $\hat{j}$ and an acute angle θ with $\hat{k}$, then find θ and hence, the components of $\vec{a}$.

4. Show that
$$(\vec{a} - \vec{b}) \times (\vec{a} + \vec{b}) = 2(\vec{a} \times \vec{b})$$

5. Find λ and μ if $(2\hat{i} + 6\hat{j} + 27\hat{k}) \times (\hat{i} + \lambda\hat{j} + \mu\hat{k}) = \vec{0}$.

6. Given that $\vec{a} \cdot \vec{b} = 0$ and $\vec{a} \times \vec{b} = \vec{0}$. What can you conclude about the vectors $\vec{a}$ and $\vec{b}$?

7. Let the vectors $\vec{a}, \vec{b}, \vec{c}$ be given as $a_1\hat{i} + a_2\hat{j} + a_3\hat{k}$, $b_1\hat{i} + b_2\hat{j} + b_3\hat{k}$, $c_1\hat{i} + c_2\hat{j} + c_3\hat{k}$. Then show that $\vec{a} \times (\vec{b} + \vec{c}) = \vec{a} \times \vec{b} + \vec{a} \times \vec{c}$.

8. If either $\vec{a} = \vec{0}$ or $\vec{b} = \vec{0}$, then $\vec{a} \times \vec{b} = \vec{0}$. Is the converse true? Justify your answer with an example.

9. Find the area of the triangle with vertices A(1, 1, 2), B(2, 3, 5) and C(1, 5, 5).

10. Find the area of the parallelogram whose adjacent sides are determined by the vectors $\vec{a} = \hat{i} - \hat{j} + 3\hat{k}$ and $\vec{b} = 2\hat{i} - 7\hat{j} + \hat{k}$.

11. Let the vectors $\vec{a}$ and $\vec{b}$ be such that $|\vec{a}| = 3$ and $|\vec{b}| = \dfrac{\sqrt{2}}{3}$, then $\vec{a} \times \vec{b}$ is a unit vector, if the angle between $\vec{a}$ and $\vec{b}$ is
(A) $\pi/6$ (B) $\pi/4$ (C) $\pi/3$ (D) $\pi/2$

12. Area of a rectangle having vertices A, B, C and D with position vectors

$$-\hat{i} + \frac{1}{2}\hat{j} + 4\hat{k}, \ \hat{i} + \frac{1}{2}\hat{j} + 4\hat{k}, \ \hat{i} - \frac{1}{2}\hat{j} + 4\hat{k} \ \text{ and } \ -\hat{i} - \frac{1}{2}\hat{j} + 4\hat{k}, \text{ respectively is}$$

(A) $\dfrac{1}{2}$ (B) 1

(C) 2   (D) 4

Miscellaneous Examples

Example 26 Write all the unit vectors in XY-plane.

Solution Let $\vec{r} = x\hat{i} + y\hat{j}$ be a unit vector in XY-plane (Fig 10.28). Then, from the figure, we have $x = \cos\theta$ and $y = \sin\theta$ (since $|\vec{r}| = 1$). So, we may write the vector $\vec{r}$ as

$$\vec{r} (= \overrightarrow{OP}) = \cos\theta\,\hat{i} + \sin\theta\,\hat{j} \qquad \qquad \text{.... (1)}$$

Clearly, $|\vec{r}| = \sqrt{\cos^2\theta + \sin^2\theta} = 1$

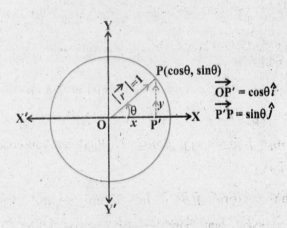

Fig 10.28

Also, as θ varies from 0 to 2π, the point P (Fig 10.28) traces the circle $x^2 + y^2 = 1$ counterclockwise, and this covers all possible directions. So, (1) gives every unit vector in the XY-plane.

Example 27 If $\hat{i}+\hat{j}+\hat{k}$, $2\hat{i}+5\hat{j}$, $3\hat{i}+2\hat{j}-3\hat{k}$ and $\hat{i}-6\hat{j}-\hat{k}$ are the position vectors of points A, B, C and D respectively, then find the angle between $\overrightarrow{AB}$ and $\overrightarrow{CD}$. Deduce that $\overrightarrow{AB}$ and $\overrightarrow{CD}$ are collinear.

Solution Note that if θ is the angle between AB and CD, then θ is also the angle between $\overrightarrow{AB}$ and $\overrightarrow{CD}$.

Now

$$\overrightarrow{AB} = \text{Position vector of B} - \text{Position vector of A}$$

$$= (2\hat{i}+5\hat{j})-(\hat{i}+\hat{j}+\hat{k}) = \hat{i}+4\hat{j}-\hat{k}$$

Therefore

$$|\overrightarrow{AB}| = \sqrt{(1)^2+(4)^2+(-1)^2} = 3\sqrt{2}$$

Similarly

$$\overrightarrow{CD} = -2\hat{i}-8\hat{j}+2\hat{k} \text{ and } |\overrightarrow{CD}| = 6\sqrt{2}$$

Thus

$$\cos\theta = \frac{\overrightarrow{AB}\cdot\overrightarrow{CD}}{|\overrightarrow{AB}||\overrightarrow{CD}|}$$

$$= \frac{1(-2)+4(-8)+(-1)(2)}{(3\sqrt{2})(6\sqrt{2})} = \frac{-36}{36} = -1$$

Since $0 \le \theta \le \pi$, it follows that $\theta = \pi$. This shows that $\overrightarrow{AB}$ and $\overrightarrow{CD}$ are collinear.

Alternatively, $\overrightarrow{AB} = -\dfrac{1}{2}\overrightarrow{CD}$ which implies that $\overrightarrow{AB}$ and $\overrightarrow{CD}$ are collinear vectors.

Example 28 Let $\vec{a}, \vec{b}$ and $\vec{c}$ be three vectors such that $|\vec{a}|=3, |\vec{b}|=4, |\vec{c}|=5$ and each one of them being perpendicular to the sum of the other two, find $|\vec{a}+\vec{b}+\vec{c}|$.

Solution Given $\vec{a}\cdot(\vec{b}+\vec{c}) = 0$, $\vec{b}\cdot(\vec{c}+\vec{a})=0$, $\vec{c}\cdot(\vec{a}+\vec{b})=0$.

Now

$$|\vec{a}+\vec{b}+\vec{c}|^2 = (\vec{a}+\vec{b}+\vec{c})^2 = (\vec{a}+\vec{b}+\vec{c})\cdot(\vec{a}+\vec{b}+\vec{c})$$

$$= \vec{a}\cdot\vec{a}+\vec{a}\cdot(\vec{b}+\vec{c})+\vec{b}\cdot\vec{b}+\vec{b}\cdot(\vec{a}+\vec{c})$$

$$+ \vec{c}\cdot(\vec{a}+\vec{b})+\vec{c}\cdot\vec{c}$$

$$= |\vec{a}|^2+|\vec{b}|^2+|\vec{c}|^2$$

$$= 9+16+25 = 50$$

Therefore

$$|\vec{a}+\vec{b}+\vec{c}| = \sqrt{50} = 5\sqrt{2}$$

Example 29 Three vectors $\vec{a}$, $\vec{b}$ and $\vec{c}$ satisfy the condition $\vec{a}+\vec{b}+\vec{c}=\vec{0}$. Evaluate the quantity $\mu = \vec{a}\cdot\vec{b}+\vec{b}\cdot\vec{c}+\vec{c}\cdot\vec{a}$, if $|\vec{a}|=1$, $|\vec{b}|=4$ and $|\vec{c}|=2$.

Solution Since $\vec{a}+\vec{b}+\vec{c}=\vec{0}$, we have

$$\vec{a}\cdot(\vec{a}+\vec{b}+\vec{c})=0$$

or

$$\vec{a}\cdot\vec{a}+\vec{a}\cdot\vec{b}+\vec{a}\cdot\vec{c}=0$$

Therefore

$$\vec{a}\cdot\vec{b}+\vec{a}\cdot\vec{c}=-|\vec{a}|^2=-1 \qquad\qquad \dots(1)$$

Again,

$$\vec{b}\cdot(\vec{a}+\vec{b}+\vec{c})=0$$

or

$$\vec{a}\cdot\vec{b}+\vec{b}\cdot\vec{c}=-|\vec{b}|^2=-16 \qquad\qquad \dots(2)$$

Similarly

$$\vec{a}\cdot\vec{c}+\vec{b}\cdot\vec{c}=-4. \qquad\qquad \dots(3)$$

Adding (1), (2) and (3), we have

$$2(\vec{a}\cdot\vec{b}+\vec{b}\cdot\vec{c}+\vec{a}\cdot\vec{c})=-21$$

or

$$2\mu=-21, \text{ i.e., } \mu=\frac{-21}{2}$$

Example 30 If with reference to the right handed system of mutually perpendicular unit vectors $\hat{i}$, $\hat{j}$ and $\hat{k}$, $\vec{\alpha}=3\hat{i}-\hat{j}$, $\vec{\beta}=2\hat{i}+\hat{j}-3\hat{k}$, then express $\vec{\beta}$ in the form $\vec{\beta}=\vec{\beta}_1+\vec{\beta}_2$, where $\vec{\beta}_1$ is parallel to $\vec{\alpha}$ and $\vec{\beta}_2$ is perpendicular to $\vec{\alpha}$.

Solution Let $\vec{\beta}_1=\lambda\vec{\alpha}$, λ is a scalar, i.e., $\vec{\beta}_1=3\lambda\hat{i}-\lambda\hat{j}$.

Now

$$\vec{\beta}_2=\vec{\beta}-\vec{\beta}_1=(2-3\lambda)\hat{i}+(1+\lambda)\hat{j}-3\hat{k}.$$

Now, since $\vec{\beta}_2$ is to be perpendicular to $\vec{\alpha}$, we should have $\vec{\alpha}\cdot\vec{\beta}_2=0$. i.e.,

$$3(2-3\lambda)-(1+\lambda)=0$$

or

$$\lambda=\frac{1}{2}$$

Therefore

$$\vec{\beta}_1=\frac{3}{2}\hat{i}-\frac{1}{2}\hat{j} \text{ and } \vec{\beta}_2=\frac{1}{2}\hat{i}+\frac{3}{2}\hat{j}-3\hat{k}$$

Miscellaneous Exercise on Chapter 10

1. Write down a unit vector in XY-plane, making an angle of 30° with the positive direction of x-axis.

2. Find the scalar components and magnitude of the vector joining the points $P(x_1, y_1, z_1)$ and $Q(x_2, y_2, z_2)$.

3. A girl walks 4 km towards west, then she walks 3 km in a direction 30° east of north and stops. Determine the girl's displacement from her initial point of departure.

4. If $\vec{a} = \vec{b} + \vec{c}$, then is it true that $|\vec{a}| = |\vec{b}| + |\vec{c}|$? Justify your answer.

5. Find the value of x for which $x(\hat{i} + \hat{j} + \hat{k})$ is a unit vector.

6. Find a vector of magnitude 5 units, and parallel to the resultant of the vectors $\vec{a} = 2\hat{i} + 3\hat{j} - \hat{k}$ and $\vec{b} = \hat{i} - 2\hat{j} + \hat{k}$.

7. If $\vec{a} = \hat{i} + \hat{j} + \hat{k}$, $\vec{b} = 2\hat{i} - \hat{j} + 3\hat{k}$ and $\vec{c} = \hat{i} - 2\hat{j} + \hat{k}$, find a unit vector parallel to the vector $2\vec{a} - \vec{b} + 3\vec{c}$.

8. Show that the points $A(1, -2, -8)$, $B(5, 0, -2)$ and $C(11, 3, 7)$ are collinear, and find the ratio in which B divides AC.

9. Find the position vector of a point R which divides the line joining two points P and Q whose position vectors are $(2\vec{a} + \vec{b})$ and $(\vec{a} - 3\vec{b})$ externally in the ratio 1 : 2. Also, show that P is the mid point of the line segment RQ.

10. The two adjacent sides of a parallelogram are $2\hat{i} - 4\hat{j} + 5\hat{k}$ and $\hat{i} - 2\hat{j} - 3\hat{k}$. Find the unit vector parallel to its diagonal. Also, find its area.

11. Show that the direction cosines of a vector equally inclined to the axes OX, OY and OZ are $\dfrac{1}{\sqrt{3}}, \dfrac{1}{\sqrt{3}}, \dfrac{1}{\sqrt{3}}$.

12. Let $\vec{a} = \hat{i} + 4\hat{j} + 2\hat{k}$, $\vec{b} = 3\hat{i} - 2\hat{j} + 7\hat{k}$ and $\vec{c} = 2\hat{i} - \hat{j} + 4\hat{k}$. Find a vector $\vec{d}$ which is perpendicular to both $\vec{a}$ and $\vec{b}$, and $\vec{c} \cdot \vec{d} = 15$.

13. The scalar product of the vector $\hat{i} + \hat{j} + \hat{k}$ with a unit vector along the sum of vectors $2\hat{i} + 4\hat{j} - 5\hat{k}$ and $\lambda\hat{i} + 2\hat{j} + 3\hat{k}$ is equal to one. Find the value of λ.

14. If $\vec{a}, \vec{b}, \vec{c}$ are mutually perpendicular vectors of equal magnitudes, show that the vector $\vec{a} + \vec{b} + \vec{c}$ is equally inclined to $\vec{a}, \vec{b}$ and $\vec{c}$.

15. Prove that $(\vec{a}+\vec{b})\cdot(\vec{a}+\vec{b})=|\vec{a}|^2+|\vec{b}|^2$, if and only if $\vec{a},\vec{b}$ are perpendicular, given $\vec{a}\neq\vec{0},\vec{b}\neq\vec{0}$.

Choose the correct answer in Exercises 16 to 19.

16. If θ is the angle between two vectors $\vec{a}$ and $\vec{b}$, then $\vec{a}\cdot\vec{b}\geq0$ only when

(A) $0<\theta<\dfrac{\pi}{2}$ (B) $0\leq\theta\leq\dfrac{\pi}{2}$

(C) $0<\theta<\pi$ (D) $0\leq\theta\leq\pi$

17. Let $\vec{a}$ and $\vec{b}$ be two unit vectors and θ is the angle between them. Then $\vec{a}+\vec{b}$ is a unit vector if

(A) $\theta=\dfrac{\pi}{4}$ (B) $\theta=\dfrac{\pi}{3}$ (C) $\theta=\dfrac{\pi}{2}$ (D) $\theta=\dfrac{2\pi}{3}$

18. The value of $\hat{i}\cdot(\hat{j}\times\hat{k})+\hat{j}\cdot(\hat{i}\times\hat{k})+\hat{k}\cdot(\hat{i}\times\hat{j})$ is

(A) 0 (B) –1 (C) 1 (D) 3

19. If θ is the angle between any two vectors $\vec{a}$ and $\vec{b}$, then $|\vec{a}\cdot\vec{b}|=|\vec{a}\times\vec{b}|$ when θ is equal to

(A) 0 (B) $\dfrac{\pi}{4}$ (C) $\dfrac{\pi}{2}$ (D) π

Summary

◆ Position vector of a point P(x,y,z) is given as $\overrightarrow{OP}(=\vec{r})=x\hat{i}+y\hat{j}+z\hat{k}$, and its magnitude by $\sqrt{x^2+y^2+z^2}$.

◆ The scalar components of a vector are its direction ratios, and represent its projections along the respective axes.

◆ The magnitude (r), direction ratios (a, b, c) and direction cosines (l, m, n) of any vector are related as:

$$l=\frac{a}{r},\quad m=\frac{b}{r},\quad n=\frac{c}{r}$$

◆ The vector sum of the three sides of a triangle taken in order is $\vec{0}$.

◆ The vector sum of two coinitial vectors is given by the diagonal of the parallelogram whose adjacent sides are the given vectors.

◆ The multiplication of a given vector by a scalar λ, changes the magnitude of the vector by the multiple $|\lambda|$, and keeps the direction same (or makes it opposite) according as the value of λ is positive (or negative).

◆ For a given vector $\vec{a}$, the vector $\hat{a} = \dfrac{\vec{a}}{|\vec{a}|}$ gives the unit vector in the direction of $\vec{a}$.

◆ The position vector of a point R dividing a line segment joining the points P and Q whose position vectors are $\vec{a}$ and $\vec{b}$ respectively, in the ratio $m : n$

(i)   internally, is given by $\dfrac{n\vec{a} + m\vec{b}}{m + n}$.

(ii) externally, is given by $\dfrac{m\vec{b} - n\vec{a}}{m - n}$.

◆ The scalar product of two given vectors $\vec{a}$ and $\vec{b}$ having angle θ between them is defined as

$$\vec{a} \cdot \vec{b} = |\vec{a}||\vec{b}|\cos\theta.$$

Also, when $\vec{a} \cdot \vec{b}$ is given, the angle 'θ' between the vectors $\vec{a}$ and $\vec{b}$ may be determined by

$$\cos\theta = \frac{\vec{a} \cdot \vec{b}}{|\vec{a}||\vec{b}|}$$

◆ If θ is the angle between two vectors $\vec{a}$ and $\vec{b}$, then their cross product is given as

$$\vec{a} \times \vec{b} = |\vec{a}||\vec{b}|\sin\theta\,\hat{n}$$

where $\hat{n}$ is a unit vector perpendicular to the plane containing $\vec{a}$ and $\vec{b}$. Such that $\vec{a}, \vec{b}, \hat{n}$ form right handed system of coordinate axes.

◆ If we have two vectors $\vec{a}$ and $\vec{b}$, given in component form as $\vec{a} = a_1\hat{i} + a_2\hat{j} + a_3\hat{k}$ and $\vec{b} = b_1\hat{i} + b_2\hat{j} + b_3\hat{k}$ and λ any scalar, then $\quad \vec{a}+\vec{b} = (a_1+b_1)\hat{i}+(a_2+b_2)\hat{j}+(a_3+b_3)\hat{k}$;

$\quad\quad\quad \lambda\vec{a} = (\lambda a_1)\hat{i}+(\lambda a_2)\hat{j}+(\lambda a_3)\hat{k}$;

$\quad\quad\quad \vec{a}.\vec{b} = a_1 b_1 + a_2 b_2 + a_3 b_3$;

and $\quad \vec{a}\times\vec{b} = \begin{vmatrix} \hat{i} & \hat{j} & \hat{k} \\ a_1 & b_1 & c_1 \\ a_2 & b_2 & c_2 \end{vmatrix}$.

Historical Note

The word *vector* has been derived from a Latin word *vectus*, which means "to carry". The germinal ideas of modern vector theory date from around 1800 when Caspar Wessel (1745-1818) and Jean Robert Argand (1768-1822) described that how a complex number $a + ib$ could be given a geometric interpretation with the help of a directed line segment in a coordinate plane. William Rowen Hamilton (1805-1865) an Irish mathematician was the first to use the term vector for a directed line segment in his book *Lectures on Quaternions* (1853). Hamilton's method of quaternions (an ordered set of four real numbers given as:

$a + b\hat{i} + c\hat{j} + d\hat{k}, \hat{i}, \hat{j}, \hat{k}$ following certain algebraic rules) was a solution to the problem of multiplying vectors in three dimensional space. Though, we must mention here that in practice, the idea of vector concept and their addition was known much earlier ever since the time of Aristotle (384-322 B.C.), a Greek philosopher, and pupil of Plato (427-348 B.C.). That time it was supposed to be known that the combined action of two or more forces could be seen by adding them according to parallelogram law. The correct law for the composition of forces, that forces add vectorially, had been discovered in the case of perpendicular forces by Stevin-Simon (1548-1620). In 1586 A.D., he analysed the principle of geometric addition of forces in his treatise *DeBeghinselen der Weeghconst* ("Principles of the Art of Weighing"), which caused a major breakthrough in the development of mechanics. But it took another 200 years for the general concept of vectors to form.

In the 1880, Josaih Willard Gibbs (1839-1903), an American physicist and mathematician, and Oliver Heaviside (1850-1925), an English engineer, created what we now know as *vector analysis*, essentially by separating the real (*scalar*) part of quaternion from its imaginary (*vector*) part. In 1881 and 1884, Gibbs printed a treatise entitled *Element of Vector Analysis*. This book gave a systematic and concise account of vectors. However, much of the credit for demonstrating the applications of vectors is due to the D. Heaviside and P.G. Tait (1831-1901) who contributed significantly to this subject.

— ❖ —

Chapter 11

THREE DIMENSIONAL GEOMETRY

❖ *The moving power of mathematical invention is not*
reasoning but imagination. – *A. DEMORGAN* ❖

11.1 Introduction

In Class XI, while studying Analytical Geometry in two
dimensions, and the introduction to three dimensional
geometry, we confined to the Cartesian methods only. In
the previous chapter of this book, we have studied some
basic concepts of vectors. We will now use vector algebra
to three dimensional geometry. The purpose of this
approach to 3-dimensional geometry is that it makes the
study simple and elegant*.

Leonhard Euler
(1707-1783)

In this chapter, we shall study the direction cosines
and direction ratios of a line joining two points and also
discuss about the equations of lines and planes in space
under different conditions, angle between two lines, two
planes, a line and a plane, shortest distance between two
skew lines and distance of a point from a plane. Most of
the above results are obtained in vector form. Nevertheless, we shall also translate
these results in the Cartesian form which, at times, presents a more clear geometric
and analytic picture of the situation.

11.2 Direction Cosines and Direction Ratios of a Line

From Chapter 10, recall that if a directed line L passing through the origin makes
angles α, β and γ with x, y and z-axes, respectively, called direction angles, then cosine
of these angles, namely, cos α, cos β and cos γ are called direction cosines of the
directed line L.

If we reverse the direction of L, then the direction angles are replaced by their supplements,
i.e., $\pi - \alpha$, $\pi - \beta$ and $\pi - \gamma$. Thus, the signs of the direction cosines are reversed.

---

* For various activities in three dimensional geometry, one may refer to the Book

"A Hand Book for designing Mathematics Laboratory in Schools", NCERT, 2005

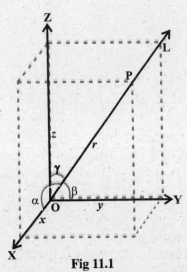

Fig 11.1

Note that a given line in space can be extended in two opposite directions and so it has two sets of direction cosines. In order to have a unique set of direction cosines for a given line in space, we must take the given line as a directed line. These unique direction cosines are denoted by l, m and n.

Remark If the given line in space does not pass through the origin, then, in order to find its direction cosines, we draw a line through the origin and parallel to the given line. Now take one of the directed lines from the origin and find its direction cosines as two parallel line have same set of direction cosines.

Any three numbers which are proportional to the direction cosines of a line are called the *direction ratios* of the line. If l, m, n are direction cosines and a, b, c are direction ratios of a line, then $a = \lambda l$, $b = \lambda m$ and $c = \lambda n$, for any nonzero $\lambda \in \mathbf{R}$.

> **Note** Some authors also call direction ratios as direction numbers.

Let a, b, c be direction ratios of a line and let l, m and n be the direction cosines ($d.c$'s) of the line. Then

$$\frac{l}{a} = \frac{m}{b} = \frac{n}{c} = k \text{ (say), } k \text{ being a constant.}$$

Therefore $l = ak$, $m = bk$, $n = ck$ ... (1)

But $l^2 + m^2 + n^2 = 1$

Therefore $k^2 (a^2 + b^2 + c^2) = 1$

or

$$k = \pm \frac{1}{\sqrt{a^2 + b^2 + c^2}}$$

Hence, from (1), the *d.c.'s* of the line are

$$l=\pm\frac{a}{\sqrt{a^2+b^2+c^2}}, m=\pm\frac{b}{\sqrt{a^2+b^2+c^2}}, n=\pm\frac{c}{\sqrt{a^2+b^2+c^2}}$$

where, depending on the desired sign of k, either a positive or a negative sign is to be taken for l, m and $\dot{n}$.

For any line, if a, b, c are direction ratios of a line, then ka, kb, kc; $k \neq 0$ is also a set of direction ratios. So, any two sets of direction ratios of a line are also proportional. Also, for any line there are infinitely many sets of direction ratios.

11.2.1 *Relation between the direction cosines of a line*

Consider a line RS with direction cosines l, m, n. Through the origin draw a line parallel to the given line and take a point P(x, y, z) on this line. From P draw a perpendicular PA on the x-axis (Fig. 11.2).

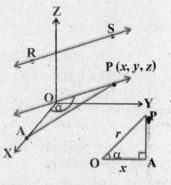

Let OP $= r$. Then $\cos\alpha = \dfrac{OA}{OP} = \dfrac{x}{r}$. This gives $x = lr$.

Similarly, $y = mr$ and $z = nr$

Thus $x^2 + y^2 + z^2 = r^2(l^2 + m^2 + n^2)$

But $x^2 + y^2 + z^2 = r^2$

Hence $l^2 + m^2 + n^2 = 1$

Fig 11.2

11.2.2 *Direction cosines of a line passing through two points*

Since one and only one line passes through two given points, we can determine the direction cosines of a line passing through the given points P(x_1, y_1, z_1) and Q(x_2, y_2, z_2) as follows (Fig 11.3 (a)).

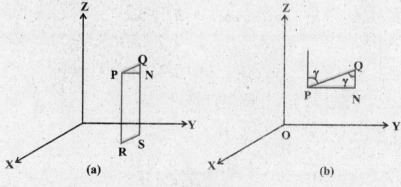

(a)   (b)

Fig 11.3

Let l, m, n be the direction cosines of the line PQ and let it makes angles α, β and γ with the x, y and z-axis, respectively.

Draw perpendiculars from P and Q to XY-plane to meet at R and S. Draw a perpendicular from P to QS to meet at N. Now, in right angle triangle PNQ. $\angle PQN = \gamma$ (Fig 11.3 (b).

Therefore, $\cos\gamma = \dfrac{NQ}{PQ} = \dfrac{z_2 - z_1}{PQ}$

Similarly $\cos\alpha = \dfrac{x_2 - x_1}{PQ}$ and $\cos\beta = \dfrac{y_2 - y_1}{PQ}$

Hence, the direction cosines of the line segment joining the points $P(x_1, y_1, z_1)$ and $Q(x_2, y_2, z_2)$ are

$$\frac{x_2 - x_1}{PQ}, \frac{y_2 - y_1}{PQ}, \frac{z_2 - z_1}{PQ}$$

where $PQ = \sqrt{(x_2 - x_1)^2 + (y_2 - y_1)^2 + (z_2 - z_1)^2}$

Note The direction ratios of the line segment joining $P(x_1, y_1, z_1)$ and $Q(x_2, y_2, z_2)$ may be taken as

$$x_2 - x_1, y_2 - y_1, z_2 - z_1 \text{ or } x_1 - x_2, y_1 - y_2, z_1 - z_2$$

Example 1 If a line makes angle 90°, 60° and 30° with the positive direction of x, y and z-axis respectively, find its direction cosines.

Solution Let the $d.c.$'s of the lines be l, m, n. Then $l = \cos 90^0 = 0$, $m = \cos 60^0 = \dfrac{1}{2}$,

$n = \cos 30^0 = \dfrac{\sqrt{3}}{2}$.

Example 2 If a line has direction ratios 2, -1, -2, determine its direction cosines.

Solution Direction cosines are

$$\frac{2}{\sqrt{2^2 + (-1)^2 + (-2)^2}}, \frac{-1}{\sqrt{2^2 + (-1)^2 + (-2)^2}}, \frac{-2}{\sqrt{2^2 + (-1)^2 + (-2)^2}}$$

or $\dfrac{2}{3}, \dfrac{-1}{3}, \dfrac{-2}{3}$

Example 3 Find the direction cosines of the line passing through the two points $(-2, 4, -5)$ and $(1, 2, 3)$.

Solution We know the direction cosines of the line passing through two points $P(x_1, y_1, z_1)$ and $Q(x_2, y_2, z_2)$ are given by

$$\frac{x_2 - x_1}{PQ}, \frac{y_2 - y_1}{PQ}, \frac{z_2 - z_1}{PQ}$$

where

$$PQ = \sqrt{(x_2 - x_1)^2 + (y_2 - y_1)^2 + (z_2 - z_1)^2}$$

Here P is $(-2, 4, -5)$ and Q is $(1, 2, 3)$.

So

$$PQ = \sqrt{(1 - (-2))^2 + (2 - 4)^2 + (3 - (-5))^2} = \sqrt{77}$$

Thus, the direction cosines of the line joining two points is

$$\frac{3}{\sqrt{77}}, \frac{-2}{\sqrt{77}}, \frac{8}{\sqrt{77}}$$

Example 4 Find the direction cosines of x, y and z-axis.

Solution The x-axis makes angles $0°$, $90°$ and $90°$ respectively with x, y and z-axis. Therefore, the direction cosines of x-axis are $\cos 0°$, $\cos 90°$, $\cos 90°$ i.e., $1, 0, 0$. Similarly, direction cosines of y-axis and z-axis are $0, 1, 0$ and $0, 0, 1$ respectively.

Example 5 Show that the points A $(2, 3, -4)$, B $(1, -2, 3)$ and C $(3, 8, -11)$ are collinear.

Solution Direction ratios of line joining A and B are

$1 - 2, -2 - 3, 3 + 4$ i.e., $-1, -5, 7$.

The direction ratios of line joining B and C are

$3 - 1, 8 + 2, -11 - 3$, i.e., $2, 10, -14$.

It is clear that direction ratios of AB and BC are proportional, hence, AB is parallel to BC. But point B is common to both AB and BC. Therefore, A, B, C are collinear points.

EXERCISE 11.1

1. If a line makes angles $90°$, $135°$, $45°$ with the x, y and z-axes respectively, find its direction cosines.

2. Find the direction cosines of a line which makes equal angles with the coordinate axes.

3. If a line has the direction ratios $-18, 12, -4$, then what are its direction cosines ?

4. Show that the points $(2, 3, 4)$, $(-1, -2, 1)$, $(5, 8, 7)$ are collinear.

5. Find the direction cosines of the sides of the triangle whose vertices are $(3, 5, -4)$, $(-1, 1, 2)$ and $(-5, -5, -2)$.

11.3 Equation of a Line in Space

We have studied equation of lines in two dimensions in Class XI, we shall now study the vector and cartesian equations of a line in space.

A line is uniquely determined if

(i) it passes through a given point and has given direction, or

(ii) it passes through two given points.

11.3.1 *Equation of a line through a given point and parallel to d given vector $\vec{b}$*

Let $\vec{a}$ be the position vector of the given point A with respect to the origin O of the rectangular coordinate system. Let l be the line which passes through the point A and is parallel to a given vector $\vec{b}$. Let $\vec{r}$ be the position vector of an arbitrary point P on the line (Fig 11.4).

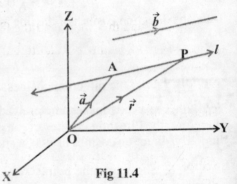

Fig 11.4

Then $\overrightarrow{AP}$ is parallel to the vector $\vec{b}$, i.e.,

$\overrightarrow{AP} = \lambda \vec{b}$, where λ is some real number.

But $\overrightarrow{AP} = \overrightarrow{OP} - \overrightarrow{OA}$

i.e. $\lambda \vec{b} = \vec{r} - \vec{a}$

Conversely, for each value of the parameter λ, this equation gives the position vector of a point P on the line. Hence, the vector equation of the line is given by

$$\vec{r} = \vec{a} + \lambda \vec{b} \qquad \qquad \dots (1)$$

Remark If $\vec{b} = a\hat{i} + b\hat{j} + c\hat{k}$, then a, b, c are direction ratios of the line and conversely, if a, b, c are direction ratios of a line, then $\vec{b} = a\hat{i} + b\hat{j} + c\hat{k}$ will be the parallel to the line. Here, b should not be confused with $|\vec{b}|$.

Derivation of cartesian form from vector form

Let the coordinates of the given point A be (x_1, y_1, z_1) and the direction ratios of the line be a, b, c. Consider the coordinates of any point P be (x, y, z). Then

$$\vec{r} = x\hat{i} + y\hat{j} + z\hat{k}; \ \vec{a} = x_1\hat{i} + y_1\hat{j} + z_1\hat{k}$$

and $\vec{b} = a\hat{i} + b\hat{j} + c\hat{k}$

Substituting these values in (1) and equating the coefficients of $\hat{i}, \hat{j}$ and $\hat{k}$, we get

$$x = x_1 + \lambda a; \ y = y_1 + \lambda b; \ z = z_1 + \lambda c \qquad \qquad \dots (2)$$

These are parametric equations of the line. Eliminating the parameter λ from (2), we get

$$\frac{x - x_1}{a} = \frac{y - y_1}{b} = \frac{z - z_1}{c} \qquad \text{... (3)}$$

This is the Cartesian equation of the line.

> **☞ Note** If l, m, n are the direction cosines of the line, the equation of the line is
>
> $$\frac{x - x_1}{l} = \frac{y - y_1}{m} = \frac{z - z_1}{n}$$

Example 6 Find the vector and the Cartesian equations of the line through the point $(5, 2, - 4)$ and which is parallel to the vector $3\hat{i} + 2\hat{j} - 8\hat{k}$.

Solution We have

$$\vec{a} = 5\hat{i} + 2\hat{j} - 4\hat{k} \text{ and } \vec{b} = 3\hat{i} + 2\hat{j} - 8\hat{k}$$

Therefore, the vector equation of the line is

$$\vec{r} = 5\hat{i} + 2\hat{j} - 4\hat{k} + \lambda(3\hat{i} + 2\hat{j} - 8\hat{k})$$

Now, $\vec{r}$ is the position vector of any point P(x, y, z) on the line.

Therefore, $x\hat{i} + y\hat{j} + z\hat{k} = 5\hat{i} + 2\hat{j} - 4\hat{k} + \lambda(3\hat{i} + 2\hat{j} - 8\hat{k})$

$$= (5 + 3\lambda)\hat{i} + (2 + 2\lambda)\hat{j} + (-4 - 8\lambda)\hat{k}$$

Eliminating λ, we get

$$\frac{x - 5}{3} = \frac{y - 2}{2} = \frac{z + 4}{-8}$$

which is the equation of the line in Cartesian form.

11.3.2 *Equation of a line passing through two given points*

Let $\vec{a}$ and $\vec{b}$ be the position vectors of two points A(x_1, y_1, z_1) and B(x_2, y_2, z_2), respectively that are lying on a line (Fig 11.5).

Let $\vec{r}$ be the position vector of an arbitrary point P(x, y, z), then P is a point on the line if and only if $\overrightarrow{AP} = \vec{r} - \vec{a}$ and $\overrightarrow{AB} = \vec{b} - \vec{a}$ are collinear vectors. Therefore, P is on the line if and only if

$$\vec{r} - \vec{a} = \lambda(\vec{b} - \vec{a})$$

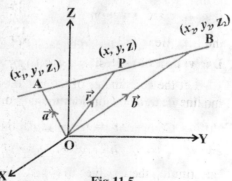

Fig 11.5

or $\quad\vec{r}=\vec{a}+\lambda(\vec{b}-\vec{a})$, $\lambda\in$ R.   ... (1)

This is the vector equation of the line.

Derivation of cartesian form from vector form

We have

$$\vec{r}=x\hat{i}+y\,\hat{j}+z\,\hat{k},\ \vec{a}=x_1\hat{i}+y_1\,\hat{j}+z_1\,\hat{k}\ \text{and}\ \vec{b}=x_2\hat{i}+y_2\,\hat{j}+z_2\,\hat{k},$$

Substituting these values in (1), we get

$$x\hat{i}+y\,\hat{j}+z\,\hat{k}=x_1\,\hat{i}+y_1\,\hat{j}+z_1\hat{k}+\lambda[(x_2-x_1)\hat{i}+(y_2-y_1)\,\hat{j}+(z_2-z_1)\hat{k}]$$

Equating the like coefficients of $\hat{i}$, $\hat{j}$, $\hat{k}$, we get

$$x=x_1+\lambda\,(x_2-x_1);\ y=y_1+\lambda\,(y_2-y_1);\ z=z_1+\lambda\,(z_2-z_1)$$

On eliminating λ, we obtain

$$\frac{x-x_1}{x_2-x_1}=\frac{y-y_1}{y_2-y_1}=\frac{z-z_1}{z_2-z_1}$$

which is the equation of the line in Cartesian form.

Example 7 Find the vector equation for the line passing through the points (–1, 0, 2) and (3, 4, 6).

Solution Let $\vec{a}$ and $\vec{b}$ be the position vectors of the point A $(-1, 0, 2)$ and B $(3, 4, 6)$.

Then $\qquad\qquad\qquad\vec{a}=-\hat{i}+2\hat{k}$

and $\qquad\qquad\qquad\vec{b}=3\hat{i}+4\hat{j}+6\hat{k}$

Therefore $\qquad\qquad\vec{b}-\vec{a}=4\hat{i}+4\hat{j}+4\hat{k}$

Let $\vec{r}$ be the position vector of any point on the line. Then the vector equation of the line is

$$\vec{r}=-\hat{i}+2\hat{k}+\lambda(4\hat{i}+4\hat{j}+4\hat{k})$$

Example 8 The Cartesian equation of a line is

$$\frac{x+3}{2}=\frac{y-5}{4}=\frac{z+6}{2}$$

Find the vector equation for the line.

Solution Comparing the given equation with the standard form

$$\frac{x-x_1}{a}=\frac{y-y_1}{b}=\frac{z-z_1}{c}$$

We observe that $\qquad x_1=-3, y_1=5, z_1=-6;\ a=2, b=4, c=2.$

Thus, the required line passes through the point $(-3, 5, -6)$ and is parallel to the vector $2\hat{i}+4\hat{j}+2\hat{k}$. Let $\vec{r}$ be the position vector of any point on the line, then the vector equation of the line is given by

$$\vec{r}=(-3\,\hat{i}+5\,\hat{j}-6\hat{k})+\lambda\;(2\hat{i}+4\hat{j}+2\hat{k})$$

11.4 Angle between Two Lines

Let L_1 and L_2 be two lines passing through the origin and with direction ratios a_1, b_1, c_1 and a_2, b_2, c_2, respectively. Let P be a point on L_1 and Q be a point on L_2. Consider the directed lines OP and OQ as given in Fig 11.6. Let θ be the acute angle between OP and OQ. Now recall that the directed line segments OP and OQ are vectors with components a_1, b_1, c_1 and a_2, b_2, c_2, respectively. Therefore, the angle θ between them is given by

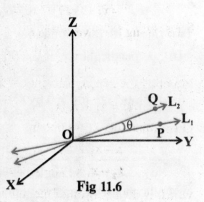

Fig 11.6

$$\cos\theta = \left|\frac{a_1a_2+b_1b_2+c_1c_2}{\sqrt{a_1^2+b_1^2+c_1^2}\,\sqrt{a_2^2+b_2^2+c_2^2}}\right| \qquad \ldots (1)$$

The angle between the lines in terms of $\sin\theta$ is given by

$$\sin\theta = \sqrt{1-\cos^2\theta}$$

$$= \sqrt{1-\frac{(a_1a_2+b_1b_2+c_1c_2)^2}{(a_1^2+b_1^2+c_1^2)(a_2^2+b_2^2+c_2^2)}}$$

$$= \frac{\sqrt{(a_1^2+b_1^2+c_1^2)(a_2^2+b_2^2+c_2^2)-(a_1a_2+b_1b_2+c_1c_2)^2}}{\sqrt{(a_1^2+b_1^2+c_1^2)}\sqrt{(a_2^2+b_2^2+c_2^2)}}$$

$$= \frac{\sqrt{(a_1 b_2 - a_2 b_1)^2 + (b_1 c_2 - b_2 c_1)^2 + (c_1 a_2 - c_2 a_1)^2}}{\sqrt{a_1^2 + b_1^2 + c_1^2}\,\sqrt{a_2^2 + b_2^2 + c_2^2}} \qquad \ldots (2)$$

> **☞ Note** In case the lines L_1 and L_2 do not pass through the origin, we may take lines L_1' and L_2' which are parallel to L_1 and L_2 respectively and pass through the origin.

If instead of direction ratios for the lines L_1 and L_2, direction cosines, namely, l_1, m_1, n_1 for L_1 and l_2, m_2, n_2 for L_2 are given, then (1) and (2) takes the following form:

$$\cos \theta = |l_1 l_2 + m_1 m_2 + n_1 n_2| \quad (\text{as } l_1^2 + m_1^2 + n_1^2 = 1 = l_2^2 + m_2^2 + n_2^2) \quad \ldots (3)$$

and

$$\sin \theta = \sqrt{(l_1 m_2 - l_2 m_1)^2 - (m_1 n_2 - m_2 n_1)^2 + (n_1 l_2 - n_2 l_1)^2} \quad \ldots (4)$$

Two lines with direction ratios a_1, b_1, c_1 and a_2, b_2, c_2 are

(i) perpendicular i.e. if $\theta = 90°$ by (1)

$$a_1 a_2 + b_1 b_2 + c_1 c_2 = 0$$

(ii) parallel i.e. if $\theta = 0$ by (2)

$$\frac{a_1}{a_2} = \frac{b_1}{b_2} = \frac{c_1}{c_2}$$

Now, we find the angle between two lines when their equations are given. If θ is acute the angle between the lines

$$\vec{r} = \vec{a}_1 + \lambda \vec{b}_1 \text{ and } \vec{r} = \vec{a}_2 + \mu \vec{b}_2$$

then

$$\cos \theta = \left| \frac{\vec{b}_1 \cdot \vec{b}_2}{|\vec{b}_1||\vec{b}_2|} \right|$$

In Cartesian form, if θ is the angle between the lines

$$\frac{x - x_1}{a_1} = \frac{y - y_1}{b_1} = \frac{z - z_1}{c_1} \quad \ldots (1)$$

and

$$\frac{x - x_2}{a_2} = \frac{y - y_2}{b_2} = \frac{z - z_2}{c_2} \quad \ldots (2)$$

where, a_1, b_1, c_1 and a_2, b_2, c_2 are the direction ratios of the lines (1) and (2), respectively, then

$$\cos \theta = \left| \frac{a_1 a_2 + b_1 b_2 + c_1 c_2}{\sqrt{a_1^2 + b_1^2 + c_1^2} \sqrt{a_2^2 + b_2^2 + c_2^2}} \right|$$

Example 9 Find the angle between the pair of lines given by

$$\vec{r} = 3\hat{i} + 2\hat{j} - 4\hat{k} + \lambda(\hat{i} + 2\hat{j} + 2\hat{k})$$

and

$$\vec{r} = 5\hat{i} - 2\hat{j} + \mu(3\hat{i} + 2\hat{j} + 6\hat{k})$$

Solution Here $\vec{b_1} = \hat{i} + 2\hat{j} + 2\hat{k}$ and $\vec{b_2} = 3\hat{i} + 2\hat{j} + 6\hat{k}$

The angle θ between the two lines is given by

$$\cos\theta = \left| \frac{\vec{b_1} \cdot \vec{b_2}}{|\vec{b_1}||\vec{b_2}|} \right| = \left| \frac{(\hat{i} + 2\hat{j} + 2\hat{k}) \cdot (3\hat{i} + 2\hat{j} + 6\hat{k})}{\sqrt{1+4+4}\ \sqrt{9+4+36}} \right|$$

$$= \left| \frac{3+4+12}{3\times 7} \right| = \frac{19}{21}$$

Hence $\theta = \cos^{-1}\left(\dfrac{19}{21}\right)$

Example 10 Find the angle between the pair of lines

$$\frac{x+3}{3} = \frac{y-1}{5} = \frac{z+3}{4}$$

and

$$\frac{x+1}{1} = \frac{y-4}{1} = \frac{z-5}{2}$$

Solution The direction ratios of the first line are 3, 5, 4 and the direction ratios of the second line are 1, 1, 2. If θ is the angle between them, then

$$\cos\theta = \left| \frac{3.1+5.1+4.2}{\sqrt{3^2+5^2+4^2}\ \sqrt{1^2+1^2+2^2}} \right| = \frac{16}{\sqrt{50}\ \sqrt{6}} = \frac{16}{5\sqrt{2}\ \sqrt{6}} = \frac{8\sqrt{3}}{15}$$

Hence, the required angle is $\cos^{-1}\left(\dfrac{8\sqrt{3}}{15}\right)$.

11.5 Shortest Distance between Two Lines

If two lines in space intersect at a point, then the shortest distance between them is zero. Also, if two lines in space are parallel, then the shortest distance between them will be the perpendicular distance, i.e. the length of the perpendicular drawn from a point on one line onto the other line.

Further, in a space, there are lines which are neither intersecting nor parallel. In fact, such pair of lines are *non coplanar* and are called *skew lines*. For example, let us consider a room of size 1, 3, 2 units along x, y and z-axes respectively Fig 11.7.

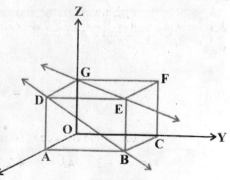

Fig 11.7

The line GE that goes diagonally across the ceiling and the line DB passes through one corner of the ceiling directly above A and goes diagonally down the wall. These lines are skew because they are not parallel and also never meet.

By the shortest distance between two lines we mean the join of a point in one line with one point on the other line so that the length of the segment so obtained is the smallest.

For skew lines, the line of the shortest distance will be perpendicular to both the lines.

11.5.1 *Distance between two skew lines*

We now determine the shortest distance between two skew lines in the following way:

Let l_1 and l_2 be two skew lines with equations (Fig. 11.8)

$$\vec{r} = \vec{a}_1 + \lambda \vec{b}_1 \qquad \qquad \ldots (1)$$

and

$$\vec{r} = \vec{a}_2 + \mu \vec{b}_2 \qquad \qquad \ldots (2)$$

Take any point S on l_1 with position vector $\vec{a}_1$ and T on l_2, with position vector $\vec{a}_2$. Then the magnitude of the shortest distance vector will be equal to that of the projection of ST along the direction of the line of shortest distance (See 10.6.2).

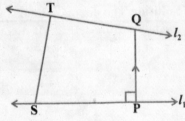

If $\overrightarrow{PQ}$ is the shortest distance vector between l_1 and l_2, then it being perpendicular to both $\vec{b}_1$ and $\vec{b}_2$, the unit vector $\hat{n}$ along $\overrightarrow{PQ}$ would therefore be

Fig 11.8

$$\hat{n} = \frac{\vec{b}_1 \times \vec{b}_2}{|\vec{b}_1 \times \vec{b}_2|} \qquad \qquad \ldots (3)$$

Then

$$\overrightarrow{PQ} = d\,\hat{n}$$

where, d is the magnitude of the shortest distance vector. Let θ be the angle between $\overrightarrow{ST}$ and $\overrightarrow{PQ}$. Then

$$PQ = ST\,|\cos\theta|$$

But

$$\cos\theta = \left| \frac{\overrightarrow{PQ}\cdot\overrightarrow{ST}}{|\overrightarrow{PQ}||\overrightarrow{ST}|} \right|$$

$$= \left| \frac{d\,\hat{n}\cdot(\vec{a}_2 - \vec{a}_1)}{d\,ST} \right| \qquad (\text{since } \overrightarrow{ST} = \vec{a}_2 - \vec{a}_1)$$

$$= \left| \frac{(\vec{b}_1 \times \vec{b}_2)\cdot(\vec{a}_2 - \vec{a}_1)}{ST\,|\vec{b}_1 \times \vec{b}_2|} \right| \qquad [\text{From (3)}]$$

Hence, the required shortest distance is

$$d = PQ = ST \, |\cos \theta|$$

or

$$d = \left| \frac{(\vec{b}_1 \times \vec{b}_2) \cdot (\vec{a}_2 - \vec{a}_1)}{|\vec{b}_1 \times \vec{b}_2|} \right|$$

Cartesian form

The shortest distance between the lines

$$l_1 : \frac{x - x_1}{a_1} = \frac{y - y_1}{b_1} = \frac{z - z_1}{c_1}$$

and

$$l_2 : \frac{x - x_2}{a_2} = \frac{y - y_2}{b_2} = \frac{z - z_2}{c_2}$$

is

$$\frac{\begin{vmatrix} x_2 - x_1 & y_2 - y_1 & z_2 - z_1 \\ a_1 & b_1 & c_1 \\ a_2 & b_2 & c_2 \end{vmatrix}}{\sqrt{(b_1 c_2 - b_2 c_1)^2 + (c_1 a_2 - c_2 a_1)^2 + (a_1 b_2 - a_2 b_1)^2}}$$

11.5.2 *Distance between parallel lines*

If two lines l_1 and l_2 are parallel, then they are coplanar. Let the lines be given by

$$\vec{r} = \vec{a}_1 + \lambda \vec{b} \qquad \qquad \dots (1)$$

and

$$\vec{r} = \vec{a}_2 + \mu \vec{b} \qquad \qquad \dots (2)$$

where, $\vec{}$ is the position vector of a point S on l_1 and

$\vec{}$ is the position vector of a point T on l_2 Fig 11.9.

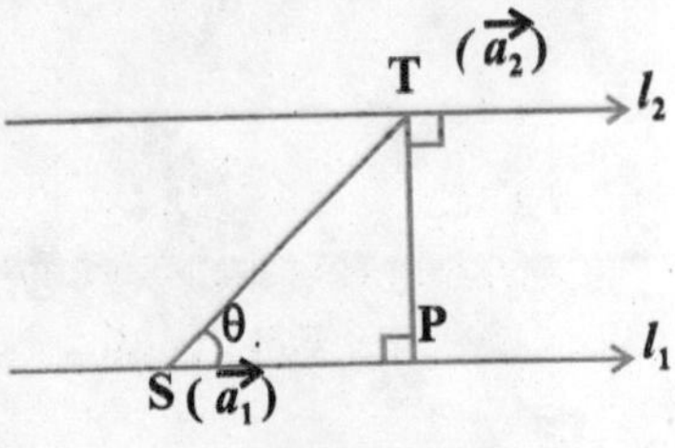

As l_1, l_2 are coplanar, if the foot of the perpendicular from T on the line l_1 is P, then the distance between the lines l_1 and $l_2 = |TP|$.

Fig 11.9

Let θ be the angle between the vectors $\overrightarrow{ST}$ and $\vec{b}$. Then

$$\vec{b} \times \overrightarrow{ST} = (|\vec{b}||\overrightarrow{ST}| \sin \theta)\hat{n} \qquad \qquad \dots (3)$$

where $\hat{n}$ is the unit vector perpendicular to the plane of the lines l_1 and l_2.

But

$$\overrightarrow{ST} = \vec{a}_2 - \vec{a}_1$$

Therefore, from (3), we get

$$\vec{b} \times (\vec{a}_2 - \vec{a}_1) = |\vec{b}| \, PT \, \hat{n} \qquad \text{(since PT = ST sin } \theta)$$

i.e.,
$$|\vec{b} \times (\vec{a}_2 - \vec{a}_1)| = |\vec{b}| \, PT \cdot 1 \qquad \text{(as } |\hat{n}| = 1)$$

Hence, the distance between the given parallel lines is

$$d = |\overrightarrow{PT}| = \left| \frac{\vec{b} \times (\vec{a}_2 - \vec{a}_1)}{|\vec{b}|} \right|$$

Example 11 Find the shortest distance between the lines l_1 and l_2 whose vector equations are

$$\vec{r} = \hat{i} + \hat{j} + \lambda \, (2\hat{i} - \hat{j} + \hat{k}) \qquad \text{... (1)}$$

and
$$\vec{r} = 2\hat{i} + \hat{j} - \hat{k} + \mu \, (3\hat{i} - 5\hat{j} + 2\hat{k}) \qquad \text{... (2)}$$

Solution Comparing (1) and (2) with $\vec{r} = \vec{a}_1 + \lambda \, \vec{b}_1$ and $\vec{r} = \vec{a}_2 + \mu \, \vec{b}_2$ respectively,
we get
$$\vec{a}_1 = \hat{i} + \hat{j}, \; \vec{b}_1 = 2\hat{i} - \hat{j} + \hat{k}$$

$$\vec{a}_2 = 2\hat{i} + \hat{j} - \hat{k} \text{ and } \vec{b}_2 = 3\hat{i} - 5\hat{j} + 2\hat{k}$$

Therefore
$$\vec{a}_2 - \vec{a}_1 = \hat{i} - \hat{k}$$

and
$$\vec{b}_1 \times \vec{b}_2 = (2\hat{i} - \hat{j} + \hat{k}) \times (3\hat{i} - 5\hat{j} + 2\hat{k})$$

$$= \begin{vmatrix} \hat{i} & \hat{j} & \hat{k} \\ 2 & -1 & 1 \\ 3 & -5 & 2 \end{vmatrix} = 3\hat{i} - \hat{j} - 7\hat{k}$$

So
$$|\vec{b}_1 \times \vec{b}_2| = \sqrt{9 + 1 + 49} = \sqrt{59}$$

Hence, the shortest distance between the given lines is given by

$$d = \left| \frac{(\vec{b}_1 \times \vec{b}_2) \cdot (\vec{a}_2 - \vec{a}_1)}{|\vec{b}_1 \times \vec{b}_2|} \right| = \frac{|3 - 0 + 7|}{\sqrt{59}} = \frac{10}{\sqrt{59}}$$

Example 12 Find the distance between the lines l_1 and l_2 given by

$$\vec{r} = \hat{i} + 2\hat{j} - 4\hat{k} + \lambda (2\hat{i} + 3\hat{j} + 6\hat{k})$$

and
$$\vec{r} = 3\hat{i} + 3\hat{j} - 5\hat{k} + \mu (2\hat{i} + 3\hat{j} + 6\hat{k})$$

Solution The two lines are parallel (Why?) We have

$$\vec{a_1} = \hat{i} + 2\hat{j} - 4\hat{k}, \ \vec{a_2} = 3\hat{i} + 3\hat{j} - 5\hat{k} \text{ and } \vec{b} = 2\hat{i} + 3\hat{j} + 6\hat{k}$$

Therefore, the distance between the lines is given by

$$d = \left| \frac{\vec{b} \times (\vec{a_2} - \vec{a_1})}{|\vec{b}|} \right| = \frac{\begin{vmatrix} \hat{i} & \hat{j} & \hat{k} \\ 2 & 3 & 6 \\ 2 & 1 & -1 \end{vmatrix}}{\sqrt{4 + 9 + 36}}$$

or

$$= \frac{\left| -9\hat{i} + 14\hat{j} - 4\hat{k} \right|}{\sqrt{49}} = \frac{\sqrt{293}}{\sqrt{49}} = \frac{\sqrt{293}}{7}$$

EXERCISE 11.2

1. Show that the three lines with direction cosines

   $$\frac{12}{13}, \frac{-3}{13}, \frac{-4}{13}; \ \frac{4}{13}, \frac{12}{13}, \frac{3}{13}; \ \frac{3}{13}, \frac{-4}{13}, \frac{12}{13} \text{ are mutually perpendicular.}$$

2. Show that the line through the points $(1, -1, 2), (3, 4, -2)$ is perpendicular to the line through the points $(0, 3, 2)$ and $(3, 5, 6)$.

3. Show that the line through the points $(4, 7, 8), (2, 3, 4)$ is parallel to the line through the points $(-1, -2, 1), (1, 2, 5)$.

4. Find the equation of the line which passes through the point $(1, 2, 3)$ and is parallel to the vector $3\hat{i} + 2\hat{j} - 2\hat{k}$.

5. Find the equation of the line in vector and in cartesian form that passes through the point with position vector $2\hat{i} - j + 4\hat{k}$ and is in the direction $\hat{i} + 2\hat{j} - \hat{k}$.

6. Find the cartesian equation of the line which passes through the point $(-2, 4, -5)$ and parallel to the line given by $\dfrac{x+3}{3} = \dfrac{y-4}{5} = \dfrac{z+8}{6}$.

7. The cartesian equation of a line is $\dfrac{x-5}{3} = \dfrac{y+4}{7} = \dfrac{z-6}{2}$. Write its vector form.

8. Find the vector and the cartesian equations of the lines that passes through the origin and $(5, -2, 3)$.

9. Find the vector and the cartesian equations of the line that passes through the points $(3, -2, -5)$, $(3, -2, 6)$.

10. Find the angle between the following pairs of lines:

   (i) $\vec{r} = 2\hat{i} - 5\hat{j} + \hat{k} + \lambda(3\hat{i} + 2\hat{j} + 6\hat{k})$ and

   $\vec{r} = 7\hat{i} - 6\hat{k} + \mu(\hat{i} + 2\hat{j} + 2\hat{k})$

   (ii) $\vec{r} = 3\hat{i} + \hat{j} - 2\hat{k} + \lambda(\hat{i} - \hat{j} - 2\hat{k})$ and

   $\vec{r} = 2\hat{i} - \hat{j} - 56\hat{k} + \mu(3\hat{i} - 5\hat{j} - 4\hat{k})$

11. Find the angle between the following pair of lines:

   (i) $\dfrac{x-2}{2} = \dfrac{y-1}{5} = \dfrac{z+3}{-3}$ and $\dfrac{x+2}{-1} = \dfrac{y-4}{8} = \dfrac{z-5}{4}$

   (ii) $\dfrac{x}{2} = \dfrac{y}{2} = \dfrac{z}{1}$ and $\dfrac{x-5}{4} = \dfrac{y-2}{1} = \dfrac{z-3}{8}$

12. Find the values of p so that the lines $\dfrac{1-x}{3} = \dfrac{7y-14}{2p} = \dfrac{z-3}{2}$

   and $\dfrac{7-7x}{3p} = \dfrac{y-5}{1} = \dfrac{6-z}{5}$ are at right angles.

13. Show that the lines $\dfrac{x-5}{7} = \dfrac{y+2}{-5} = \dfrac{z}{1}$ and $\dfrac{x}{1} = \dfrac{y}{2} = \dfrac{z}{3}$ are perpendicular to each other.

14. Find the shortest distance between the lines

   $\vec{r} = (\hat{i} + 2\hat{j} + \hat{k}) + \lambda(\hat{i} - \hat{j} + \hat{k})$ and

   $\vec{r} = 2\hat{i} - \hat{j} - \hat{k} + \mu(2\hat{i} + \hat{j} + 2\hat{k})$

15. Find the shortest distance between the lines

   $\dfrac{x+1}{7} = \dfrac{y+1}{-6} = \dfrac{z+1}{1}$ and $\dfrac{x-3}{1} = \dfrac{y-5}{-2} = \dfrac{z-7}{1}$

16. Find the shortest distance between the lines whose vector equations are

   $\vec{r} = (\hat{i} + 2\hat{j} + 3\hat{k}) + \lambda(\hat{i} - 3\hat{j} + 2\hat{k})$

   and $\vec{r} = 4\hat{i} + 5\hat{j} + 6\hat{k} + \mu(2\hat{i} + 3\hat{j} + \hat{k})$

17. Find the shortest distance between the lines whose vector equations are

   $\vec{r} = (1-t)\hat{i} + (t-2)\hat{j} + (3-2t)\hat{k}$ and

   $\vec{r} = (s+1)\hat{i} + (2s-1)\hat{j} - (2s+1)\hat{k}$

11.6 Plane

A plane is determined uniquely if any one of the following is known:

(i) the normal to the plane and its distance from the origin is given, i.e., equation of a plane in normal form.

(ii) it passes through a point and is perpendicular to a given direction.

(iii) it passes through three given non collinear points.

Now we shall find vector and Cartesian equations of the planes.

11.6.1 *Equation of a plane in normal form*

Consider a plane whose perpendicular distance from the origin is d $(d \neq 0)$. Fig 11.10.

If $\overrightarrow{ON}$ is the normal from the origin to the plane, and $\hat{n}$ is the unit normal vector

along $\overrightarrow{ON}$. Then $\overrightarrow{ON} = d\,\hat{n}$. Let P be any

point on the plane. Therefore, $\overrightarrow{NP}$ is

perpendicular to $\overrightarrow{ON}$.

Therefore, $\overrightarrow{NP} \cdot \overrightarrow{ON} = 0$ ... (1)

Let $\vec{r}$ be the position vector of the point P,

then $\overrightarrow{NP} = \vec{r} - d\,\hat{n}$ (as $\overrightarrow{ON} + \overrightarrow{NP} = \overrightarrow{OP}$)

Therefore, (1) becomes

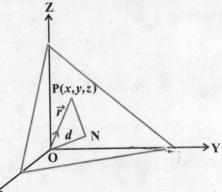

$$(\vec{r} - d\,\hat{n}) \cdot d\,\hat{n} = 0$$

Fig 11.10

or $$(\vec{r} - d\,\hat{n}) \cdot \hat{n} = 0 \quad (d \neq 0)$$

or $$\vec{r} \cdot \hat{n} - d\,\hat{n} \cdot \hat{n} = 0$$

i.e., $$\vec{r} \cdot \hat{n} = d \qquad (\text{as } \hat{n} \cdot \hat{n} = 1) \qquad \qquad \text{... (2)}$$

This is the vector form of the equation of the plane.

Cartesian form

Equation (2) gives the vector equation of a plane, where $\hat{n}$ is the unit vector normal to the plane. Let P(x, y, z) be any point on the plane. Then

$$\overrightarrow{OP} = \vec{r} = x\hat{i} + y\hat{j} + z\hat{k}$$

Let l, m, n be the direction cosines of $\hat{n}$. Then

$$\hat{n} = l\hat{i} + m\hat{j} + n\hat{k}$$

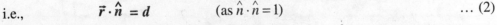

Therefore, (2) gives

$$(x\,\hat{i} + y\,\hat{j} + z\,\hat{k})\cdot(l\,\hat{i} + m\,\hat{j} + n\,\hat{k}) = d$$

i.e., $$lx + my + nz = d$$ ... (3)

This is the cartesian equation of the plane in the normal form.

> **Note** Equation (3) shows that if $\vec{r}\cdot(a\,\hat{i} + b\,\hat{j} + c\,\hat{k}) = d$ is the vector equation of a plane, then $ax + by + cz = d$ is the Cartesian equation of the plane, where a, b and c are the direction ratios of the normal to the plane.

Example 13 Find the vector equation of the plane which is at a distance of $\dfrac{6}{\sqrt{29}}$ from the origin and its normal vector from the origin is $2\hat{i} - 3\hat{j} + 4\hat{k}$. Also find its cartesian form.

Solution Let $\vec{n} = 2\,\hat{i} - 3\,\hat{j} + 4\,\hat{k}$. Then

$$\hat{n} = \frac{\vec{n}}{|\vec{n}|} = \frac{2\,\hat{i} - 3\,\hat{j} + 4\,\hat{k}}{\sqrt{4 + 9 + 16}} = \frac{2\,\hat{i} - 3\,\hat{j} + 4\,\hat{k}}{\sqrt{29}}$$

Hence, the required equation of the plane is

$$\vec{r}\cdot\left(\frac{2}{\sqrt{29}}\,\hat{i} + \frac{-3}{\sqrt{29}}\,\hat{j} + \frac{4}{\sqrt{29}}\,\hat{k}\right) = \frac{6}{\sqrt{29}}$$

Example 14 Find the direction cosines of the unit vector perpendicular to the plane $\vec{r}\cdot(6\hat{i} - 3\hat{j} - 2\hat{k}) + 1 = 0$ passing through the origin.

Solution The given equation can be written as

$$\vec{r}\cdot(-6\,\hat{i} + 3\,\hat{j} + 2\,\hat{k}) = 1$$ ... (1)

Now $$\left|-6\hat{i} + 3\hat{j} + 2\hat{k}\right| = \sqrt{36 + 9 + 4} = 7$$

Therefore, dividing both sides of (1) by 7, we get

$$\vec{r}\cdot\left(-\frac{6}{7}\,\hat{i} + \frac{3}{7}\,\hat{j} + \frac{2}{7}\,\hat{k}\right) = \frac{1}{7}$$

which is the equation of the plane in the form $\vec{r}\cdot\hat{n} = d$.

This shows that $\hat{n} = -\dfrac{6}{7}\,\hat{i} + \dfrac{3}{7}\,\hat{j} + \dfrac{2}{7}\,\hat{k}$ is a unit vector perpendicular to the

plane through the origin. Hence, the direction cosines of $\hat{n}$ are $\dfrac{-6}{7}, \dfrac{3}{7}, \dfrac{2}{7}$.

Example 15 Find the distance of the plane $2x - 3y + 4z - 6 = 0$ from the origin.

Solution Since the direction ratios of the normal to the plane are $2, -3, 4$; the direction cosines of it are

$$\frac{2}{\sqrt{2^2 + (-3)^2 + 4^2}}, \frac{-3}{\sqrt{2^2 + (-3)^2 + 4^2}}, \frac{4}{\sqrt{2^2 + (-3)^2 + 4^2}}, \text{ i.e., } \frac{2}{\sqrt{29}}, \frac{-3}{\sqrt{29}}, \frac{4}{\sqrt{29}}$$

Hence, dividing the equation $2x - 3y + 4z - 6 = 0$ i.e., $2x - 3y + 4z = 6$ throughout by $\sqrt{29}$, we get

$$\frac{2}{\sqrt{29}} x + \frac{-3}{\sqrt{29}} y + \frac{4}{\sqrt{29}} z = \frac{6}{\sqrt{29}}$$

This is of the form $lx + my + nz = d$, where d is the distance of the plane from the origin. So, the distance of the plane from the origin is $\dfrac{6}{\sqrt{29}}$.

Example 16 Find the coordinates of the foot of the perpendicular drawn from the origin to the plane $2x - 3y + 4z - 6 = 0$.

Solution Let the coordinates of the foot of the perpendicular P from the origin to the plane is (x_1, y_1, z_1) (Fig 11.11).

Then, the direction ratios of the line OP are x_1, y_1, z_1.

Writing the equation of the plane in the normal form, we have

$$\frac{2}{\sqrt{29}} x - \frac{3}{\sqrt{29}} y + \frac{4}{\sqrt{29}} z = \frac{6}{\sqrt{29}}$$

where, $\dfrac{2}{\sqrt{29}}, \dfrac{-3}{\sqrt{29}}, \dfrac{4}{\sqrt{29}}$ are the direction cosines of the OP.

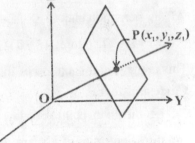

Fig 11.11

Since d.c.'s and direction ratios of a line are proportional, we have

$$\frac{x_1}{\dfrac{2}{\sqrt{29}}} = \frac{y_1}{\dfrac{-3}{\sqrt{29}}} = \frac{z_1}{\dfrac{4}{\sqrt{29}}} = k$$

i.e.,

$$x_1 = \frac{2k}{\sqrt{29}}, y_1 = \frac{-3k}{\sqrt{29}}, z_1 = \frac{4k}{\sqrt{29}}$$

Substituting these in the equation of the plane, we get $k = \dfrac{6}{\sqrt{29}}$.

Hence, the foot of the perpendicular is $\left(\dfrac{12}{29}, \dfrac{-18}{29}, \dfrac{24}{29}\right)$.

> **☞ Note** If d is the distance from the origin and l, m, n are the direction cosines of the normal to the plane through the origin, then the foot of the perpendicular is (ld, md, nd).

11.6.2 *Equation of a plane perpendicular to a given vector and passing through a given point*

In the space, there can be many planes that are perpendicular to the given vector, but through a given point $P(x_1, y_1, z_1)$, only one such plane exists (see Fig 11.12).

Let a plane pass through a point A with position vector $\vec{a}$ and perpendicular to the vector $\vec{N}$.

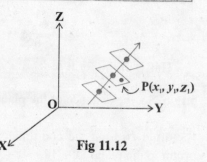

Fig 11.12

Let $\vec{r}$ be the position vector of any point P(x, y, z) in the plane. (Fig 11.13).

Then the point P lies in the plane if and only if $\overrightarrow{AP}$ is perpendicular to $\vec{N}$. i.e., $\overrightarrow{AP} \cdot \vec{N} = 0$. But $\overrightarrow{AP} = \vec{r} - \vec{a}$. Therefore, $(\vec{r} - \vec{a}) \cdot \vec{N} = 0$ ... (1)

This is the vector equation of the plane.

Cartesian form

Let the given point A be (x_1, y_1, z_1), P be (x, y, z) and direction ratios of $\vec{N}$ are A, B and C. Then,

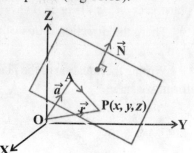

Fig 11.13

$$\vec{a} = x_1\hat{i} + y_1\hat{j} + z_1\hat{k}, \quad \vec{r} = x\hat{i} + y\hat{j} + z\hat{k} \quad \text{and} \quad \vec{N} = A\hat{i} + B\hat{j} + C\hat{k}$$

Now $(\vec{r} - \vec{a}) \cdot \vec{N} = 0$

So $\left[(x - x_1)\hat{i} + (y - y_1)\hat{j} + (z - z_1)\hat{k}\right] \cdot (A\hat{i} + B\hat{j} + C\hat{k}) = 0$

i.e. $A(x - x_1) + B(y - y_1) + C(z - z_1) = 0$

Example 17 Find the vector and cartesian equations of the plane which passes through the point (5, 2, − 4) and perpendicular to the line with direction ratios 2, 3, − 1.

Solution We have the position vector of point $(5, 2, -4)$ as $\vec{a}=5\hat{i}+2\hat{j}-4\hat{k}$ and the

normal vector $\vec{N}$ perpendicular to the plane as $\vec{N}=2\hat{i}+3\hat{j}-\hat{k}$

Therefore, the vector equation of the plane is given by $(\vec{r}-\vec{a}).\vec{N}=0$

or $\qquad [\vec{r}-(5\hat{i}+2\hat{j}-4\hat{k})]\cdot(2\hat{i}+3\hat{j}-\hat{k})=0$ ... (1)

Transforming (1) into Cartesian form, we have

$$[(x-5)\hat{i}+(y-2)\hat{j}+(z+4)\hat{k}]\cdot(2\hat{i}+3\hat{j}-\hat{k})=0$$

or $\qquad 2(x-5)+3(y-2)-1(z+4)=0$

i.e. $\qquad 2x+3y-z=20$

which is the cartesian equation of the plane.

11.6.3 *Equation of a plane passing through three non collinear points*

Let R, S and T be three non collinear points on the plane with position vectors $\vec{a}$, $\vec{b}$ and $\vec{c}$ respectively (Fig 11.14).

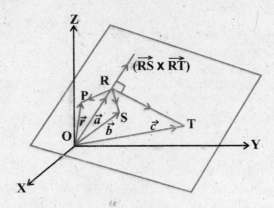

Fig 11.14

The vectors $\overrightarrow{RS}$ and $\overrightarrow{RT}$ are in the given plane. Therefore, the vector $\overrightarrow{RS}\times\overrightarrow{RT}$ is perpendicular to the plane containing points R, S and T. Let $\vec{r}$ be the position vector of any point P in the plane. Therefore, the equation of the plane passing through R and perpendicular to the vector $\overrightarrow{RS}\times\overrightarrow{RT}$ is

$$(\vec{r}-\vec{a})\cdot(\overrightarrow{RS}\times\overrightarrow{RT})=0$$

or $\qquad (\vec{r}-\vec{a}).[(\vec{b}-\vec{a})\times(\vec{c}-\vec{a})]=0$ ... (1)

This is the equation of the plane in vector form passing through three noncollinear points.

> **Note** Why was it necessary to say that the three points had to be non collinear? If the three points were on the same line, then there will be many planes that will contain them (Fig 11.15).

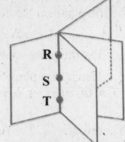

These planes will resemble the pages of a book where the line containing the points R, S and T are members in the binding of the book.

Cartesian form

Fig 11.15

Let (x_1, y_1, z_1), (x_2, y_2, z_2) and (x_3, y_3, z_3) be the coordinates of the points R, S and T respectively. Let (x, y, z) be the coordinates of any point P on the plane with position vector $\vec{r}$. Then

$$\overrightarrow{RP} = (x - x_1)\hat{i} + (y - y_1)\hat{j} + (z - z_1)\hat{k}$$

$$\overrightarrow{RS} = (x_2 - x_1)\hat{i} + (y_2 - y_1)\hat{j} + (z_2 - z_1)\hat{k}$$

$$\overrightarrow{RT} = (x_3 - x_1)\hat{i} + (y_3 - y_1)\hat{j} + (z_3 - z_1)\hat{k}$$

Substituting these values in equation (1) of the vector form and expressing it in the form of a determinant, we have

$$\begin{vmatrix} x - x_1 & y - y_1 & z - z_1 \\ x_2 - x_1 & y_2 - y_1 & z_2 - z_1 \\ x_3 - x_1 & y_3 - y_1 & z_3 - z_1 \end{vmatrix} = 0$$

which is the equation of the plane in Cartesian form passing through three non collinear points (x_1, y_1, z_1), (x_2, y_2, z_2) and (x_3, y_3, z_3).

Example 18 Find the vector equations of the plane passing through the points R$(2, 5, -3)$, S$(-2, -3, 5)$ and T$(5, 3, -3)$.

Solution Let $\vec{a} = 2\hat{i} + 5\hat{j} - 3\hat{k}$, $\vec{b} = -2\hat{i} - 3\hat{j} + 5\hat{k}$, $\vec{c} = 5\hat{i} + 3\hat{j} - 3\hat{k}$

Then the vector equation of the plane passing through $\vec{a}$, $\vec{b}$ and $\vec{c}$ and is given by

$$(\vec{r} - \vec{a}) \cdot (\overrightarrow{RS} \times \overrightarrow{RT}) = 0 \quad \text{(Why?)}$$

or
$$(\vec{r} - \vec{a}) \cdot [(\vec{b} - \vec{a}) \times (\vec{c} - \vec{a})] = 0$$

i.e.
$$[\vec{r} - (2\hat{i} + 5\hat{j} - 3\hat{k})] \cdot [(-4\hat{i} - 8\hat{j} + 8\hat{k}) \times (3\hat{i} - 2\hat{j})] = 0$$

11.6.4 *Intercept form of the equation of a plane*

In this section, we shall deduce the equation of a plane in terms of the intercepts made by the plane on the coordinate axes. Let the equation of the plane be

$$Ax + By + Cz + D = 0 \ (D \neq 0) \tag{1}$$

Let the plane make intercepts a, b, c on x, y and z axes, respectively (Fig 11.16).

Hence, the plane meets x, y and z-axes at $(a, 0, 0)$, $(0, b, 0)$, $(0, 0, c)$, respectively.

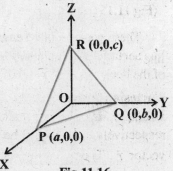

Fig 11.16

Therefore $Aa + D = 0$ or $A = \dfrac{-D}{a}$

$Bb + D = 0$ or $B = \dfrac{-D}{b}$

$Cc + D = 0$ or $C = \dfrac{-D}{c}$

Substituting these values in the equation (1) of the plane and simplifying, we get

$$\frac{x}{a} + \frac{y}{b} + \frac{z}{c} = 1 \tag{1}$$

which is the required equation of the plane in the intercept form.

Example 19 Find the equation of the plane with intercepts 2, 3 and 4 on the x, y and z-axis respectively.

Solution Let the equation of the plane be

$$\frac{x}{a} + \frac{y}{b} + \frac{z}{c} = 1 \tag{1}$$

Here $a = 2, b = 3, c = 4.$

Substituting the values of a, b and c in (1), we get the required equation of the

plane as $\dfrac{x}{2} + \dfrac{y}{3} + \dfrac{z}{4} = 1$ or $6x + 4y + 3z = 12.$

11.6.5 *Plane passing through the intersection of two given planes*

Let π_1 and π_2 be two planes with equations $\vec{r} \cdot \hat{n}_1 = d_1$ and $\vec{r} \cdot \hat{n}_2 = d_2$ respectively. The position vector of any point on the line of intersection must satisfy both the equations (Fig 11.17).

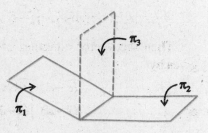

Fig 11.17

If $\vec{t}$ is the position vector of a point on the line, then

$$\vec{t} \cdot \hat{n}_1 = d_1 \text{ and } \vec{t} \cdot \hat{n}_2 = d_2$$

Therefore, for all real values of λ, we have

$$\vec{t} \cdot (\hat{n}_1 + \lambda \hat{n}_2) = d_1 + \lambda d_2$$

Since $\vec{t}$ is arbitrary, it satisfies for any point on the line.

Hence, the equation $\vec{r} \cdot (\vec{n}_1 + \lambda \vec{n}_2) = d_1 + \lambda d_2$ represents a plane π_3 which is such that if any vector $\vec{r}$ satisfies both the equations π_1 and π_2, it also satisfies the equation π_3 i.e., any plane passing through the intersection of the planes

$$\vec{r} \cdot \vec{n}_1 = d_1 \text{ and } \vec{r} \cdot \vec{n}_2 = d_2$$

has the equation $\vec{r} \cdot (\vec{n}_1 + \lambda \vec{n}_2) = d_1 + \lambda d_2$ ... (1)

Cartesian form

In Cartesian system, let

$$\vec{n}_1 = A_1 \hat{i} + B_2 \hat{j} + C_1 \hat{k}$$

$$\vec{n}_2 = A_2 \hat{i} + B_2 \hat{j} + C_2 \hat{k}$$

and

$$\vec{r} = x\hat{i} + y\hat{j} + z\hat{k}$$

Then (1) becomes

$$x(A_1 + \lambda A_2) + y(B_1 + \lambda B_2) + z(C_1 + \lambda C_2) = d_1 + \lambda d_2$$

or $(A_1 x + B_1 y + C_1 z - d_1) + \lambda(A_2 x + B_2 y + C_2 z - d_2) = 0$ ... (2)

which is the required Cartesian form of the equation of the plane passing through the intersection of the given planes for each value of λ.

Example 20 Find the vector equation of the plane passing through the intersection of the planes $\vec{r} \cdot (\hat{i} + \hat{j} + \hat{k}) = 6$ and $\vec{r} \cdot (2\hat{i} + 3\hat{j} + 4\hat{k}) = -5$, and the point $(1, 1, 1)$.

Solution Here, $\vec{n}_1 = \hat{i} + \hat{j} + \hat{k}$ and $\vec{n}_2 = 2\hat{i} + 3\hat{j} + 4\hat{k}$;

and $d_1 = 6$ and $d_2 = -5$

Hence, using the relation $\vec{r} \cdot (\vec{n}_1 + \lambda \vec{n}_2) = d_1 + \lambda d_2$, we get

$$\vec{r} \cdot [\hat{i} + \hat{j} + \hat{k} + \lambda(2\hat{i} + 3\hat{j} + 4\hat{k})] = 6 - 5\lambda$$

or $\vec{r} \cdot [(1 + 2\lambda)\hat{i} + (1 + 3\lambda)\hat{j} + (1 + 4\lambda)\hat{k}] = 6 - 5\lambda$ ... (1)

where, λ is some real number.

Taking $\qquad \vec{r} = x\hat{i} + y\hat{j} + z\hat{k}$, we get

$$(x\hat{i} + y\hat{j} + z\hat{k})\cdot[(1+2\lambda)\hat{i} + (1+3\lambda)\hat{j} + (1+4\lambda)\hat{k}] = 6 - 5\lambda$$

or $\qquad (1 + 2\lambda)\, x + (1 + 3\lambda)\, y + (1 + 4\lambda)\, z = 6 - 5\lambda$

or $\qquad (x + y + z - 6) + \lambda\ (2x + 3y + 4z + 5) = 0 \qquad \qquad$ ... (2)

Given that the plane passes through the point $(1,1,1)$, it must satisfy (2), i.e.

$$(1 + 1 + 1 - 6) + \lambda\ (2 + 3 + 4 + 5) = 0$$

or $\qquad \lambda = \dfrac{3}{14}$

Putting the values of λ in (1), we get

$$\vec{r}\cdot\left[\left(1 + \frac{3}{7}\right)\hat{i} + \left(1 + \frac{9}{14}\right)\hat{j} + \left(1 + \frac{6}{7}\right)\hat{k}\right] = 6 - \frac{15}{14}$$

or $\qquad \vec{r}\cdot\left(\dfrac{10}{7}\hat{i} + \dfrac{23}{14}\hat{j} + \dfrac{13}{7}\hat{k}\right) = \dfrac{69}{14}$

or $\qquad \vec{r}\cdot(20\hat{i} + 23\hat{j} + 26\hat{k}) = 69$

which is the required vector equation of the plane.

11.7 Coplanarity of Two Lines

Let the given lines be

$$\vec{r} = \vec{a}_1 + \lambda\vec{b}_1 \qquad\qquad \text{... (1)}$$

and $\qquad \vec{r} = \vec{a}_2 + \mu\vec{b}_2 \qquad\qquad$ ... (2)

The line (1) passes through the point, say A, with position vector $\vec{a}_1$ and is parallel to $\vec{b}_1$. The line (2) passes through the point, say B with position vector $\vec{a}_2$ and is parallel to $\vec{b}_2$.

Thus, $\qquad \overrightarrow{AB} = \vec{a}_2 - \vec{a}_1$

The given lines are coplanar if and only if $\overrightarrow{AB}$ is perpendicular to $\vec{b}_1 \times \vec{b}_2$.

i.e. $\qquad \overrightarrow{AB}\cdot(\vec{b}_1 \times \vec{b}_2) = 0$ or $(\vec{a}_2 - \vec{a}_1)\cdot(\vec{b}_1 \times \vec{b}_2) = 0$

Cartesian form

Let (x_1, y_1, z_1) and (x_2, y_2, z_2) be the coordinates of the points A and B respectively.

Let a_1, b_1, c_1 and a_2, b_2, c_2 be the direction ratios of $\vec{b}_1$ and $\vec{b}_2$, respectively. Then

$$\overrightarrow{AB} = (x_2 - x_1)\hat{i} + (y_2 - y_1)\hat{j} + (z_2 - z_1)\hat{k}$$

$$\vec{b}_1 = a_1\hat{i} + b_1\hat{j} + c_1\hat{k} \text{ and } \vec{b}_2 = a_2\hat{i} + b_2\hat{j} + c_2\hat{k}$$

The given lines are coplanar if and only if $\overrightarrow{AB} \cdot (\vec{b}_1 \times \vec{b}_2) = 0$. In the cartesian form, it can be expressed as

$$\begin{vmatrix} x_2 - x_1 & y_2 - y_1 & z_2 - z_1 \\ a_1 & b_2 & c_1 \\ a_2 & b_2 & c_2 \end{vmatrix} = 0 \qquad \qquad \dots (4)$$

Example 21 Show that the lines

$$\frac{x+3}{-3} = \frac{y-1}{1} = \frac{z-5}{5} \text{ and } \frac{x+1}{-1} = \frac{y-2}{2} = \frac{z-5}{5} \text{ are coplanar.}$$

Solution Here, $x_1 = -3$, $y_1 = 1$, $z_1 = 5$, $a_1 = -3$, $b_1 = 1$, $c_1 = 5$
$$x_2 = -1, \ y_2 = 2, \ z_2 = 5, \ a_2 = -1, \ b_2 = 2, \ c_2 = 5$$

Now, consider the determinant

$$\begin{vmatrix} x_2 - x_1 & y_2 - y_1 & z_2 - z_1 \\ a_1 & b_1 & c_1 \\ a_2 & b_2 & c_2 \end{vmatrix} = \begin{vmatrix} 2 & 1 & 0 \\ -3 & 1 & 5 \\ -1 & 2 & 5 \end{vmatrix} = 0$$

Therefore, lines are coplanar.

11.8 Angle between Two Planes

Definition 2 The angle between two planes is defined as the angle between their normals (Fig 11.18 (a)). Observe that if θ is an angle between the two planes, then so is $180 - \theta$ (Fig 11.18 (b)). We shall take the acute angle as the angles between two planes.

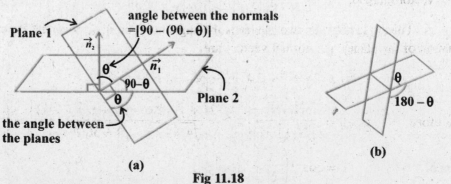

(a)

(b)

Fig 11.18

If $\vec{n}_1$ and $\vec{n}_2$ are normals to the planes and θ be the angle between the planes

$$\vec{r} \cdot \vec{n}_1 = d_1 \text{ and } \vec{r} \cdot \vec{n}_2 = d_2.$$

Then θ is the angle between the normals to the planes drawn from some common point.

We have,
$$\cos \theta = \left| \frac{\vec{n}_1 \cdot \vec{n}_2}{|\vec{n}_1||\vec{n}_2|} \right|$$

> **Note** The planes are perpendicular to each other if $\vec{n}_1 . \vec{n}_2 = 0$ and parallel if $\vec{n}_1$ is parallel to $\vec{n}_2$.

Cartesian form Let θ be the angle between the planes,

$$A_1 x + B_1 y + C_1 z + D_1 = 0 \text{ and } A_2 x + B_2 y + C_2 z + D_2 = 0$$

The direction ratios of the normal to the planes are A_1, B_1, C_1 and A_2, B_2, C_2 respectively.

Therefore,
$$\cos \theta = \left| \frac{A_1 A_2 + B_1 B_2 + C_1 C_2}{\sqrt{A_1^2 + B_1^2 + C_1^2} \ \sqrt{A_2^2 + B_2^2 + C_2^2}} \right|$$

> **Note**
> 1. If the planes are at right angles, then $\theta = 90°$ and so $\cos \theta = 0$. Hence, $\cos \theta = A_1 A_2 + B_1 B_2 + C_1 C_2 = 0$.
> 2. If the planes are parallel, then $\dfrac{A_1}{A_2} = \dfrac{B_1}{B_2} = \dfrac{C_1}{C_2}$.

Example 22 Find the angle between the two planes $2x + y - 2z = 5$ and $3x - 6y - 2z = 7$ using vector method.

Solution The angle between two planes is the angle between their normals. From the equation of the planes, the normal vectors are

$$\vec{N}_1 = 2\hat{i} + \hat{j} - 2\hat{k} \text{ and } \vec{N}_2 = 3\hat{i} - 6\hat{j} - 2\hat{k}$$

Therefore
$$\cos \theta = \left| \frac{\vec{N}_1 \cdot \vec{N}_2}{|\vec{N}_1||\vec{N}_2|} \right| = \left| \frac{(2\hat{i} + \hat{j} - 2\hat{k}) \cdot (3\hat{i} - 6\hat{j} - 2\hat{k})}{\sqrt{4+1+4} \ \sqrt{9+36+4}} \right| = \left(\frac{4}{21} \right)$$

Hence
$$\theta = \cos^{-1}\left(\frac{4}{21} \right)$$

Example 23 Find the angle between the two planes $3x - 6y + 2z = 7$ and $2x + 2y - 2z = 5$.

Solution Comparing the given equations of the planes with the equations

$$A_1 x + B_1 y + C_1 z + D_1 = 0 \text{ and } A_2 x + B_2 y + C_2 z + D_2 = 0$$

We get

$$A_1 = 3, B_1 = -6, C_1 = 2$$
$$A_2 = 2, B_2 = 2, C_2 = -2$$

$$\cos \theta = \left| \frac{3 \times 2 + (-6)(2) + (2)(-2)}{\sqrt{(3^2 + (-6)^2 + (-2)^2)} \sqrt{(2^2 + 2^2 + (-2)^2)}} \right|$$

$$= \left| \frac{-10}{7 \times 2\sqrt{3}} \right| = \frac{5}{7\sqrt{3}} = \frac{5\sqrt{3}}{21}$$

Therefore,

$$\theta = \cos^{-1} \left(\frac{5\sqrt{3}}{21} \right)$$

11.9 Distance of a Point from a Plane
Vector form

Consider a point P with position vector $\vec{a}$ and a plane π_1 whose equation is $\vec{r} \cdot \hat{n} = d$ (Fig 11.19).

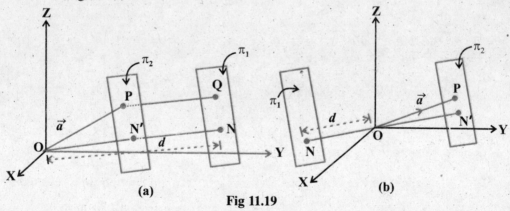

Fig 11.19

Consider a plane π_2 through P parallel to the plane π_1. The unit vector normal to π_2 is $\hat{n}$. Hence, its equation is $(\vec{r} - \vec{a}) \cdot \hat{n} = 0$

i.e.,

$$\vec{r} \cdot \hat{n} = \vec{a} \cdot \hat{n}$$

Thus, the distance ON′ of this plane from the origin is $|\vec{a} \cdot \hat{n}|$. Therefore, the distance PQ from the plane π_1 is (Fig. 11.21 (a))

i.e.,

$$ON - ON' = |d - \vec{a} \cdot \hat{n}|$$

which is the length of the perpendicular from a point to the given plane.

We may establish the similar results for (Fig 11.19 (b)).

> **Note**
>
> 1. If the equation of the plane π_2 is in the form $\vec{r} \cdot \overline{N} = d$, where $\overline{N}$ is normal
>
>   to the plane, then the perpendicular distance is $\dfrac{\left| \vec{a} \cdot \overline{N} - d \right|}{\left| \overline{N} \right|}$.
>
> 2. The length of the perpendicular from origin O to the plane $\vec{r} \cdot \overline{N} = d$ is $\dfrac{|d|}{|\overline{N}|}$
>
>   (since $\vec{a} = 0$).

Cartesian form

Let $P(x_1, y_1, z_1)$ be the given point with position vector $\vec{a}$ and
$$Ax + By + Cz = D$$
be the Cartesian equation of the given plane. Then

$$\vec{a} = x_1 \hat{i} + y_1 \hat{j} + z_1 \hat{k}$$

$$\overline{N} = A \hat{i} + B \hat{j} + C \hat{k}$$

Hence, from Note 1, the perpendicular from P to the plane is

$$\left| \frac{(x_1 \hat{i} + y_1 \hat{j} + z_1 \hat{k}) \cdot (A \hat{i} + B \hat{j} + C \hat{k}) - D}{\sqrt{A^2 + B^2 + C^2}} \right|$$

$$= \left| \frac{A x_1 + B y_1 + C z_1 - D}{\sqrt{A^2 + B^2 + C^2}} \right|$$

Example 24 Find the distance of a point $(2, 5, -3)$ from the plane

$$\vec{r} \cdot (6\hat{i} - 3\hat{j} + 2\hat{k}) = 4$$

Solution Here, $\vec{a} = 2\hat{i} + 5\hat{j} - 3\hat{k}$, $\overline{N} = 6\hat{i} - 3\hat{j} + 2\hat{k}$ and $d = 4$.

Therefore, the distance of the point $(2, 5, -3)$ from the given plane is

$$\frac{\left| (2\hat{i} + 5\hat{j} - 3\hat{k}) \cdot (6\hat{i} - 3\hat{j} + 2\hat{k}) - 4 \right|}{\left| 6\hat{i} - 3\hat{j} + 2\hat{k} \right|} = \frac{\left| 12 - 15 - 6 - 4 \right|}{\sqrt{36 + 9 + 4}} = \frac{13}{7}$$

11.10 Angle between a Line and a Plane

Definition 3 The angle between a line and a plane is the complement of the angle between the line and normal to the plane (Fig 11.20).

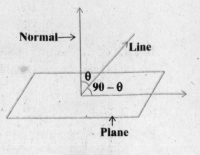

Fig 11.20

Vector form If the equation of the line is $\vec{r} = \vec{a} + \lambda \vec{b}$ and the equation of the plane is $\vec{r} \cdot \vec{n} = d$. Then the angle θ between the line and the normal to the plane is

$$\cos \theta = \left| \frac{\vec{b} \cdot \vec{n}}{|\vec{b}| \cdot |\vec{n}|} \right|$$

and so the angle ϕ between the line and the plane is given by $90 - \theta$, i.e.,

$$\sin (90 - \theta) = \cos \theta$$

i.e.

$$\sin \phi = \left| \frac{\vec{b} \cdot \vec{n}}{|\vec{b}| \, |\vec{n}|} \right| \text{ or } \phi = \sin^{-1} \left| \frac{\vec{b} \cdot \vec{n}}{|\vec{b}| |\vec{n}|} \right|$$

Example 25 Find the angle between the line

$$\frac{x+1}{2} = \frac{y}{3} = \frac{z-3}{6}$$

and the plane $10\,x + 2y - 11\,z = 3$.

Solution Let θ be the angle between the line and the normal to the plane. Converting the given equations into vector form, we have

$$\vec{r} = (-\hat{i} + 3\hat{k}) + \lambda (2\hat{i} + 3\hat{j} + 6\hat{k})$$

and $\qquad \vec{r} \cdot (10\hat{i} + 2\hat{j} - 11\hat{k}) = 3$

Here $\qquad \vec{b} = 2\hat{i} + 3\hat{j} + 6\hat{k} \quad$ and $\quad \vec{n} = 10\hat{i} + 2\hat{j} - 11\hat{k}$

$$\sin \phi = \left| \frac{(2\hat{i} + 3\hat{j} + 6\hat{k}) \cdot (10\hat{i} + 2\hat{j} - 11\hat{k})}{\sqrt{2^2 + 3^2 + 6^2} \ \sqrt{10^2 + 2^2 + 11^2}} \right|$$

$$= \left| \frac{-40}{7 \times 15} \right| = \left| \frac{8}{21} \right| = \frac{8}{21} \text{ or } \phi = \sin^{-1} \left(\frac{8}{21} \right)$$

EXERCISE 11.3

1. In each of the following cases, determine the direction cosines of the normal to the plane and the distance from the origin.

   (a) $z = 2$
   (b) $x + y + z = 1$
   (c) $2x + 3y - z = 5$
   (d) $5y + 8 = 0$

2. Find the vector equation of a plane which is at a distance of 7 units from the origin and normal to the vector $3\,\hat{i} + 5\,\hat{j} - 6\,\hat{k}$.

3. Find the Cartesian equation of the following planes:

   (a) $\vec{r} \cdot (\hat{i} + \hat{j} - \hat{k}) = 2$
   (b) $\vec{r} \cdot (2\hat{i} + 3\hat{j} - 4\hat{k}) = 1$
   (c) $\vec{r} \cdot [(s - 2t)\,\hat{i} + (3 - t)\,\hat{j} + (2\,s + t)\,\hat{k}] = 15$

4. In the following cases, find the coordinates of the foot of the perpendicular drawn from the origin.

   (a) $2x + 3y + 4z - 12 = 0$
   (b) $3y + 4z - 6 = 0$
   (c) $x + y + z = 1$
   (d) $5y + 8 = 0$

5. Find the vector and cartesian equations of the planes

   (a) that passes through the point $(1, 0, -2)$ and the normal to the plane is $\hat{i} + \hat{j} - \hat{k}$.

   (b) that passes through the point $(1, 4, 6)$ and the normal vector to the plane is $\hat{i} - 2\hat{j} + \hat{k}$.

6. Find the equations of the planes that passes through three points.

   (a) $(1, 1, -1), (6, 4, -5), (-4, -2, 3)$
   (b) $(1, 1, 0), (1, 2, 1), (-2, 2, -1)$

7. Find the intercepts cut off by the plane $2x + y - z = 5$.

8. Find the equation of the plane with intercept 3 on the y-axis and parallel to ZOX plane.

9. Find the equation of the plane through the intersection of the planes $3x - y + 2z - 4 = 0$ and $x + y + z - 2 = 0$ and the point $(2, 2, 1)$.

10. Find the vector equation of the plane passing through the intersection of the planes $\vec{r} \cdot (2\hat{i} + 2\hat{j} - 3\hat{k}) = 7$, $\vec{r} \cdot (2\hat{i} + 5\hat{j} + 3\hat{k}) = 9$ and through the point $(2, 1, 3)$.

11. Find the equation of the plane through the line of intersection of the planes $x + y + z = 1$ and $2x + 3y + 4z = 5$ which is perpendicular to the plane $x - y + z = 0$.

12. Find the angle between the planes whose vector equations are

$\vec{r} \cdot (2\hat{i} + 2\hat{j} - 3\hat{k}) = 5$ and $\vec{r} \cdot (3\hat{i} - 3\hat{j} + 5\hat{k}) = 3$.

13. In the following cases, determine whether the given planes are parallel or perpendicular, and in case they are neither, find the angles between them.

(a) $7x + 5y + 6z + 30 = 0$ and $3x - y - 10z + 4 = 0$

(b) $2x + y + 3z - 2 = 0$ and $x - 2y + 5 = 0$

(c) $2x - 2y + 4z + 5 = 0$ and $3x - 3y + 6z - 1 = 0$

(d) $2x - y + 3z - 1 = 0$ and $2x - y + 3z + 3 = 0$

(e) $4x + 8y + z - 8 = 0$ and $y + z - 4 = 0$

14. In the following cases, find the distance of each of the given points from the corresponding given plane.

Point	Plane
(a) $(0, 0, 0)$	$3x - 4y + 12z = 3$
(b) $(3, -2, 1)$	$2x - y + 2z + 3 = 0$
(c) $(2, 3, -5)$	$x + 2y - 2z = 9$
(d) $(-6, 0, 0)$	$2x - 3y + 6z - 2 = 0$

Miscellaneous Examples

Example 26 A line makes angles α, β, γ and δ with the diagonals of a cube, prove that

$$\cos^2 \alpha + \cos^2 \beta + \cos^2 \gamma + \cos^2 \delta = \frac{4}{3}$$

Solution A cube is a rectangular parallelopiped having equal length, breadth and height. Let OADBFEGC be the cube with each side of length a units. (Fig 11.21) The four diagonals are OE, AF, BG and CD.

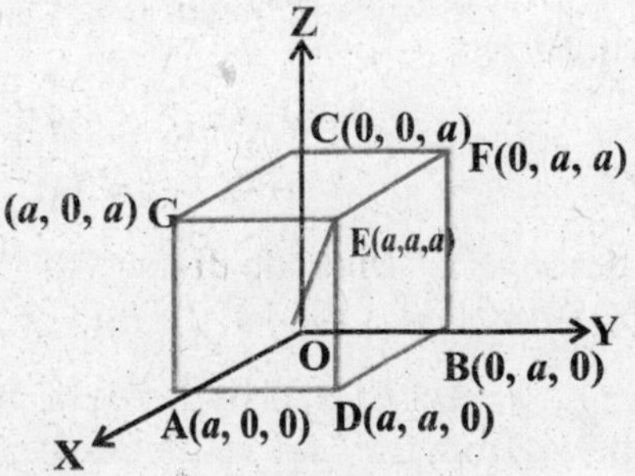

The direction cosines of the diagonal OE which is the line joining two points O and E are

$$\frac{a-0}{\sqrt{a^2 + a^2 + a^2}}, \frac{a-0}{\sqrt{a^2 + a^2 + a^2}}, \frac{a-0}{\sqrt{a^2 + a^2 + a^2}}$$

i.e., $\dfrac{1}{\sqrt{3}}, \dfrac{1}{\sqrt{3}}, \dfrac{1}{\sqrt{3}}$

Fig 11.21

Similarly, the direction cosines of AF, BG and CD are $\dfrac{-1}{\sqrt{3}}, \dfrac{1}{\sqrt{3}}, \dfrac{1}{\sqrt{3}}; \dfrac{1}{\sqrt{3}},$

$\dfrac{-1}{\sqrt{3}}, \dfrac{1}{\sqrt{3}}$ and $\dfrac{1}{\sqrt{3}}, \dfrac{1}{\sqrt{3}}, \dfrac{-1}{\sqrt{3}}$, respectively.

Let l, m, n be the direction cosines of the given line which makes angles $\alpha, \beta, \gamma, \delta$ with OE, AF, BG, CD, respectively. Then

$$\cos\alpha = \frac{1}{\sqrt{3}}\,(l + m + n); \cos\beta = \frac{1}{\sqrt{3}}\,(-l + m + n);$$

$$\cos\gamma = \frac{1}{\sqrt{3}}\,(l - m + n); \cos\delta = \frac{1}{\sqrt{3}}\,(l + m - n) \quad \text{(Why?)}$$

Squaring and adding, we get

$$\cos^2\alpha + \cos^2\beta + \cos^2\gamma + \cos^2\delta$$

$$= \frac{1}{3}\,[\,(l + m + n\,)^2 + (-l + m + n)^2\,] + (l - m + n)^2 + (l + m - n)^2]$$

$$= \frac{1}{3}\,[\,4\,(l^2 + m^2 + n^2\,)\,] = \frac{4}{3} \qquad \text{(as } l^2 + m^2 + n^2 = 1)$$

Example 27 Find the equation of the plane that contains the point $(1, -1, 2)$ and is perpendicular to each of the planes $2x + 3y - 2z = 5$ and $x + 2y - 3z = 8$.

Solution The equation of the plane containing the given point is
$$A\,(x - 1) + B(y + 1) + C\,(z - 2) = 0 \qquad \qquad \text{... (1)}$$
Applying the condition of perpendicularly to the plane given in (1) with the planes
$$2x + 3y - 2z = 5 \text{ and } x + 2y - 3z = 8, \text{ we have}$$
$$2A + 3B - 2C = 0 \text{ and } A + 2B - 3C = 0$$

Solving these equations, we find $A = -5C$ and $B = 4C$. Hence, the required equation is

$$-5C\,(x - 1) + 4\,C\,(y + 1) + C(z - 2) = 0$$
i.e. $\qquad\qquad 5x - 4y - z = 7$

Example 28 Find the distance between the point $P(6, 5, 9)$ and the plane determined by the points $A\,(3, -1, 2)$, $B\,(5, 2, 4)$ and $C(-1, -1, 6)$.

Solution Let A, B, C be the three points in the plane. D is the foot of the perpendicular drawn from a point P to the plane. PD is the required distance to be determined, which is the projection of $\overrightarrow{AP}$ on $\overrightarrow{AB} \times \overrightarrow{AC}$.

Hence, PD = the dot product of $\overrightarrow{AP}$ with the unit vector along $\overrightarrow{AB} \times \overrightarrow{AC}$.

So
$$\overrightarrow{AP} = 3\,\hat{i} + 6\,\hat{j} + 7\,\hat{k}$$

and
$$\overrightarrow{AB} \times \overrightarrow{AC} = \begin{vmatrix} \hat{i} & \hat{j} & \hat{k} \\ 2 & 3 & 2 \\ -4 & 0 & 4 \end{vmatrix} = 12\hat{i} - 16\hat{j} + 12\hat{k}$$

Unit vector along $\overrightarrow{AB} \times \overrightarrow{AC} = \dfrac{3\,\hat{i} - 4\,\hat{j} + 3\,\hat{k}}{\sqrt{34}}$

Hence
$$PD = (3\,\hat{i} + 6\,\hat{j} + 7\,\hat{k}) \cdot \frac{3\,\hat{i} - 4\,\hat{j} + 3\,\hat{k}}{\sqrt{34}}$$

$$= \frac{3\sqrt{34}}{17}$$

Alternatively, find the equation of the plane passing through A, B and C and then compute the distance of the point P from the plane.

Example 29 Show that the lines

$$\frac{x-a+d}{\alpha-\delta} = \frac{y-a}{\alpha} = \frac{z-a-d}{\alpha+\delta}$$

and
$$\frac{x-b+c}{\beta-\gamma} = \frac{y-b}{\beta} = \frac{z-b-c}{\beta+\gamma} \quad \text{are coplanar.}$$

Solution

Here

$$\begin{array}{ll} x_1 = a - d & x_2 = b - c \\ y_1 = a & y_2 = b \\ z_1 = a + d & z_2 = b + c \\ a_1 = \alpha - \delta & a_2 = \beta - \gamma \\ b_1 = \alpha & b_2 = \beta \\ c_1 = \alpha + \delta & c_2 = \beta + \gamma \end{array}$$

Now consider the determinant

$$\begin{vmatrix} x_2 - x_1 & y_2 - y_1 & z_2 - z_1 \\ a_1 & b_1 & c_1 \\ a_2 & b_2 & c_2 \end{vmatrix} = \begin{vmatrix} b-c-a+d & b-a & b+c-a-d \\ \alpha-\delta & \alpha & \alpha+\delta \\ \beta-\gamma & \beta & \beta+\gamma \end{vmatrix}$$

Adding third column to the first column, we get

$$2 \begin{vmatrix} b-a & b-a & b+c-a-d \\ \alpha & \alpha & \alpha+\delta \\ \beta & \beta & \beta+\gamma \end{vmatrix} = 0$$

Since the first and second columns are identical. Hence, the given two lines are coplanar.

Example 30 Find the coordinates of the point where the line through the points A $(3, 4, 1)$ and B $(5, 1, 6)$ crosses the XY-plane.

Solution The vector equation of the line through the points A and B is

$$\vec{r} = 3\hat{i} + 4\hat{j} + \hat{k} + \lambda[\,(5-3)\hat{i} + (1-4)\hat{j} + (6-1)\hat{k}\,]$$

i.e.

$$\vec{r} = 3\hat{i} + 4\hat{j} + \hat{k} + \lambda(\,2\hat{i} - 3\hat{j} + 5\hat{k}\,) \qquad \ldots (1)$$

Let P be the point where the line AB crosses the XY-plane. Then the position vector of the point P is of the form $x\hat{i} + y\hat{j}$.

This point must satisfy the equation (1).   (Why ?)

i.e.

$$x\hat{i} + y\hat{j} = (3+2\lambda)\hat{i} + (4-3\lambda)\hat{j} + (1+5\lambda)\hat{k}$$

Equating the like coefficients of $\hat{i}$, $\hat{j}$ and $\hat{k}$, we have

$$x = 3 + 2\lambda$$
$$y = 4 - 3\lambda$$
$$0 = 1 + 5\lambda$$

Solving the above equations, we get

$$x = \frac{13}{5} \text{ and } y = \frac{23}{5}$$

Hence, the coordinates of the required point are $\left(\dfrac{13}{5}, \dfrac{23}{5}, 0 \right)$.

Miscellaneous Exercise on Chapter 11

1. Show that the line joining the origin to the point $(2, 1, 1)$ is perpendicular to the line determined by the points $(3, 5, -1)$, $(4, 3, -1)$.

2. If l_1, m_1, n_1 and l_2, m_2, n_2 are the direction cosines of two mutually perpendicular lines, show that the direction cosines of the line perpendicular to both of these are $m_1 n_2 - m_2 n_1$, $n_1 l_2 - n_2 l_1$, $l_1 m_2 - l_2 m_1$

3. Find the angle between the lines whose direction ratios are a, b, c and $b - c, c - a, a - b$.

4. Find the equation of a line parallel to x-axis and passing through the origin.

5. If the coordinates of the points A, B, C, D be $(1, 2, 3), (4, 5, 7), (-4, 3, -6)$ and $(2, 9, 2)$ respectively, then find the angle between the lines AB and CD.

6. If the lines $\dfrac{x - 1}{-3} = \dfrac{y - 2}{2k} = \dfrac{z - 3}{2}$ and $\dfrac{x - 1}{3k} = \dfrac{y - 1}{1} = \dfrac{z - 6}{-5}$ are perpendicular, find the value of k.

7. Find the vector equation of the line passing through $(1, 2, 3)$ and perpendicular to the plane $\vec{r} \cdot (\hat{i} + 2\hat{j} - 5\hat{k}) + 9 = 0$.

8. Find the equation of the plane passing through (a, b, c) and parallel to the plane $\vec{r} \cdot (\hat{i} + \hat{j} + \hat{k}) = 2$.

9. Find the shortest distance between lines $\vec{r} = 6\hat{i} + 2\hat{j} + 2\hat{k} + \lambda(\hat{i} - 2\hat{j} + 2\hat{k})$ and $\vec{r} = -4\hat{i} - \hat{k} + \mu(3\hat{i} - 2\hat{j} - 2\hat{k})$.

10. Find the coordinates of the point where the line through $(5, 1, 6)$ and $(3, 4, 1)$ crosses the YZ-plane.

11. Find the coordinates of the point where the line through $(5, 1, 6)$ and $(3, 4, 1)$ crosses the ZX-plane.

12. Find the coordinates of the point where the line through $(3, -4, -5)$ and $(2, -3, 1)$ crosses the plane $2x + y + z = 7$.

13. Find the equation of the plane passing through the point $(-1, 3, 2)$ and perpendicular to each of the planes $x + 2y + 3z = 5$ and $3x + 3y + z = 0$.

14. If the points $(1, 1, p)$ and $(-3, 0, 1)$ be equidistant from the plane $\vec{r} \cdot (3\hat{i} + 4\hat{j} - 12\hat{k}) + 13 = 0$, then find the value of p.

15. Find the equation of the plane passing through the line of intersection of the planes $\vec{r} \cdot (\hat{i} + \hat{j} + \hat{k}) = 1$ and $\vec{r} \cdot (2\hat{i} + 3\hat{j} - \hat{k}) + 4 = 0$ and parallel to x-axis.

16. If O be the origin and the coordinates of P be $(1, 2, -3)$, then find the equation of the plane passing through P and perpendicular to OP.

17. Find the equation of the plane which contains the line of intersection of the planes $\vec{r} \cdot (\hat{i} + 2\hat{j} + 3\hat{k}) - 4 = 0, \vec{r} \cdot (2\hat{i} + \hat{j} - \hat{k}) + 5 = 0$ and which is perpendicular to the plane $\vec{r} \cdot (5\hat{i} + 3\hat{j} - 6\hat{k}) + 8 = 0$.

18. Find the distance of the point $(-1, -5, -10)$ from the point of intersection of the line $\vec{r} = 2\hat{i} - \hat{j} + 2\hat{k} + \lambda(3\hat{i} + 4\hat{j} + 2\hat{k})$ and the plane $\vec{r} \cdot (\hat{i} - \hat{j} + \hat{k}) = 5$.

19. Find the vector equation of the line passing through $(1, 2, 3)$ and parallel to the planes $\vec{r} \cdot (\hat{i} - \hat{j} + 2\hat{k}) = 5$ and $\vec{r} \cdot (3\hat{i} + \hat{j} + \hat{k}) = 6$.

20. Find the vector equation of the line passing through the point $(1, 2, -4)$ and perpendicular to the two lines:

$$\frac{x-8}{3} = \frac{y+19}{-16} = \frac{z-10}{7} \quad \text{and} \quad \frac{x-15}{3} = \frac{y-29}{8} = \frac{z-5}{-5}.$$

21. Prove that if a plane has the intercepts a, b, c and is at a distance of p units from the origin, then $\dfrac{1}{a^2} + \dfrac{1}{b^2} + \dfrac{1}{c^2} = \dfrac{1}{p^2}$.

Choose the correct answer in Exercises 22 and 23.

22. Distance between the two planes: $2x + 3y + 4z = 4$ and $4x + 6y + 8z = 12$ is

(A) 2 units   (B) 4 units   (C) 8 units   (D) $\dfrac{2}{\sqrt{29}}$ units

23. The planes: $2x - y + 4z = 5$ and $5x - 2.5y + 10z = 6$ are

(A) Perpendicular   (B) Parallel

(C) intersect y-axis   (D) passes through $\left(0, 0, \dfrac{5}{4}\right)$

Summary

- **Direction cosines of a line** are the cosines of the angles made by the line with the positive directions of the coordinate axes.

- If l, m, n are the direction cosines of a line, then $l^2 + m^2 + n^2 = 1$.

- Direction cosines of a line joining two points $P(x_1, y_1, z_1)$ and $Q(x_2, y_2, z_2)$ are

$$\frac{x_2 - x_1}{PQ}, \frac{y_2 - y_1}{PQ}, \frac{z_2 - z_1}{PQ}$$

where PQ = $\sqrt{(x_2 - x_1)^2 + (y_2 - y_1)^2 + (z_2 - z_1)^2}$

- **Direction ratios of a line** are the numbers which are proportional to the direction cosines of a line.

- If l, m, n are the direction cosines and a, b, c are the direction ratios of a line then

$$l = \frac{a}{\sqrt{a^2 + b^2 + c^2}} \; ; m = \frac{b}{\sqrt{a^2 + b^2 + c^2}} \; ; n = \frac{c}{\sqrt{a^2 + b^2 + c^2}}$$

- **Skew lines** are lines in space which are neither parallel nor intersecting. They lie in different planes.

- **Angle between skew lines** is the angle between two intersecting lines drawn from any point (preferably through the origin) parallel to each of the skew lines.

- If l_1, m_1, n_1 and l_2, m_2, n_2 are the direction cosines of two lines; and θ is the acute angle between the two lines; then

$$\cos\theta = |l_1 l_2 + m_1 m_2 + n_1 n_2|$$

- If a_1, b_1, c_1 and a_2, b_2, c_2 are the direction ratios of two lines and θ is the acute angle between the two lines; then

$$\cos\theta = \left| \frac{a_1 a_2 + b_1 b_2 + c_1 c_2}{\sqrt{a_1^2 + b_1^2 + c_1^2} \; \sqrt{a_2^2 + b_2^2 + c_2^2}} \right|$$

- Vector equation of a line that passes through the given point whose position vector is $\vec{a}$ and parallel to a given vector $\vec{b}$ is $\vec{r} = \vec{a} + \lambda \vec{b}$.

- Equation of a line through a point (x_1, y_1, z_1) and having direction cosines l, m, n is

$$\frac{x - x_1}{l} = \frac{y - y_1}{m} = \frac{z - z_1}{n}$$

- The vector equation of a line which passes through two points whose position vectors are $\vec{a}$ and $\vec{b}$ is $\vec{r} = \vec{a} + \lambda (\vec{b} - \vec{a})$.

- Cartesian equation of a line that passes through two points (x_1, y_1, z_1) and (x_2, y_2, z_2) is $\dfrac{x - x_1}{x_2 - x_1} = \dfrac{y - y_1}{y_2 - y_1} = \dfrac{z - z_1}{z_2 - z_1}$.

- If θ is the acute angle between $\vec{r} = \vec{a}_1 + \lambda \vec{b}_1$ and $\vec{r} = \vec{a}_2 + \lambda \vec{b}_2$, then

$$\cos\theta = \left| \frac{\vec{b}_1 \cdot \vec{b}_2}{|\vec{b}_1| |\vec{b}_2|} \right|$$

- If $\dfrac{x - x_1}{l_1} = \dfrac{y - y_1}{m_1} = \dfrac{z - z_1}{n_1}$ and $\dfrac{x - x_2}{l_2} = \dfrac{y - y_2}{m_2} = \dfrac{z - z_2}{n_2}$

are the equations of two lines, then the acute angle between the two lines is given by $\cos\theta = |l_1 l_2 + m_1 m_2 + n_1 n_2|$.

Shortest distance between two skew lines is the line segment perpendicular to both the lines.

Shortest distance between $\vec{r} = \vec{a}_1 + \lambda \vec{b}_1$ and $\vec{r} = \vec{a}_2 + \mu \vec{b}_2$ is

$$\left| \frac{(\vec{b}_1 \times \vec{b}_2) \cdot (\vec{a}_2 - \vec{a}_1)}{|\vec{b}_1 \times \vec{b}_2|} \right|$$

Shortest distance between the lines: $\dfrac{x - x_1}{a_1} = \dfrac{y - y_1}{b_1} = \dfrac{z - z_1}{c_1}$ and

$\dfrac{x - x_2}{a_2} = \dfrac{y - y_2}{b_2} = \dfrac{z - z_2}{c_2}$ is

$$\frac{\begin{vmatrix} x_2 - x_1 & y_2 - y_1 & z_2 - z_1 \\ a_1 & b_1 & c_1 \\ a_2 & b_2 & c_2 \end{vmatrix}}{\sqrt{(b_1 c_2 - b_2 c_1)^2 + (c_1 a_2 - c_2 a_1)^2 + (a_1 b_2 - a_2 b_1)^2}}$$

Distance between parallel lines $\vec{r} = \vec{a}_1 + \lambda \vec{b}$ and $\vec{r} = \vec{a}_2 + \mu \vec{b}$ is

$$\left| \frac{\vec{b} \times (\vec{a}_2 - \vec{a}_1)}{|\vec{b}|} \right|$$

In the vector form, equation of a plane which is at a distance d from the origin, and $\hat{n}$ is the unit vector normal to the plane through the origin is $\vec{r} \cdot \hat{n} = d$.

Equation of a plane which is at a distance of d from the origin and the direction cosines of the normal to the plane as l, m, n is $lx + my + nz = d$.

The equation of a plane through a point whose position vector is $\vec{a}$ and perpendicular to the vector $\overrightarrow{N}$ is $(\vec{r} - \vec{a}) \cdot \overrightarrow{N} = 0$.

Equation of a plane perpendicular to a given line with direction ratios A, B, C and passing through a given point (x_1, y_1, z_1) is
$$A(x - x_1) + B(y - y_1) + C(z - z_1) = 0$$

Equation of a plane passing through three non collinear points (x_1, y_1, z_1),

(x_2, y_2, z_2) and (x_3, y_3, z_3) is

$$\begin{vmatrix} x - x_1 & y - y_1 & z - z_1 \\ x_2 - x_1 & y_2 - y_1 & z_2 - z_1 \\ x_3 - x_1 & y_3 - y_1 & z_3 - z_1 \end{vmatrix} = 0$$

♦ Vector equation of a plane that contains three non collinear points having position vectors $\vec{a}$, $\vec{b}$ and $\vec{c}$ is $(\vec{r} - \vec{a}) \cdot [(\vec{b} - \vec{a}) \times (\vec{c} - \vec{a})] = 0$

♦ Equation of a plane that cuts the coordinates axes at $(a, 0, 0)$, $(0, b, 0)$ and $(0, 0, c)$ is

$$\frac{x}{a} + \frac{y}{b} + \frac{z}{c} = 1$$

♦ Vector equation of a plane that passes through the intersection of planes $\vec{r} \cdot \vec{n}_1 = d_1$ and $\vec{r} \cdot \vec{n}_2 = d_2$ is $\vec{r} \cdot (\vec{n}_1 + \lambda \vec{n}_2) = d_1 + \lambda d_2$, where λ is any nonzero constant.

♦ Vector equation of a plane that passes through the intersection of two given planes $A_1 x + B_1 y + C_1 z + D_1 = 0$ and $A_2 x + B_2 y + C_2 z + D_2 = 0$ is $(A_1 x + B_1 y + C_1 z + D_1) + \lambda(A_2 x + B_2 y + C_2 z + D_2) = 0$.

♦ Two lines $\vec{r} = \vec{a}_1 + \lambda \vec{b}_1$ and $\vec{r} = \vec{a}_2 + \mu \vec{b}_2$ are coplanar if

$$(\vec{a}_2 - \vec{a}_1) \cdot (\vec{b}_1 \times \vec{b}_2) = 0$$

♦ In the cartesian form two lines $= \dfrac{x - x_1}{a_1} = \dfrac{y - y_1}{b_1} = \dfrac{z - z_1}{C_1}$ and $\dfrac{x - x_2}{a_2}$

$= \dfrac{y - y_2}{b_2} = \dfrac{z - z_2}{C_2}$ are coplanar if $\begin{vmatrix} x_2 - x_1 & y_2 - y_1 & z_2 - z_1 \\ a_1 & b_1 & c_1 \\ a_2 & b_2 & c_2 \end{vmatrix} = 0$.

♦ In the vector form, if θ is the angle between the two planes, $\vec{r} \cdot \vec{n}_1 = d_1$ and $\vec{r} \cdot \vec{n}_2 = d_2$, then $\theta = \cos^{-1} \dfrac{|\vec{n}_1 \cdot \vec{n}_2|}{|\vec{n}_1| |\vec{n}_2|}$.

♦ The angle ϕ between the line $\vec{r} = \vec{a} + \lambda \vec{b}$ and the plane $\vec{r} \cdot \hat{n} = d$ is

$$\sin \phi = \left| \frac{\vec{b} \cdot \hat{n}}{|\vec{b}||\hat{n}|} \right|$$

◆ The angle θ between the planes $A_1 x + B_1 y + C_1 z + D_1 = 0$ and $A_2 x + B_2 y + C_2 z + D_2 = 0$ is given by

$$\cos \theta = \left| \frac{A_1 A_2 + B_1 B_2 + C_1 C_2}{\sqrt{A_1^2 + B_1^2 + C_1^2}\ \sqrt{A_2^2 + B_2^2 + C_2^2}} \right|$$

◆ The distance of a point whose position vector is $\vec{a}$ from the plane $\vec{r} \cdot \hat{n} = d$ is $|d - \vec{a} \cdot \hat{n}|$

◆ The distance from a point (x_1, y_1, z_1) to the plane $Ax + By + Cz + D = 0$ is

$$\left| \frac{Ax_1 + By_1 + Cz_1 + D}{\sqrt{A^2 + B^2 + C^2}} \right|$$

— ❖ —

Chapter 12

⬭ LINEAR PROGRAMMING ⬭

❖ *The mathematical experience of the student is incomplete if he never had the opportunity to solve a problem invented by himself. – G. POLYA* ❖

12.1 Introduction

In earlier classes, we have discussed systems of linear equations and their applications in day to day problems. In Class XI, we have studied linear inequalities and systems of linear inequalities in two variables and their solutions by graphical method. Many applications in mathematics involve systems of inequalities/equations. In this chapter, we shall apply the systems of linear inequalities/equations to solve some real life problems of the type as given below:

L. Kantorovich

A furniture dealer deals in only two items–tables and chairs. He has Rs 50,000 to invest and has storage space of at most 60 pieces. A table costs Rs 2500 and a chair Rs 500. He estimates that from the sale of one table, he can make a profit of Rs 250 and that from the sale of one chair a profit of Rs 75. He wants to know how many tables and chairs he should buy from the available money so as to maximise his total profit, assuming that he can sell all the items which he buys.

Such type of problems which seek to maximise (or, minimise) profit (or, cost) form a general class of problems called **optimisation problems**. Thus, an optimisation problem may involve finding maximum profit, minimum cost, or minimum use of resources etc.

A special but a very important class of optimisation problems is **linear programming problem.** The above stated optimisation problem is an example of linear programming problem. Linear programming problems are of much interest because of their wide applicability in industry, commerce, management science etc.

In this chapter, we shall study some linear programming problems and their solutions by graphical method only, though there are many other methods also to solve such problems.

12.2 Linear Programming Problem and its Mathematical Formulation

We begin our discussion with the above example of furniture dealer which will further lead to a mathematical formulation of the problem in two variables. In this example, we observe

(i) The dealer can invest his money in buying tables or chairs or combination thereof. Further he would earn different profits by following different investment strategies.

(ii) There are certain **overriding conditions** or **constraints** viz., his investment is limited to a **maximum** of Rs 50,000 and so is his storage space which is for a maximum of 60 pieces.

Suppose he decides to buy tables only and no chairs, so he can buy $50000 \div 2500$, i.e., 20 tables. His profit in this case will be Rs (250×20), i.e., **Rs 5000.**

Suppose he chooses to buy chairs only and no tables. With his capital of Rs 50,000, he can buy $50000 \div 500$, i.e. 100 chairs. But he can store only 60 pieces. Therefore, he is forced to buy only 60 chairs which will give him a total profit of Rs (60×75), i.e., **Rs 4500**.

There are many other possibilities, for instance, he may choose to buy 10 tables and 50 chairs, as he can store only 60 pieces. Total profit in this case would be Rs $(10 \times 250 + 50 \times 75)$, i.e., **Rs 6250** and so on.

We, thus, find that the dealer can invest his money in different ways and he would earn different profits by following different investment strategies.

Now the problem is : How should he invest his money in order to get maximum profit? To answer this question, let us try to formulate the problem mathematically.

12.2.1 *Mathematical formulation of the problem*

Let x be the number of tables and y be the number of chairs that the dealer buys. Obviously, x and y must be non-negative, i.e.,

$$\left. \begin{array}{l} x \geq 0 \\ y \geq 0 \end{array} \right\} \text{(Non-negative constraints)}$$

... (1)
... (2)

The dealer is constrained by the maximum amount he can invest (Here it is Rs 50,000) and by the maximum number of items he can store (Here it is 60).

Stated mathematically,

$$2500x + 500y \leq 50000 \text{ (investment constraint)}$$

or

$$5x + y \leq 100 \qquad \text{... (3)}$$

and

$$x + y \leq 60 \text{ (storage constraint)} \qquad \text{... (4)}$$

The dealer wants to invest in such a way so as to maximise his profit, say, Z which stated as a function of x and y is given by

$Z = 250x + 75y$ (called *objective function*)   ... (5)

Mathematically, the given problems now reduces to:

Maximise $Z = 250x + 75y$

subject to the constraints:

$$5x + y \leq 100$$

$$x + y \leq 60$$

$$x \geq 0, \ y \geq 0$$

So, we have to maximise the linear function Z subject to certain conditions determined by a set of linear inequalities with variables as non-negative. There are also some other problems where we have to minimise a linear function subject to certain conditions determined by a set of linear inequalities with variables as non-negative. Such problems are called **Linear Programming Problems.**

Thus, a Linear Programming Problem is one that is concerned with finding the **optimal value** (maximum or minimum value) of a linear function (called **objective function**) of several variables (say x and y), subject to the conditions that the variables are **non-negative** and satisfy a set of linear inequalities (called **linear constraints**). The term **linear** implies that all the mathematical relations used in the problem are **linear relations** while the term programming refers to the method of determining a particular **programme** or plan of action.

Before we proceed further, we now formally define some terms (which have been used above) which we shall be using in the linear programming problems:

Objective function Linear function $Z = ax + by$, where a, b are constants, which has to be maximised or minimized is called a linear **objective function.**

In the above example, $Z = 250x + 75y$ is a linear objective function. Variables x and y are called **decision variables**.

Constraints The linear inequalities or equations or restrictions on the variables of a linear programming problem are called **constraints**. The conditions $x \geq 0$, $y \geq 0$ are called non-negative restrictions. In the above example, the set of inequalities (1) to (4) are **constraints**.

Optimisation problem A problem which seeks to maximise or minimise a linear function (say of two variables x and y) subject to certain constraints as determined by a set of linear inequalities is called an **optimisation problem**. Linear programming problems are special type of optimisation problems. The above problem of investing a given sum by the dealer in purchasing chairs and tables is an example of an optimisation problem as well as of a linear programming problem.

We will now discuss how to find solutions to a linear programming problem. In this chapter, we will be concerned only with the graphical method.

12.2.2 *Graphical method of solving linear programming problems*

In Class XI, we have learnt how to graph a system of linear inequalities involving two variables x and y and to find its solutions graphically. Let us refer to the problem of investment in tables and chairs discussed in Section 12.2. We will now solve this problem graphically. Let us graph the constraints stated as linear inequalities:

$$5x + y \le 100 \qquad \qquad \dots (1)$$
$$x + y \le 60 \qquad \qquad \dots (2)$$
$$x \ge 0 \qquad \qquad \dots (3)$$
$$y \ge 0 \qquad \qquad \dots (4)$$

The graph of this system (shaded region) consists of the points common to all half planes determined by the inequalities (1) to (4) (Fig 12.1). Each point in this region represents a **feasible choice** open to the dealer for investing in tables and chairs. The region, therefore, is called the **feasible region** for the problem. Every point of this region is called a **feasible solution** to the problem. Thus, we have,

Feasible region The common region determined by all the constraints including non-negative constraints $x, y \ge 0$ of a linear programming problem is called the **feasible region** (or solution region) for the problem. In Fig 12.1, the region OABC (shaded) is the feasible region for the problem. The region other than feasible region is called an **infeasible region**.

Feasible solutions Points within and on the boundary of the feasible region represent feasible solutions of the constraints. In Fig 12.1, every point within and on the boundary of the feasible region OABC represents feasible solution to the problem. For example, the point (10, 50) is a feasible solution of the problem and so are the points (0, 60), (20, 0) etc.

Any point outside the feasible region is called an **infeasible solution.** For example, the point (25, 40) is an infeasible solution of the problem.

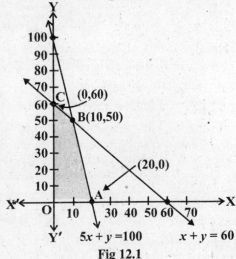

Fig 12.1

Optimal (feasible) solution: Any point in the feasible region that gives the optimal value (maximum or minimum) of the objective function is called an **optimal solution.**

Now, we see that every point in the feasible region OABC satisfies all the constraints as given in (1) to (4), and since there are **infinitely many points**, it is not evident how we should go about finding a point that gives a maximum value of the objective function $Z = 250x + 75y$. To handle this situation, we use the following theorems which are fundamental in solving linear programming problems. The proofs of these theorems are beyond the scope of the book.

Theorem 1 Let R be the feasible region (convex polygon) for a linear programming problem and let $Z = ax + by$ be the objective function. When Z has an optimal value (maximum or minimum), where the variables x and y are subject to constraints described by linear inequalities, this optimal value must occur at a corner point* (vertex) of the feasible region.

Theorem 2 Let R be the feasible region for a linear programming problem, and let $Z = ax + by$ be the objective function. If R is **bounded****, then the objective function Z has both a **maximum** and a **minimum** value on R and each of these occurs at a corner point (vertex) of R.

Remark If R is **unbounded**, then a maximum or a minimum value of the objective function may not exist. However, if it exists, it must occur at a corner point of R. (By Theorem 1).

In the above example, the corner points (vertices) of the bounded (feasible) region are: O, A, B and C and it is easy to find their coordinates as (0, 0), (20, 0), (10, 50) and (0, 60) respectively. Let us now compute the values of Z at these points.

We have

Vertex of the Feasible Region	Corresponding value of Z (in Rs)
O (0,0)	0
C (0,60)	4500
B (10,50)	6250 ← Maximum
A (20,0)	5000

---

*   A corner point of a feasible region is a point in the region which is the intersection of two boundary lines.

**   A feasible region of a system of linear inequalities is said to be bounded if it can be enclosed within a circle. Otherwise, it is called unbounded. Unbounded means that the feasible region does extend indefinitely in any direction.

We observe that the maximum profit to the dealer results from the investment strategy (10, 50), i.e. buying 10 tables and 50 chairs.

This method of solving linear programming problem is referred as **Corner Point Method**. The method comprises of the following steps:

1. Find the feasible region of the linear programming problem and determine its corner points (vertices) either by inspection or by solving the two equations of the lines intersecting at that point.

2. Evaluate the objective function $Z = ax + by$ at each corner point. Let M and m, respectively denote the largest and smallest values of these points.

3. (i) When the feasible region is **bounded**, M and m are the maximum and minimum values of Z.

   (ii) In case, the feasible region is **unbounded**, we have:

4. (a) M is the maximum value of Z, if the open half plane determined by $ax + by > M$ has no point in common with the feasible region. Otherwise, Z has no maximum value.

   (b) Similarly, m is the minimum value of Z, if the open half plane determined by $ax + by < m$ has no point in common with the feasible region. Otherwise, Z has no minimum value.

We will now illustrate these steps of Corner Point Method by considering some examples:

Example 1 Solve the following linear programming problem graphically:

Maximise $Z = 4x + y$ ... (1)

subject to the constraints:

$$x + y \leq 50 \qquad \qquad \text{... (2)}$$

$$3x + y \leq 90 \qquad \qquad \text{... (3)}$$

$$x \geq 0, y \geq 0 \qquad \qquad \text{... (4)}$$

Solution The shaded region in Fig 12.2 is the feasible region determined by the system of constraints (2) to (4). We observe that the feasible region OABC is **bounded**. So, we now use Corner Point Method to determine the maximum value of Z.

The coordinates of the corner points O, A, B and C are (0, 0), (30, 0), (20, 30) and (0, 50) respectively. Now we evaluate Z at each corner point.

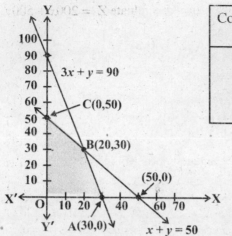

Corner Point	Corresponding value of Z	
(0, 0)	0	
(30, 0)	120 ←	Maximum
(20, 30)	110	
(0, 50)	50	

Fig 12.2

Hence, maximum value of Z is 120 at the point (30, 0).

Example 2 Solve the following linear programming problem graphically:

Minimise $Z = 200 x + 500 y$ ... (1)

subject to the constraints:

$$x + 2y \geq 10 \qquad ... (2)$$
$$3x + 4y \leq 24 \qquad ... (3)$$
$$x \geq 0, y \geq 0 \qquad ... (4)$$

Solution The shaded region in Fig 12.3 is the feasible region ABC determined by the system of constraints (2) to (4), which is **bounded**. The coordinates of corner points

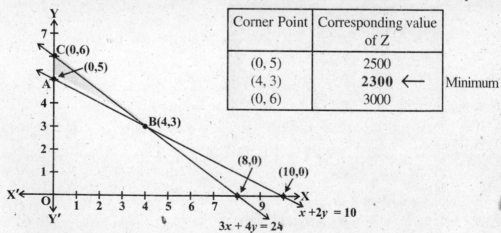

Corner Point	Corresponding value of Z	
(0, 5)	2500	
(4, 3)	2300 ←	Minimum
(0, 6)	3000	

Fig 12.3

A, B and C are (0,5), (4,3) and (0,6) respectively. Now we evaluate $Z = 200x + 500y$ at these points.

Hence, minimum value of Z is 2300 at...

Example 3 Solve the following problem graphically:

Minimise and Maximise $Z = 3x + 9y$ ... (1)

subject to the constraints: $x + 3y \leq 60$ ... (2)

$x + y \geq 10$ ... (3)

$x \leq y$ ... (4)

$x \geq 0, y \geq 0$ ... (5)

Solution First of all, let us graph the feasible region of the system of linear inequalities (2) to (5). The feasible region ABCD is shown in the Fig 12.4. Note that the region is bounded. The coordinates of the corner points A, B, C and D are (0, 10), (5, 5); (15,15) and (0, 20) respectively.

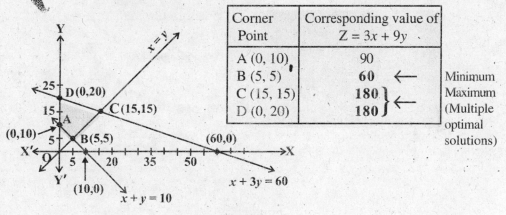

Corner Point	Corresponding value of $Z = 3x + 9y$	
A (0, 10)	90	
B (5, 5)	60	← Minimum
C (15, 15)	180 ⎫	← Maximum
D (0, 20)	180 ⎭	(Multiple optimal solutions)

Fig 12.4

We now find the minimum and maximum value of Z. From the table, we find that the minimum value of Z is 60 at the point B (5, 5) of the feasible region.

The maximum value of Z on the feasible region occurs at the two corner points C (15, 15) and D (0, 20) and it is 180 in each case.

Remark Observe that in the above example, the problem has multiple optimal solutions at the corner points C and D, i.e. the both points produce same maximum value 180. In such cases, you can see that every point on the line segment CD joining the two corner points C and D also give the same maximum value. Same is also true in the case if the two points produce same minimum value.

Example 4 Determine graphically the minimum value of the objective function

$$Z = -50x + 20y \quad\quad\quad ... (1)$$

subject to the constraints:

$$2x - y \geq -5 \quad\quad\quad ... (2)$$
$$3x + y \geq 3 \quad\quad\quad ... (3)$$
$$2x - 3y \leq 12 \quad\quad\quad ... (4)$$
$$x \geq 0, y \geq 0 \quad\quad\quad ... (5)$$

Solution First of all, let us graph the feasible region of the system of inequalities (2) to (5). The feasible region (shaded) is shown in the Fig 12.5. Observe that the feasible region is **unbounded.**.

We now evaluate Z at the corner points.

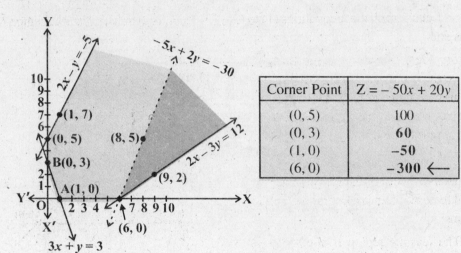

Corner Point	$Z = -50x + 20y$
(0, 5)	100
(0, 3)	60
(1, 0)	−50
(6, 0)	−300 ⟵ smallest

Fig 12.5

From this table, we find that − 300 is the smallest value of Z at the corner point (6, 0). Can we say that minimum value of Z is − 300? Note that if the region would have been bounded, this smallest value of Z is the minimum value of Z (Theorem 2). But here we see that the feasible region is unbounded. Therefore, − 300 may or may not be the minimum value of Z. To decide this issue, we graph the inequality

$$-50x + 20y < -300 \text{ (see Step 3(ii) of corner Point Method.)}$$

i.e.,

$$-5x + 2y < -30$$

and check whether the resulting open half plane has points in common with feasible region or not. If it has common points, then −300 will not be the minimum value of Z. Otherwise, −300 will be the minimum value of Z.

As shown in the Fig 12.5, it has common points. Therefore, Z = –50 x + 20 y has no minimum value subject to the given constraints.

In the above example, can you say whether $z = -50 x + 20 y$ has the maximum value 100 at (0,5)? For this, check whether the graph of $-50 x + 20 y > 100$ has points in common with the feasible region. (Why?)

Example 5 Minimise Z = 3x + 2y

subject to the constraints:

$$x + y \geq 8 \qquad \qquad \dots (1)$$
$$3x + 5y \leq 15 \qquad \qquad \dots (2)$$
$$x \geq 0, y \geq 0 \qquad \qquad \dots (3)$$

Solution Let us graph the inequalities (1) to (3) (Fig 12.6). Is there any feasible region? Why is so?

From Fig 12.6, you can see that there is no point satisfying all the constraints simultaneously. Thus, the problem is having no feasible region and hence no feasible solution.

Remarks From the examples which we have discussed so far, we notice some general features of linear programming problems:

(i) The feasible region is always a convex region.

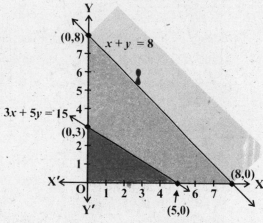

Fig 12.6

(ii) The maximum (or minimum) solution of the objective function occurs at the vertex (corner) of the feasible region. If two corner points produce the same maximum (or minimum) value of the objective function, then every point on the line segment joining these points will also give the same maximum (or minimum) value.

$$\boxed{\text{EXERCISE 12.1}}$$

Solve the following Linear Programming Problems graphically:

1. Maximise Z = 3x + 4y

   subject to the constraints : $x + y \leq 4, x \geq 0, y \geq 0$.

2. Minimise $Z = -3x + 4y$

   subject to $x + 2y \le 8$, $3x + 2y \le 12$, $x \ge 0$, $y \ge 0$.

3. Maximise $Z = 5x + 3y$

   subject to $3x + 5y \le 15$, $5x + 2y \le 10$, $x \ge 0$, $y \ge 0$.

4. Minimise $Z = 3x + 5y$

   such that $x + 3y \ge 3$, $x + y \ge 2$, $x, y \ge 0$.

5. Maximise $Z = 3x + 2y$

   subject to $x + 2y \le 10$, $3x + y \le 15$, $x, y \ge 0$.

6. Minimise $Z = x + 2y$

   subject to $2x + y \ge 3$, $x + 2y \ge 6$, $x, y \ge 0$.

   Show that the minimum of Z occurs at more than two points.

7. Minimise and Maximise $Z = 5x + 10y$

   subject to $x + 2y \le 120$, $x + y \ge 60$, $x - 2y \ge 0$, $x, y \ge 0$.

8. Minimise and Maximise $Z = x + 2y$

   subject to $x + 2y \ge 100$, $2x - y \le 0$, $2x + y \le 200$; $x, y \ge 0$.

9. Maximise $Z = -x + 2y$, subject to the constraints:

   $x \ge 3$, $x + y \ge 5$, $x + 2y \ge 6$, $y \ge 0$.

10. Maximise $Z = x + y$, subject to $x - y \le -1$, $-x + y \le 0$, $x, y \ge 0$.

12.3 Different Types of Linear Programming Problems

A few important linear programming problems are listed below:

1. **Manufacturing problems** In these problems, we determine the number of units of different products which should be produced and sold by a firm when each product requires a fixed manpower, machine hours, labour hour per unit of product, warehouse space per unit of the output etc., in order to make maximum profit.

2. **Diet problems** In these problems, we determine the amount of different kinds of constituents/nutrients which should be included in a diet so as to minimise the cost of the desired diet such that it contains a certain minimum amount of each constituent/nutrients.

3. **Transportation problems** In these problems, we determine a transportation schedule in order to find the cheapest way of transporting a product from plants/factories situated at different locations to different markets.

Let us now solve some of these types of linear programming problems:

Example 6 (Diet problem): A dietician wishes to mix two types of foods in such a way that vitamin contents of the mixture contain atleast 8 units of vitamin A and 10 units of vitamin C. Food 'I' contains 2 units/kg of vitamin A and 1 unit/kg of vitamin C. Food 'II' contains 1 unit/kg of vitamin A and 2 units/kg of vitamin C. It costs Rs 50 per kg to purchase Food 'I' and Rs 70 per kg to purchase Food 'II'. Formulate this problem as a linear programming problem to minimise the cost of such a mixture.

Solution Let the mixture contain x kg of Food 'I' and y kg of Food 'II'. Clearly, $x \geq 0$, $y \geq 0$. We make the following table from the given data:

Resources	Food I (x)	Food II (y)	Requirement
Vitamin A (units/kg)	2	1	8
Vitamin C (units/kg)	1	2	10
Cost (Rs/kg)	50	70	

Since the mixture must contain at least 8 units of vitamin A and 10 units of vitamin C, we have the constraints:

$$2x + y \geq 8$$
$$x + 2y \geq 10$$

Total cost Z of purchasing x kg of food 'I' and y kg of Food 'II' is

$$Z = 50x + 70y$$

Hence, the mathematical formulation of the problem is:

Minimise $\qquad\qquad Z = 50x + 70y$ $\qquad\qquad\qquad$ ... (1)

subject to the constraints:

$$2x + y \geq 8 \qquad\qquad\qquad \text{... (2)}$$
$$x + 2y \geq 10 \qquad\qquad\qquad \text{... (3)}$$
$$x, y \geq 0 \qquad\qquad\qquad \text{... (4)}$$

Let us graph the inequalities (2) to (4). The feasible region determined by the system is shown in the Fig 12.7. Here again, observe that the feasible region is **unbounded**.

Let us evaluate Z at the corner points A(0,8), B(2,4) and C(10,0).

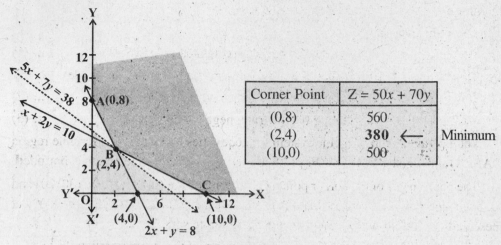

Corner Point	Z = 50x + 70y	
(0,8)	560	
(2,4)	**380** ←	Minimum
(10,0)	500	

Fig 12.7

In the table, we find that smallest value of Z is 380 at the point (2,4). Can we say that the minimum value of Z is 380? Remember that the feasible region is unbounded. Therefore, we have to draw the graph of the inequality

$$50x + 70y < 380 \text{ i.e., } 5x + 7y < 38$$

to check whether the resulting open half plane has any point common with the feasible region. From the Fig 12.7, we see that it has no points in common.

Thus, the minimum value of Z is 380 attained at the point (2, 4). Hence, the optimal mixing strategy for the dietician would be to mix 2 kg of Food 'I' and 4 kg of Food 'II', and with this strategy, the minimum cost of the mixture will be Rs 380.

Example 7 (Allocation problem) A cooperative society of farmers has 50 hectare of land to grow two crops X and Y. The profit from crops X and Y per hectare are estimated as Rs 10,500 and Rs 9,000 respectively. To control weeds, a liquid herbicide has to be used for crops X and Y at rates of 20 litres and 10 litres per hectare. Further, no more than 800 litres of herbicide should be used in order to protect fish and wild life using a pond which collects drainage from this land. How much land should be allocated to each crop so as to maximise the total profit of the society?

Solution Let x hectare of land be allocated to crop X and y hectare to crop Y. Obviously, $x \geq 0, y \geq 0$.

Profit per hectare on crop X = Rs 10500

Profit per hectare on crop Y = Rs 9000

Therefore, total profit   = Rs $(10500x + 9000y)$

The mathematical formulation of the problem is as follows:

Maximise $Z = 10500\,x + 9000\,y$

subject to the constraints:

$$x + y \leq 50 \quad \text{(constraint related to land)} \qquad \text{... (1)}$$
$$20x + 10y \leq 800 \text{ (constraint related to use of herbicide)}$$

i.e. $2x + y \leq 80 \qquad\qquad\qquad\qquad\qquad \text{... (2)}$

$$x \geq 0,\ y \geq 0 \qquad \text{(non negative constraint)} \qquad \text{... (3)}$$

Let us draw the graph of the system of inequalities (1) to (3). The feasible region OABC is shown (shaded) in the Fig 12.8. Observe that the feasible region is **bounded**.

The coordinates of the corner points O, A, B and C are (0, 0), (40, 0), (30, 20) and (0, 50) respectively. Let us evaluate the objective function $Z = 10500\,x + 9000y$ at these vertices to find which one gives the maximum profit.

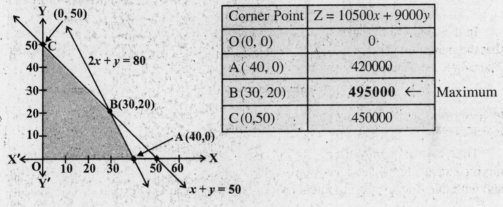

Corner Point	$Z = 10500x + 9000y$	
O(0, 0)	0	
A(40, 0)	420000	
B(30, 20)	**495000**	← Maximum
C(0,50)	450000	

Fig 12.8

Hence, the society will get the maximum profit of Rs 4,95,000 by allocating 30 hectares for crop X and 20 hectares for crop Y.

Example 8 (Manufacturing problem) A manufacturing company makes two models A and B of a product. Each piece of Model A requires 9 labour hours for fabricating and 1 labour hour for finishing. Each piece of Model B requires 12 labour hours for fabricating and 3 labour hours for finishing. For fabricating and finishing, the maximum labour hours available are 180 and 30 respectively. The company makes a profit of Rs 8000 on each piece of model A and Rs 12000 on each piece of Model B. How many pieces of Model A and Model B should be manufactured per week to realise a maximum profit? What is the maximum profit per week?

Solution Suppose x is the number of pieces of Model A and y is the number of pieces of Model B. Then

$$\text{Total profit (in Rs)} = 8000\,x + 12000\,y$$

Let $$Z = 8000\,x + 12000\,y$$

We now have the following mathematical model for the given problem.

Maximise $Z = 8000\,x + 12000\,y$ ... (1)

subject to the constraints:

$$9x + 12y \le 180 \quad \text{(Fabricating constraint)}$$

i.e. $$3x + 4y \le 60 \qquad \qquad \qquad \text{... (2)}$$

$$x + 3y \le 30 \quad \text{(Finishing constraint)} \qquad \text{... (3)}$$

$$x \ge 0,\ y \ge 0 \quad \text{(non-negative constraint)} \qquad \text{... (4)}$$

The feasible region (shaded) OABC determined by the linear inequalities (2) to (4) is shown in the Fig 12.9. Note that the feasible region is bounded.

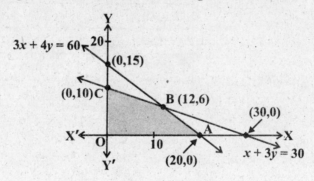

Fig 12.9

Let us evaluate the objective function Z at each corner point as shown below:

Corner Point	$Z = 8000\,x + 12000\,y$	
0 (0, 0)	0	
A (20, 0)	160000	
B (12, 6)	**168000** ←	Maximum
C (0, 10)	120000	

We find that maximum value of Z is 1,68,000 at B (12, 6). Hence, the company should produce 12 pieces of Model A and 6 pieces of Model B to realise maximum profit and maximum profit then will be Rs 1,68,000.

EXERCISE 12.2

1. Reshma wishes to mix two types of food P and Q in such a way that the vitamin contents of the mixture contain at least 8 units of vitamin A and 11 units of vitamin B. Food P costs Rs 60/kg and Food Q costs Rs 80/kg. Food P contains 3 units/kg of Vitamin A and 5 units / kg of Vitamin B while food Q contains 4 units/kg of Vitamin A and 2 units/kg of vitamin B. Determine the minimum cost of the mixture.

2. One kind of cake requires 200g of flour and 25g of fat, and another kind of cake requires 100g of flour and 50g of fat. Find the maximum number of cakes which can be made from 5kg of flour and 1 kg of fat assuming that there is no shortage of the other ingredients used in making the cakes.

3. A factory makes tennis rackets and cricket bats. A tennis racket takes 1.5 hours of machine time and 3 hours of craftman's time in its making while a cricket bat takes 3 hour of machine time and 1 hour of craftman's time. In a day, the factory has the availability of not more than 42 hours of machine time and 24 hours of craftsman's time.

   (i) What number of rackets and bats must be made if the factory is to work at full capacity?

   (ii) If the profit on a racket and on a bat is Rs 20 and Rs 10 respectively, find the maximum profit of the factory when it works at full capacity.

4. A manufacturer produces nuts and bolts. It takes 1 hour of work on machine A and 3 hours on machine B to produce a package of nuts. It takes 3 hours on machine A and 1 hour on machine B to produce a package of bolts. He earns a profit of Rs17.50 per package on nuts and Rs 7.00 per package on bolts. How many packages of each should be produced each day so as to maximise his profit, if he operates his machines for at the most 12 hours a day?

5. A factory manufactures two types of screws, A and B. Each type of screw requires the use of two machines, an automatic and a hand operated. It takes 4 minutes on the automatic and 6 minutes on hand operated machines to manufacture a package of screws A, while it takes 6 minutes on automatic and 3 minutes on the hand operated machines to manufacture a package of screws B. Each machine is available for at the most 4 hours on any day. The manufacturer can sell a package of screws A at a profit of Rs 7 and screws B at a profit of Rs 10. Assuming that he can sell all the screws he manufactures, how many packages of each type should the factory owner produce in a day in order to maximise his profit? Determine the maximum profit.

6. A cottage industry manufactures pedestal lamps and wooden shades, each requiring the use of a grinding/cutting machine and a sprayer. It takes 2 hours on grinding/cutting machine and 3 hours on the sprayer to manufacture a pedestal lamp. It takes 1 hour on the grinding/cutting machine and 2 hours on the sprayer to manufacture a shade. On any day, the sprayer is available for at the most 20 hours and the grinding/cutting machine for at the most 12 hours. The profit from the sale of a lamp is Rs 5 and that from a shade is Rs 3. Assuming that the manufacturer can sell all the lamps and shades that he produces, how should he schedule his daily production in order to maximise his profit?

7. A company manufactures two types of novelty souvenirs made of plywood. Souvenirs of type A require 5 minutes each for cutting and 10 minutes each for assembling. Souvenirs of type B require 8 minutes each for cutting and 8 minutes each for assembling. There are 3 hours 20 minutes available for cutting and 4 hours for assembling. The profit is Rs 5 each for type A and Rs 6 each for type B souvenirs. How many souvenirs of each type should the company manufacture in order to maximise the profit?

8. A merchant plans to sell two types of personal computers – a desktop model and a portable model that will cost Rs 25000 and Rs 40000 respectively. He estimates that the total monthly demand of computers will not exceed 250 units. Determine the number of units of each type of computers which the merchant should stock to get maximum profit if he does not want to invest more than Rs 70 lakhs and if his profit on the desktop model is Rs 4500 and on portable model is Rs 5000.

9. A diet is to contain at least 80 units of vitamin A and 100 units of minerals. Two foods F_1 and F_2 are available. Food F_1 costs Rs 4 per unit food and F_2 costs Rs 6 per unit. One unit of food F_1 contains 3 units of vitamin A and 4 units of minerals. One unit of food F_2 contains 6 units of vitamin A and 3 units of minerals. Formulate this as a linear programming problem. Find the minimum cost for diet that consists of mixture of these two foods and also meets the minimal nutritional requirements.

10. There are two types of fertilisers F_1 and F_2. F_1 consists of 10% nitrogen and 6% phosphoric acid and F_2 consists of 5% nitrogen and 10% phosphoric acid. After testing the soil conditions, a farmer finds that she needs atleast 14 kg of nitrogen and 14 kg of phosphoric acid for her crop. If F_1 costs Rs 6/kg and F_2 costs Rs 5/kg, determine how much of each type of fertiliser should be used so that nutrient requirements are met at a minimum cost. What is the minimum cost?

11. The corner points of the feasible region determined by the following system of linear inequalities:

$2x + y \leq 10$, $x + 3y \leq 15$, x, $y \geq 0$ are $(0, 0)$, $(5, 0)$, $(3, 4)$ and $(0, 5)$. Let $Z = px + qy$, where p, $q > 0$. Condition on p and q so that the maximum of Z occurs at both $(3, 4)$ and $(0, 5)$ is

(A) $p = q$ (B) $p = 2q$ (C) $p = 3q$ (D) $q = 3p$

Miscellaneous Examples

Example 9 (Diet problem) A dietician has to develop a special diet using two foods P and Q. Each packet (containing 30 g) of food P contains 12 units of calcium, 4 units of iron, 6 units of cholesterol and 6 units of vitamin A. Each packet of the same quantity of food Q contains 3 units of calcium, 20 units of iron, 4 units of cholesterol and 3 units of vitamin A. The diet requires atleast 240 units of calcium, atleast 460 units of iron and at most 300 units of cholesterol. How many packets of each food should be used to minimise the amount of vitamin A in the diet? What is the minimum amount of vitamin A?

Solution Let x and y be the number of packets of food P and Q respectively. Obviously $x \geq 0$, $y \geq 0$. Mathematical formulation of the given problem is as follows:

Minimise $Z = 6x + 3y$ (vitamin A)

subject to the constraints

$12x + 3y \geq 240$ (constraint on calcium), i.e. $\quad 4x + y \geq 80$ ... (1)

$4x + 20y \geq 460$ (constraint on iron), i.e. $\quad x + 5y \geq 115$ ... (2)

$6x + 4y \leq 300$ (constraint on cholesterol), i.e. $3x + 2y \leq 150$ ... (3)

$$x \geq 0, y \geq 0 \quad\quad\quad ...(4)$$

Let us graph the inequalities (1) to (4).

The feasible region (shaded) determined by the constraints (1) to (4) is shown in Fig 12.10 and note that it is bounded.

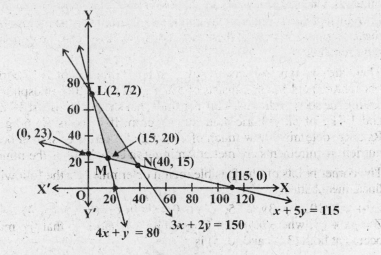

Fig 12.10

The coordinates of the corner points L, M and N are (2, 72), (15, 20) and (40, 15) respectively. Let us evaluate Z at these points:

Corner Point	Z = 6 x + 3 y	
(2, 72)	228	
(15, 20)	**150** ←	Minimum
(40, 15)	285	

From the table, we find that Z is minimum at the point (15, 20). Hence, the amount of vitamin A under the constraints given in the problem will be minimum, if 15 packets of food P and 20 packets of food Q are used in the special diet. The minimum amount of vitamin A will be 150 units.

Example 10 (**Manufacturing problem**) A manufacturer has three machines I, II and III installed in his factory. Machines I and II are capable of being operated for at most 12 hours whereas machine III must be operated for atleast 5 hours a day. She produces only two items M and N each requiring the use of all the three machines.

The number of hours required for producing 1 unit of each of M and N on the three machines are given in the following table:

Items	Number of hours required on machines		
	I	II	III
M	1	2	1
N	2	1	1.25

She makes a profit of Rs 600 and Rs 400 on items M and N respectively. How many of each item should she produce so as to maximise her profit assuming that she can sell all the items that she produced? What will be the maximum profit?

Solution Let x and y be the number of items M and N respectively.
Total profit on the production = Rs $(600 x + 400 y)$
Mathematical formulation of the given problem is as follows:
Maximise Z = 600 x + 400 y
subject to the constraints:

$$x + 2y \leq 12 \text{ (constraint on Machine I)} \qquad \text{... (1)}$$
$$2x + y \leq 12 \text{ (constraint on Machine II)} \qquad \text{... (2)}$$

$$x + \frac{5}{4} y \geq 5 \text{ (constraint on Machine III)} \qquad \text{... (3)}$$

$$x \geq 0, \ y \geq 0 \qquad \text{... (4)}$$

Let us draw the graph of constraints (1) to (4). ABCDE is the feasible region (shaded) as shown in Fig 12.11 determined by the constraints (1) to (4). Observe that the feasible region is bounded, coordinates of the corner points A, B, C, D and E are (5, 0) (6, 0), (4, 4), (0, 6) and (0, 4) respectively.

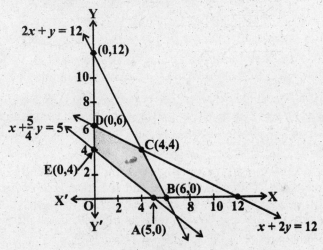

Fig 12.11

Let us evaluate Z = 600 x + 400 y at these corner points.

Corner point	$Z = 600\,x + 400\,y$
(5, 0)	3000
(6, 0)	3600
(4, 4)	**4000** ←
(0, 6)	2400
(0, 4)	1600

Maximum

We see that the point (4, 4) is giving the maximum value of Z. Hence, the manufacturer has to produce 4 units of each item to get the maximum profit of Rs 4000.

Example 11 (Transportation problem) There are two factories located one at place P and the other at place Q. From these locations, a certain commodity is to be delivered to each of the three depots situated at A, B and C. The weekly requirements of the depots are respectively 5, 5 and 4 units of the commodity while the production capacity of the factories at P and Q are respectively 8 and 6 units. The cost of transportation per unit is given below:

From/To	Cost (in Rs)		
	A	B	C
P	160	100	150
Q	100	120	100

How many units should be transported from each factory to each depot in order that the transportation cost is minimum. What will be the minimum transportation cost?

Solution The problem can be explained diagrammatically as follows (Fig 12.12):

Let x units and y units of the commodity be transported from the factory at P to the depots at A and B respectively. Then $(8 - x - y)$ units will be transported to depot at C (Why?)

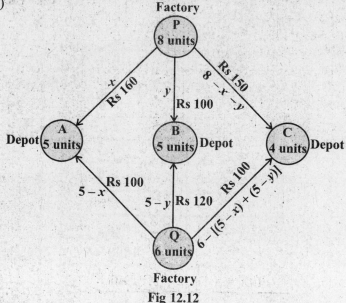

Fig 12.12

Hence, we have $\qquad x \geq 0, y \geq 0 \quad$ and $\quad 8 - x - y \geq 0$

i.e. $\qquad x \geq 0, y \geq 0 \quad$ and $\quad x + y \leq 8$

Now, the weekly requirement of the depot at A is 5 units of the commodity. Since x units are transported from the factory at P, the remaining $(5 - x)$ units need to be transported from the factory at Q. Obviously, $5 - x \geq 0$, i.e. $x \leq 5$.

Similarly, $(5 - y)$ and $6 - (5 - x + 5 - y) = x + y - 4$ units are to be transported from the factory at Q to the depots at B and C respectively.

Thus, $\qquad 5 - y \geq 0 \ , \ x + y - 4 \geq 0$

i.e. $\qquad y \leq 5 \ , \ x + y \geq 4$

Total transportation cost Z is given by

$$Z = 160\,x + 100\,y + 100\,(5 - x) + 120\,(5 - y) + 100\,(x + y - 4) + 150\,(8 - x - y)$$

$$= 10\,(x - 7\,y + 190)$$

Therefore, the problem reduces to

Minimise $Z = 10\,(x - 7y + 190)$

subject to the constraints:

$$x \geq 0,\ y \geq 0 \qquad \dots (1)$$
$$x + y \leq 8 \qquad \dots (2)$$
$$x \leq 5 \qquad \dots (3)$$
$$y \leq 5 \qquad \dots (4)$$

and $\qquad x + y \geq 4 \qquad \dots (5)$

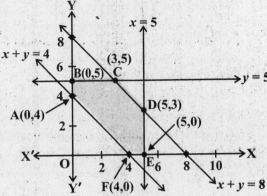

Fig 12.13

The shaded region ABCDEF represented by the constraints (1) to (5) is the feasible region (Fig 12.13).

Observe that the feasible region is bounded. The coordinates of the corner points of the feasible region are (0, 4), (0, 5), (3, 5), (5, 3), (5, 0) and (4, 0). Let us evaluate Z at these points.

Corner Point	$Z = 10\,(x - 7\,y + 190)$	
(0, 4)	1620	
(0, 5)	1550 ←	Minimum
(3, 5)	1580	
(5, 3)	1740	
(5, 0)	1950	
(4, 0)	1940	

From the table, we see that the minimum value of Z is 1550 at the point (0, 5).

Hence, the optimal transportation strategy will be to deliver 0, 5 and 3 units from the factory at P and 5, 0 and 1 units from the factory at Q to the depots at A, B and C respectively. Corresponding to this strategy, the transportation cost would be minimum, i.e., Rs 1550.

Miscellaneous Exercise on Chapter 12

1. Refer to Example 9. How many packets of each food should be used to maximise the amount of vitamin A in the diet? What is the maximum amount of vitamin A in the diet?

2. A farmer mixes two brands P and Q of cattle feed. Brand P, costing Rs 250 per bag, contains 3 units of nutritional element A, 2.5 units of element B and 2 units of element C. Brand Q costing Rs 200 per bag contains 1.5 units of nutritional element A, 11.25 units of element B, and 3 units of element C. The minimum requirements of nutrients A, B and C are 18 units, 45 units and 24 units respectively. Determine the number of bags of each brand which should be mixed in order to produce a mixture having a minimum cost per bag? What is the minimum cost of the mixture per bag?

3. A dietician wishes to mix together two kinds of food X and Y in such a way that the mixture contains at least 10 units of vitamin A, 12 units of vitamin B and 8 units of vitamin C. The vitamin contents of one kg food is given below:

Food	Vitamin A	Vitamin B	Vitamin C
X	1	2	3
Y	2	2	1

One kg of food X costs Rs 16 and one kg of food Y costs Rs 20. Find the least cost of the mixture which will produce the required diet?

4. A manufacturer makes two types of toys A and B. Three machines are needed for this purpose and the time (in minutes) required for each toy on the machines is given below:

Types of Toys	Machines		
	I	II	III
A	12	18	6
B	6	0	9

Each machine is available for a maximum of 6 hours per day. If the profit on each toy of type A is Rs 7.50 and that on each toy of type B is Rs 5, show that 15 toys of type A and 30 of type B should be manufactured in a day to get maximum profit.

5. An aeroplane can carry a maximum of 200 passengers. A profit of Rs 1000 is made on each executive class ticket and a profit of Rs 600 is made on each economy class ticket. The airline reserves at least 20 seats for executive class. However, at least 4 times as many passengers prefer to travel by economy class than by the executive class. Determine how many tickets of each type must be sold in order to maximise the profit for the airline. What is the maximum profit?

6. Two godowns A and B have grain capacity of 100 quintals and 50 quintals respectively. They supply to 3 ration shops, D, E and F whose requirements are 60, 50 and 40 quintals respectively. The cost of transportation per quintal from the godowns to the shops are given in the following table:

Transportation cost per quintal (in Rs)		
From/To	A	B
D	6	4
E	3	2
F	2.50	3

How should the supplies be transported in order that the transportation cost is minimum? What is the minimum cost?

7. An oil company has two depots A and B with capacities of 7000 L and 4000 L respectively. The company is to supply oil to three petrol pumps, D, E and F whose requirements are 4500L, 3000L and 3500L respectively. The distances (in km) between the depots and the petrol pumps is given in the following table:

Distance in (km.)		
From / To	A	B
D	7	3
E	6	4
F	3	2

Assuming that the transportation cost of 10 litres of oil is Re 1 per km, how should the delivery be scheduled in order that the transportation cost is minimum? What is the minimum cost?

8. A fruit grower can use two types of fertilizer in his garden, brand P and brand Q. The amounts (in kg) of nitrogen, phosphoric acid, potash, and chlorine in a bag of each brand are given in the table. Tests indicate that the garden needs at least 240 kg of phosphoric acid, at least 270 kg of potash and at most 310 kg of chlorine.

If the grower wants to minimise the amount of nitrogen added to the garden, how many bags of each brand should be used? What is the minimum amount of nitrogen added in the garden?

kg per bag		
	Brand P	Brand Q
Nitrogen	3	3.5
Phosphoric acid	1	2
Potash	3	1.5
Chlorine	1.5	2

9. Refer to Question 8. If the grower wants to maximise the amount of nitrogen added to the garden, how many bags of each brand should be added? What is the maximum amount of nitrogen added?

10. A toy company manufactures two types of dolls, A and B. Market tests and available resources have indicated that the combined production level should not exceed 1200 dolls per week and the demand for dolls of type B is at most half of that for dolls of type A. Further, the production level of dolls of type A can exceed three times the production of dolls of other type by at most 600 units. If the company makes profit of Rs 12 and Rs 16 per doll respectively on dolls A and B, how many of each should be produced weekly in order to maximise the profit?

Summary

◆ A linear programming problem is one that is concerned with finding the optimal value (maximum or minimum) of a linear function of several variables (called **objective function**) subject to the conditions that the variables are non-negative and satisfy a set of linear inequalities (called linear **constraints**). Variables are sometimes called **decision variables** and are **non-negative.**

◆ A few important linear programming problems are:

   (i) Diet problems

   (ii) Manufacturing problems

   (iii) Transportation problems

◆ The common region determined by all the constraints including the non-negative constraints $x \geq 0$, $y \geq 0$ of a linear programming problem is called the **feasible region** (or **solution region**) for the problem.

◆ Points within and on the boundary of the feasible region represent **feasible solutions** of the constraints.

   Any point outside the feasible region is an **infeasible solution.**

◆ Any point in the feasible region that gives the optimal value (maximum or minimum) of the objective function is called an **optimal solution.**

◆ The following Theorems are fundamental in solving linear programming problems:

Theorem 1 Let R be the feasible region (convex polygon) for a linear programming problem and let $Z = ax + by$ be the objective function. When Z has an optimal value (maximum or minimum), where the variables x and y are subject to constraints described by linear inequalities, this optimal value must occur at a corner point (vertex) of the feasible region.

Theorem 2 Let R be the feasible region for a linear programming problem, and let $Z = ax + by$ be the objective function. If R is **bounded**, then the objective function Z has both a **maximum** and a **minimum** value on R and each of these occurs at a corner point (vertex) of R.

◆ If the feasible region is unbounded, then a maximum or a minimum may not exist. However, if it exists, it must occur at a corner point of R.

◆ **Corner point method** for solving a linear programming problem. The method comprises of the following steps:

(i) Find the feasible region of the linear programming problem and determine its corner points (vertices).

(ii) Evaluate the objective function $Z = ax + by$ at each corner point. Let M and m respectively be the largest and smallest values at these points.

(iii) If the feasible region is bounded, M and m respectively are the maximum and minimum values of the objective function.

If the feasible region is unbounded, then

(i) M is the maximum value of the objective function, if the open half plane determined by $ax + by > M$ has no point in common with the feasible region. Otherwise, the objective function has no maximum value.

(ii) m is the minimum value of the objective function, if the open half plane determined by $ax + by < m$ has no point in common with the feasible region. Otherwise, the objective function has no minimum value.

◆ If two corner points of the feasible region are both optimal solutions of the same type, i.e., both produce the same maximum or minimum, then any point on the line segment joining these two points is also an optimal solution of the same type.

Historical Note

In the World War II, when the war operations had to be planned to economise expenditure, maximise damage to the enemy, linear programming problems came to the forefront.

The first problem in linear programming was formulated in 1941 by the Russian mathematician, L. Kantorovich and the American economist, F. L. Hitchcock, both of whom worked at it independently of each other. This was the well known *transportation problem*. In 1945, an English economist, G.Stigler, described yet another linear programming problem – that of determining an *optimal diet*.

In 1947, the American economist, G. B. Dantzig suggested an efficient method known as the simplex method which is an iterative procedure to solve any linear programming problem in a finite number of steps.

L. Katorovich and American mathematical economist, T. C. Koopmans were awarded the nobel prize in the year 1975 in economics for their pioneering work in linear programming. With the advent of computers and the necessary softwares, it has become possible to apply linear programming model to increasingly complex problems in many areas.

— ❖ —

Chapter 13

PROBABILITY

❖ *The theory of probabilities is simply the Science of logic*
quantitatively treated. – C.S. PEIRCE ❖

13.1 Introduction

In earlier Classes, we have studied the probability as a measure of uncertainty of events in a random experiment. We discussed the axiomatic approach formulated by Russian Mathematician, A.N. Kolmogorov (1903-1987) and treated probability as a function of outcomes of the experiment. We have also established equivalence between the axiomatic theory and the classical theory of probability in case of equally likely outcomes. On the basis of this relationship, we obtained probabilities of events associated with discrete sample spaces. We have also studied the addition rule of probability. In this chapter, we shall discuss the important concept of conditional probability of an event given that another event has occurred, which will be helpful in understanding the Bayes' theorem, multiplication rule of probability and independence of events. We shall also learn an important concept of random variable and its probability

Pierre de Fermat
(1601-1665)

distribution and also the mean and variance of a probability distribution. In the last section of the chapter, we shall study an important discrete probability distribution called Binomial distribution. Throughout this chapter, we shall take up the experiments having equally likely outcomes, unless stated otherwise.

13.2 Conditional Probability

Uptill now in probability, we have discussed the methods of finding the probability of events. If we have two events from the same sample space, does the information about the occurrence of one of the events affect the probability of the other event? Let us try to answer this question by taking up a random experiment in which the outcomes are equally likely to occur.

Consider the experiment of tossing three fair coins. The sample space of the experiment is

$$S = \{HHH, HHT, HTH, THH, HTT, THT, TTH, TTT\}$$

Since the coins are fair, we can assign the probability $\frac{1}{8}$ to each sample point. Let E be the event 'at least two heads appear' and F be the event 'first coin shows tail'. Then

$$E = \{HHH, HHT, HTH, THH\}$$

and

$$F = \{THH, THT, TTH, TTT\}$$

Therefore

$$P(E) = P(\{HHH\}) + P(\{HHT\}) + P(\{HTH\}) + P(\{THH\})$$

$$= \frac{1}{8} + \frac{1}{8} + \frac{1}{8} + \frac{1}{8} = \frac{1}{2} \text{ (Why ?)}$$

and

$$P(F) = P(\{THH\}) + P(\{THT\}) + P(\{TTH\}) + P(\{TTT\})$$

$$= \frac{1}{8} + \frac{1}{8} + \frac{1}{8} + \frac{1}{8} = \frac{1}{2}$$

Also

$$E \cap F = \{THH\}$$

with

$$P(E \cap F) = P(\{THH\}) = \frac{1}{8}$$

Now, suppose we are given that the first coin shows tail, i.e. F occurs, then what is the probability of occurrence of E? With the information of occurrence of F, we are sure that the cases in which first coin does not result into a tail should not be considered while finding the probability of E. This information reduces our sample space from the set S to its subset F for the event E. In other words, the additional information really amounts to telling us that the situation may be considered as being that of a new random experiment for which the sample space consists of all those outcomes only which are favourable to the occurrence of the event F.

Now, the sample point of F which is favourable to event E is THH.

Thus, Probability of E considering F as the sample space $= \frac{1}{4}$,

or   Probability of E given that the event F has occurred $= \frac{1}{4}$

This probability of the event E is called the *conditional probability of E given that F has already occurred*, and is denoted by P (E|F).

Thus $P(E|F) = \frac{1}{4}$

Note that the elements of F which favour the event E are the common elements of E and F, i.e. the sample points of E ∩ F.

Thus, we can also write the conditional probability of E given that F has occurred as

$$P(E|F) = \frac{\text{Number of elementary events favourable to } E \cap F}{\text{Number of elementary events which are favourable to } F}$$

$$= \frac{n(E \cap F)}{n(F)}$$

Dividing the numerator and the denominator by total number of elementary events of the sample space, we see that P(E|F) can also be written as

$$P(E|F) = \frac{\dfrac{n(E \cap F)}{n(S)}}{\dfrac{n(F)}{n(S)}} = \frac{P(E \cap F)}{P(F)} \qquad \ldots (1)$$

Note that (1) is valid only when $P(F) \neq 0$ i.e., $F \neq \phi$ (Why?)

Thus, we can define the conditional probability as follows :

Definition 1 If E and F are two events associated with the same sample space of a random experiment, the conditional probability of the event E given that F has occurred, i.e. P (E|F) is given by

$$P(E|F) = \frac{P(E \cap F)}{P(F)} \quad \text{provided } P(F) \neq 0$$

13.2.1 *Properties of conditional probability*

Let E and F be events of a sample space S of an experiment, then we have

Property 1 $P(S|F) = P(F|F) = 1$

We know that

$$P(S|F) = \frac{P(S \cap F)}{P(F)} = \frac{P(F)}{P(F)} = 1$$

Also

$$P(F|F) = \frac{P(F \cap F)}{P(F)} = \frac{P(F)}{P(F)} = 1$$

Thus

$$P(S|F) = P(F|F) = 1$$

Property 2 *If* A *and* B *are any two events of a sample space* S *and* F *is an event of* S *such that* $P(F) \neq 0$, *then*

$$P((A \cup B)|F) = P(A|F) + P(B|F) - P((A \cap B)|F)$$

In particular, if A and B are disjoint events, then

$$P((A \cup B)|F) = P(A|F) + P(B|F)$$

We have

$$P((A \cup B)|F) = \frac{P[(A \cup B) \cap F]}{P(F)}$$

$$= \frac{P[(A \cap F) \cup (B \cap F)]}{P(F)}$$

(by distributive law of union of sets over intersection)

$$= \frac{P(A \cap F) + P(B \cap F) - P(A \cap B \cap F)}{P(F)}$$

$$= \frac{P(A \cap F)}{P(F)} + \frac{P(B \cap F)}{P(F)} - \frac{P[(A \cap B) \cap F]}{P(F)}$$

$$= P(A|F) + P(B|F) - P((A \cap B)|F)$$

When A and B are disjoint events, then

$$P((A \cap B)|F) = 0$$

$$\Rightarrow \qquad P((A \cup B)|F) = P(A|F) + P(B|F)$$

Property 3 $P(E'|F) = 1 - P(E|F)$

From Property 1, we know that $P(S|F) = 1$

$$\Rightarrow \qquad P(E \cup E'|F) = 1 \qquad \qquad \text{since } S = E \cup E'$$

$$\Rightarrow \qquad P(E|F) + P(E'|F) = 1 \qquad \text{since E and E' are disjoint events}$$

Thus, $\qquad\qquad P(E'|F) = 1 - P(E|F)$

Let us now take up some examples.

Example 1 If $P(A) = \dfrac{7}{13}$, $P(B) = \dfrac{9}{13}$ and $P(A \cap B) = \dfrac{4}{13}$, evaluate $P(A|B)$.

Solution We have $P(A|B) = \dfrac{P(A \cap B)}{P(B)} = \dfrac{\frac{4}{13}}{\frac{9}{13}} = \dfrac{4}{9}$

Example 2 A family has two children. What is the probability that both the children are boys given that at least one of them is a boy ?

Solution Let b stand for boy and g for girl. The sample space of the experiment is

$$S = \{(b, b), (g, b), (b, g), (g, g)\}$$

Let E and F denote the following events :

E : 'both the children are boys'

F : 'at least one of the child is a boy'

Then $\hspace{3cm}$ E $= \{(b,b)\}$ and F $= \{(b,b), (g,b), (b,g)\}$

Now $\hspace{3cm}$ E $\cap$ F $= \{(b,b)\}$

Thus $\hspace{3cm}$ $P(F) = \dfrac{3}{4}$ and $P(E \cap F) = \dfrac{1}{4}$

Therefore $\hspace{2cm}$ $P(E|F) = \dfrac{P(E \cap F)}{P(F)} = \dfrac{\frac{1}{4}}{\frac{3}{4}} = \dfrac{1}{3}$

Example 3 Ten cards numbered 1 to 10 are placed in a box, mixed up thoroughly and then one card is drawn randomly. If it is known that the number on the drawn card is more than 3, what is the probability that it is an even number?

Solution Let A be the event 'the number on the card drawn is even' and B be the event 'the number on the card drawn is greater than 3'. We have to find P(A|B).

Now, the sample space of the experiment is S $= \{1, 2, 3, 4, 5, 6, 7, 8, 9, 10\}$

Then $\hspace{3cm}$ A $= \{2, 4, 6, 8, 10\}$, B $= \{4, 5, 6, 7, 8, 9, 10\}$

and $\hspace{3cm}$ A $\cap$ B $= \{4, 6, 8, 10\}$

Also $\hspace{3cm}$ $P(A) = \dfrac{5}{10}$, $P(B) = \dfrac{7}{10}$ and $P(A \cap B) = \dfrac{4}{10}$

Then $\hspace{3cm}$ $P(A|B) = \dfrac{P(A \cap B)}{P(B)} = \dfrac{\frac{4}{10}}{\frac{7}{10}} = \dfrac{4}{7}$

Example 4 In a school, there are 1000 students, out of which 430 are girls. It is known that out of 430, 10% of the girls study in class XII. What is the probability that a student chosen randomly studies in Class XII given that the chosen student is a girl?

Solution Let E denote the event that a student chosen randomly studies in Class XII and F be the event that the randomly chosen student is a girl. We have to find P (E|F).

Now $\qquad$ $P(F) = \dfrac{430}{1000} = 0.43$ and $P(E \cap F) = \dfrac{43}{1000} = 0.043$ (Why?)

Then $\qquad$ $P(E|F) = \dfrac{P(E \cap F)}{P(F)} = \dfrac{0.043}{0.43} = 0.1$

Example 5 A die is thrown three times. Events A and B are defined as below:

A : 4 on the third throw

B : 6 on the first and 5 on the second throw

Find the probability of A given that B has already occurred.

Solution The sample space has 216 outcomes.

Now $\qquad$ $A = \begin{cases} (1,1,4) \ (1,2,4) \ ... \ (1,6,4) \ (2,1,4) \ (2,2,4) \ ... \ (2,6,4) \\ (3,1,4) \ (3,2,4) \ ... \ (3,6,4) \ (4,1,4) \ (4,2,4) \ ...(4,6,4) \\ (5,1,4) \ (5,2,4) \ ... \ (5,6,4) \ (6,1,4) \ (6,2,4) \ ...(6,6,4) \end{cases}$

$\qquad\qquad B = \{(6,5,1), (6,5,2), (6,5,3), (6,5,4), (6,5,5), (6,5,6)\}$

and $\qquad A \cap B = \{(6,5,4)\}.$

Now $\qquad$ $P(B) = \dfrac{6}{216}$ and $P(A \cap B) = \dfrac{1}{216}$

Then $\qquad$ $P(A|B) = \dfrac{P(A \cap B)}{P(B)} = \dfrac{\dfrac{1}{216}}{\dfrac{6}{216}} = \dfrac{1}{6}$

Example 6 A die is thrown twice and the sum of the numbers appearing is observed to be 6. What is the conditional probability that the number 4 has appeared at least once?

Solution Let E be the event that 'number 4 appears at least once' and F be the event that 'the sum of the numbers appearing is 6'.

Then, $\qquad$ $E = \{(4,1), (4,2), (4,3), (4,4), (4,5), (4,6), (1,4), (2,4), (3,4), (5,4), (6,4)\}$

and $\qquad$ $F = \{(1,5), (2,4), (3,3), (4,2), (5,1)\}$

We have $\qquad$ $P(E) = \dfrac{11}{36}$ and $P(F) = \dfrac{5}{36}$

Also $\qquad$ $E \cap F = \{(2,4), (4,2)\}$

Therefore $P(E \cap F) = \dfrac{2}{36}$

Hence, the required probability

$$P(E|F) = \frac{P(E \cap F)}{P(F)} = \frac{\dfrac{2}{36}}{\dfrac{5}{36}} = \frac{2}{5}$$

For the conditional probability discussed above, we have considered the elementary events of the experiment to be equally likely and the corresponding definition of the probability of an event was used. However, the same definition can also be used in the general case where the elementary events of the sample space are not equally likely, the probabilities $P(E \cap F)$ and $P(F)$ being calculated accordingly. Let us take up the following example.

Example 7 Consider the experiment of tossing a coin. If the coin shows head, toss it again but if it shows tail, then throw a die. Find the conditional probability of the event that 'the die shows a number greater than 4' given that 'there is at least one tail'.

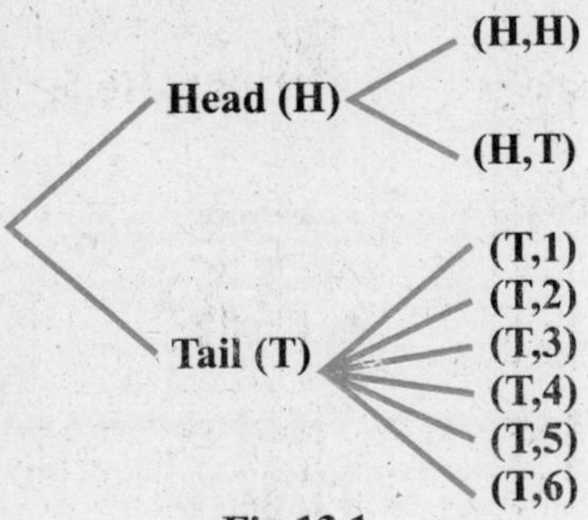

Solution The outcomes of the experiment can be represented in following diagrammatic manner called the 'tree diagram'.

The sample space of the experiment may be described as

$$S = \{(H,H), (H,T), (T,1), (T,2), (T,3), (T,4), (T,5), (T,6)\}$$

where (H, H) denotes that both the tosses result into head and (T, i) denote the first toss result into a tail and the number i appeared on the die for $i = 1,2,3,4,5,6$.

Thus, the probabilities assigned to the 8 elementary events

(H, H), (H, T), (T, 1), (T, 2), (T, 3), (T, 4), (T, 5), (T, 6)

are $\dfrac{1}{4}, \dfrac{1}{4}, \dfrac{1}{12}, \dfrac{1}{12}, \dfrac{1}{12}, \dfrac{1}{12}, \dfrac{1}{12}, \dfrac{1}{12}$ respectively which is clear from the Fig 13.2.

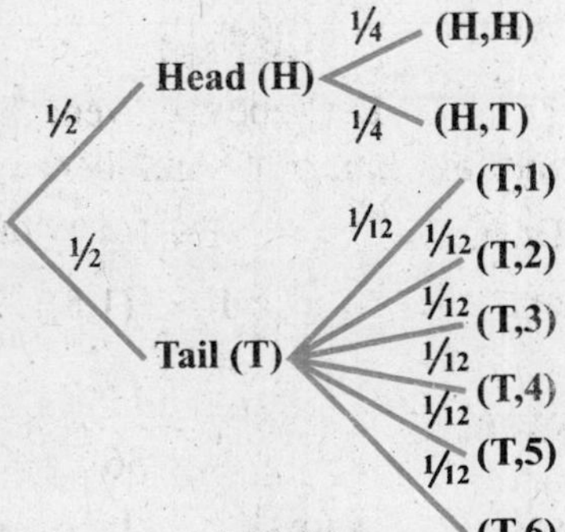

Fig 13.1

Fig 13.2

Let F be the event that 'there is at least one tail' and E be the event 'the die shows a number greater than 4'. Then

$$F = \{(H,T), (T,1), (T,2), (T,3), (T,4), (T,5), (T,6)\}$$
$$E = \{(T,5), (T,6)\} \text{ and } E \cap F = \{(T,5), (T,6)\}$$

Now
$$P(F) = P(\{(H,T)\}) + P(\{(T,1)\}) + P(\{(T,2)\}) + P(\{(T,3)\})$$
$$+ \ P(\{(T,4)\}) + P(\{(T,5)\}) + P(\{(T,6)\})$$

$$= \frac{1}{4} + \frac{1}{12} + \frac{1}{12} + \frac{1}{12} + \frac{1}{12} + \frac{1}{12} + \frac{1}{12} = \frac{3}{4}$$

and
$$P(E \cap F) = P(\{(T,5)\}) + P(\{(T,6)\}) = \frac{1}{12} + \frac{1}{12} = \frac{1}{6}$$

Hence
$$P(E|F) = \frac{P(E \cap F)}{P(F)} = \frac{\dfrac{1}{6}}{\dfrac{3}{4}} = \frac{2}{9}$$

EXERCISE 13.1

1. Given that E and F are events such that $P(E) = 0.6$, $P(F) = 0.3$ and $P(E \cap F) = 0.2$, find $P(E|F)$ and $P(F|E)$

2. Compute $P(A|B)$, if $P(B) = 0.5$ and $P(A \cap B) = 0.32$

3. If $P(A) = 0.8$, $P(B) = 0.5$ and $P(B|A) = 0.4$, find
   (i) $P(A \cap B)$ (ii) $P(A|B)$ (iii) $P(A \cup B)$

4. Evaluate $P(A \cup B)$, if $2P(A) = P(B) = \dfrac{5}{13}$ and $P(A|B) = \dfrac{2}{5}$

5. If $P(A) = \dfrac{6}{11}$, $P(B) = \dfrac{5}{11}$ and $P(A \cup B) = \dfrac{7}{11}$, find

   (i) $P(A \cap B)$ (ii) $P(A|B)$ (iii) $P(B|A)$

   Determine $P(E|F)$ in Exercises 6 to 9.

6. A coin is tossed three times, where
   (i) E : head on third toss ,   F : heads on first two tosses
   (ii) E : at least two heads ,   F : at most two heads
   (iii) E : at most two tails ,   F : at least one tail

7. Two coins are tossed once, where

(i) E : tail appears on one coin,   F : one coin shows head

(ii) E : no tail appears,   F : no head appears

8. A die is thrown three times.

    E : 4 appears on the third toss,   F : 6 and 5 appears respectively
                                            on first two tosses

9. Mother, father and son line up at random for a family picture

    E : son on one end,   F : father in middle

10. A black and a red dice are rolled.

    (a) Find the conditional probability of obtaining a sum greater than 9, given that the black die resulted in a 5.

    (b) Find the conditional probability of obtaining the sum 8, given that the red die resulted in a number less than 4.

11. A fair die is rolled. Consider events $E = \{1,3,5\}$, $F = \{2,3\}$ and $G = \{2,3,4,5\}$

    Find

      (i) $P(E|F)$ and $P(F|E)$ (ii) $P(E|G)$ and $P(G|E)$

      (iii) $P((E \cup F)|G)$ and $P((E \cap F)|G)$

12. Assume that each born child is equally likely to be a boy or a girl. If a family has two children, what is the conditional probability that both are girls given that (i) the youngest is a girl, (ii) at least one is a girl?

13. An instructor has a question bank consisting of 300 easy True / False questions, 200 difficult True / False questions, 500 easy multiple choice questions and 400 difficult multiple choice questions. If a question is selected at random from the question bank, what is the probability that it will be an easy question given that it is a multiple choice question?

14. Given that the two numbers appearing on throwing two dice are different. Find the probability of the event 'the sum of numbers on the dice is 4'.

15. Consider the experiment of throwing a die, if a multiple of 3 comes up, throw the die again and if any other number comes, toss a coin. Find the conditional probability of the event 'the coin shows a tail', given that 'at least one die shows a 3'.

In each of the Exercises 16 and 17 choose the correct answer:

16. If $P(A) = \dfrac{1}{2}$, $P(B) = 0$, then $P(A|B)$ is

    (A) 0   (B) $\dfrac{1}{2}$

    (C) not defined   (D) 1

17. If A and B are events such that P(A|B) = P(B|A), then

   (A) A ⊂ B but A ≠ B   (B) A = B

   (C) A ∩ B = φ   (D) P(A) = P(B)

13.3 Multiplication Theorem on Probability

Let E and F be two events associated with a sample space S. Clearly, the set E ∩ F denotes the event that both E and F have occurred. In other words, E ∩ F denotes the simultaneous occurrence of the events E and F. The event E ∩ F is also written as EF.

Very often we need to find the probability of the event EF. For example, in the experiment of drawing two cards one after the other, we may be interested in finding the probability of the event 'a king and a queen'. The probability of event EF is obtained by using the conditional probability as obtained below :

We know that the conditional probability of event E given that F has occurred is denoted by P(E|F) and is given by

$$P(E|F) = \frac{P(E \cap F)}{P(F)}, P(F) \neq 0$$

From this result, we can write

$$P(E \cap F) = P(F) \cdot P(E|F) \qquad \qquad \dots (1)$$

Also, we know that

$$P(F|E) = \frac{P(F \cap E)}{P(E)}, P(E) \neq 0$$

or

$$P(F|E) = \frac{P(E \cap F)}{P(E)} \quad \text{(since } E \cap F = F \cap E\text{)}$$

Thus, $$P(E \cap F) = P(E) \cdot P(F|E) \qquad \qquad \dots (2)$$

Combining (1) and (2), we find that

$$P(E \cap F) = P(E) \; P(F|E)$$

$$= P(F) \; P(E|F) \text{ provided } P(E) \neq 0 \text{ and } P(F) \neq 0.$$

The above result is known as the *multiplication rule of probability*.

Let us now take up an example.

Example 8 An urn contains 10 black and 5 white balls. Two balls are drawn from the urn one after the other without replacement. What is the probability that both drawn balls are black?

Solution Let E and F denote respectively the events that first and second ball drawn are black. We have to find P(E ∩ F) or P(EF).

Now $P(E) = P$ (black ball in first draw) $= \dfrac{10}{15}$

Also given that the first ball drawn is black, i.e., event E has occurred, now there are 9 black balls and five white balls left in the urn. Therefore, the probability that the second ball drawn is black, given that the ball in the first draw is black, is nothing but the conditional probability of F given that E has occurred.

i.e. $P(F|E) = \dfrac{9}{14}$

By multiplication rule of probability, we have

$$P(E \cap F) = P(E)\, P(F|E)$$

$$= \dfrac{10}{15} \times \dfrac{9}{14} = \dfrac{3}{7}$$

Multiplication rule of probability for more than two events If E, F and G are three events of sample space, we have

$$P(E \cap F \cap G) = P(E)\, P(F|E)\, P(G|(E \cap F)) = P(E)\, P(F|E)\, P(G|EF)$$

Similarly, the multiplication rule of probability can be extended for four or more events.

The following example illustrates the extension of multiplication rule of probability for three events.

Example 9 Three cards are drawn successively, without replacement from a pack of 52 well shuffled cards. What is the probability that first two cards are kings and the third card drawn is an ace?

Solution Let K denote the event that the card drawn is king and A be the event that the card drawn is an ace. Clearly, we have to find P (KKA)

Now $P(K) = \dfrac{4}{52}$

Also, P (K|K) is the probability of second king with the condition that one king has already been drawn. Now there are three kings in $(52 - 1) = 51$ cards.

Therefore $P(K|K) = \dfrac{3}{51}$

Lastly, P(A|KK) is the probability of third drawn card to be an ace, with the condition that two kings have already been drawn. Now there are four aces in left 50 cards.

Therefore $\qquad P(A|KK) = \dfrac{4}{50}$

By multiplication law of probability, we have

$$P(KKA) = P(K) \quad P(K|K) \quad P(A|KK)$$

$$= \frac{4}{52} \times \frac{3}{51} \times \frac{4}{50} = \frac{2}{5525}$$

13.4 Independent Events

Consider the experiment of drawing a card from a deck of 52 playing cards, in which the elementary events are assumed to be equally likely. If E and F denote the events 'the card drawn is a spade' and 'the card drawn is an ace' respectively, then

$$P(E) = \frac{13}{52} = \frac{1}{4} \text{ and } P(F) = \frac{4}{52} = \frac{1}{13}$$

Also E and F is the event ' the card drawn is the ace of spades' so that

$$P(E \cap F) = \frac{1}{52}$$

Hence $\qquad P(E|F) = \dfrac{P(E \cap F)}{P(F)} = \dfrac{\dfrac{1}{52}}{\dfrac{1}{13}} = \dfrac{1}{4}$

Since $P(E) = \dfrac{1}{4} = P(E|F)$, we can say that the occurrence of event F has not affected the probability of occurrence of the event E.

We also have

$$P(F|E) = \dfrac{P(E \cap F)}{P(E)} = \dfrac{\dfrac{1}{52}}{\dfrac{1}{4}} = \dfrac{1}{13} = P(F)$$

Again, $P(F) = \dfrac{1}{13} = P(F|E)$ shows that occurrence of event E has not affected the probability of occurrence of the event F.

Thus, E and F are two events such that the probability of occurrence of one of them is not affected by occurrence of the other.

Such events are called *independent events*.

Definition 2 Two events E and F are said to be independent, if

$$P(F|E) = P(F) \text{ provided } P(E) \neq 0$$

and
$$P(E|F) = P(E) \text{ provided } P(F) \neq 0$$

Thus, in this definition we need to have $P(E) \neq 0$ and $P(F) \neq 0$

Now, by the multiplication rule of probability, we have

$$P(E \cap F) = P(E) \cdot P(F|E) \qquad \dots (1)$$

If E and F are independent, then (1) becomes

$$P(E \cap F) = P(E) \cdot P(F) \qquad \dots (2)$$

Thus, using (2), the independence of two events is also defined as follows:

Definition 3 Let E and F be two events associated with the same random experiment, then E and F are said to be independent if

$$P(E \cap F) = P(E) \cdot P(F)$$

Remarks

(i) Two events E and F are said to be dependent if they are not independent, i.e. if

$$P(E \cap F) \neq P(E) \cdot P(F)$$

(ii) Sometimes there is a confusion between independent events and mutually exclusive events. Term 'independent' is defined in terms of 'probability of events' whereas mutually exclusive is defined in term of events (subset of sample space). Moreover, mutually exclusive events never have an outcome common, but independent events, may have common outcome. Clearly, 'independent' and 'mutually exclusive' do not have the same meaning.

In other words, two independent events having nonzero probabilities of occurrence can not be mutually exclusive, and conversely, i.e. two mutually exclusive events having nonzero probabilities of occurrence can not be independent.

(iii) Two experiments are said to be independent if for every pair of events E and F, where E is associated with the first experiment and F with the second experiment, the probability of the simultaneous occurrence of the events E and F when the two experiments are performed is the product of P(E) and P(F) calculated separately on the basis of two experiments, i.e., $P(E \cap F) = P(E) \cdot P(F)$

(iv) Three events A, B and C are said to be mutually independent, if

$$P(A \cap B) = P(A) P(B)$$
$$P(A \cap C) = P(A) P(C)$$
$$P(B \cap C) = P(B) P(C)$$

and
$$P(A \cap B \cap C) = P(A) P(B) P(C)$$

If at least one of the above is not true for three given events, we say that the events are not independent.

Example 10 A die is thrown. If E is the event 'the number appearing is a multiple of 3' and F be the event 'the number appearing is even' then find whether E and F are independent ?

Solution We know that the sample space is S = {1, 2, 3, 4, 5, 6}

Now   E = { 3, 6}, F = { 2, 4, 6} and E ∩ F = {6}

Then $P(E) = \dfrac{2}{6} = \dfrac{1}{3}$, $P(F) = \dfrac{3}{6} = \dfrac{1}{2}$ and $P(E \cap F) = \dfrac{1}{6}$

Clearly   P(E ∩ F) = P(E). P (F)

Hence   E and F are independent events.

Example 11 An unbiased die is thrown twice. Let the event A be 'odd number on the first throw' and B the event 'odd number on the second throw'. Check the independence of the events A and B.

Solution If all the 36 elementary events of the experiment are considered to be equally likely, we have

$$P(A) = \dfrac{18}{36} = \dfrac{1}{2} \text{ and } P(B) = \dfrac{18}{36} = \dfrac{1}{2}$$

Also   P(A ∩ B) = P (odd number on both throws)

$$= \dfrac{9}{36} = \dfrac{1}{4}$$

Now $P(A) P(B) = \dfrac{1}{2} \times \dfrac{1}{2} = \dfrac{1}{4}$

Clearly   P(A ∩ B) = P(A) × P(B)

Thus,   A and B are independent events

Example 12 Three coins are tossed simultaneously. Consider the event E 'three heads or three tails', F 'at least two heads' and G 'at most two heads'. Of the pairs (E,F), (E,G) and (F,G), which are independent? which are dependent?

Solution The sample space of the experiment is given by

S = {HHH, HHT, HTH, THH, HTT, THT, TTH, TTT}

Clearly   E = {HHH, TTT}, F = {HHH, HHT, HTH, THH}

and $\qquad$ G = {HHT, HTH, THH, HTT, THT, TTH, TTT}

Also $\qquad$ E ∩ F = {HHH}, E ∩ G = {TTT}, F ∩ G = { HHT, HTH, THH}

Therefore $\qquad P(E) = \dfrac{2}{8} = \dfrac{1}{4}, P(F) = \dfrac{4}{8} = \dfrac{1}{2}, P(G) = \dfrac{7}{8}$

and $\qquad P(E \cap F) = \dfrac{1}{8}, P(E \cap G) = \dfrac{1}{8}, P(F \cap G) = \dfrac{3}{8}$

Also $\qquad P(E) . P(F) = \dfrac{1}{4} \times \dfrac{1}{2} = \dfrac{1}{8}, P(E) \cdot P(G) = \dfrac{1}{4} \times \dfrac{7}{8} = \dfrac{7}{32}$

and $\qquad P(F) . P(G) = \dfrac{1}{2} \times \dfrac{7}{8} = \dfrac{7}{16}$

Thus $\qquad P(E \cap F) = P(E) . P(F)$

$\qquad\qquad P(E \cap G) \neq P(E) . P(G)$

and $\qquad P(F \cap G) \neq P (F) . P(G)$

Hence, the events (E and F) are independent, and the events (E and G) and (F and G) are dependent.

Example 13 Prove that if E and F are independent events, then so are the events E and F'.

Solution Since E and F are independent, we have

$\qquad P(E \cap F) = P(E) . P(F)$ $\qquad\qquad$ ....(1)

From the venn diagram in Fig 13.3, it is clear that E ∩ F and E ∩ F' are mutually exclusive events and also E =(E ∩ F) ∪ (E ∩ F').

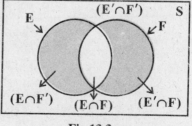

Fig 13.3

Therefore $\qquad P(E) = P(E \cap F) + P(E \cap F')$

or $\qquad P(E \cap F') = P(E) - P(E \cap F)$

$\qquad\qquad = P(E) - P(E) . P(F)$

$\qquad\qquad$ (by (1))

$\qquad\qquad = P(E) (1-P(F))$

$\qquad\qquad = P(E). \ P(F')$

Hence, E and F' are independent

> **Note** In a similar manner, it can be shown that if the events E and F are independent, then
>
> (a) E′ and F are independent,
>
> (b) E′ and F′ are independent

Example 14 If A and B are two independent events, then the probability of occurrence of at least one of A and B is given by $1 - P(A') P(B')$

Solution We have

$$P(\text{at least one of A and B}) = P(A \cup B)$$
$$= P(A) + P(B) - P(A \cap B)$$
$$= P(A) + P(B) - P(A) P(B)$$
$$= P(A) + P(B) [1 - P(A)]$$
$$= P(A) + P(B). P(A')$$
$$= 1 - P(A') + P(B) P(A')$$
$$= 1 - P(A') [1 - P(B)]$$
$$= 1 - P(A') P(B')$$

EXERCISE 13.2

1. If $P(A) = \dfrac{3}{5}$ and $P(B) = \dfrac{1}{5}$, find $P(A \cap B)$ if A and B are independent events.

2. Two cards are drawn at random and without replacement from a pack of 52 playing cards. Find the probability that both the cards are black.

3. A box of oranges is inspected by examining three randomly selected oranges drawn without replacement. If all the three oranges are good, the box is approved for sale, otherwise, it is rejected. Find the probability that a box containing 15 oranges out of which 12 are good and 3 are bad ones will be approved for sale.

4. A fair coin and an unbiased die are tossed. Let A be the event 'head appears on the coin' and B be the event '3 on the die'. Check whether A and B are independent events or not.

5. A die marked 1, 2, 3 in red and 4, 5, 6 in green is tossed. Let A be the event, 'the number is even,' and B be the event, 'the number is red'. Are A and B independent?

6. Let E and F be events with $P(E) = \dfrac{3}{5}$, $P(F) = \dfrac{3}{10}$ and $P(E \cap F) = \dfrac{1}{-}$. Are E and F independent?

7. Given that the events A and B are such that $P(A) = \dfrac{1}{2}$, $P(A \cup B) = \dfrac{3}{5}$ and $P(B) = p$. Find p if they are (i) mutually exclusive (ii) independent.

8. Let A and B be independent events with $P(A) = 0.3$ and $P(B) = 0.4$. Find

    (i) $P(A \cap B)$ (ii) $P(A \cup B)$

    (iii) $P(A|B)$ (iv) $P(B|A)$

9. If A and B are two events such that $P(A) = \dfrac{1}{4}$, $P(B) = \dfrac{1}{2}$ and $P(A \cap B) = \dfrac{1}{8}$, find P (not A and not B).

10. Events A and B are such that $P(A) = \dfrac{1}{2}$, $P(B) = \dfrac{7}{12}$ and P(not A or not B) $= \dfrac{1}{4}$. State whether A and B are independent ?

11. Given two independent events A and B such that $P(A) = 0.3$, $P(B) = 0.6$. Find

    (i) P(A and B)   (ii) P(A and not B)

    (iii) P(A or B)   (iv) P(neither A nor B)

12. A die is tossed thrice. Find the probability of getting an odd number at least once.

13. Two balls are drawn at random with replacement from a box containing 10 black and 8 red balls. Find the probability that

    (i) both balls are red.

    (ii) first ball is black and second is red.

    (iii) one of them is black and other is red.

14. Probability of solving specific problem independently by A and B are $\dfrac{1}{2}$ and $\dfrac{1}{3}$ respectively. If both try to solve the problem independently, find the probability that

    (i) the problem is solved   (ii) exactly one of them solves the problem.

15. One card is drawn at random from a well shuffled deck of 52 cards. In which of the following cases are the events E and F independent ?

    (i) E : 'the card drawn is a spade'

         F : 'the card drawn is an ace'

    (ii) E : 'the card drawn is black'

         F : 'the card drawn is a king'

    (iii) E : 'the card drawn is a king or queen'

         F : 'the card drawn is a queen or jack'.

16. In a hostel, 60% of the students read Hindi news paper, 40% read English news paper and 20% read both Hindi and English news papers. A student is selected at random.

   (a) Find the probability that she reads neither Hindi nor English news papers.

   (b) If she reads Hindi news paper, find the probability that she reads English news paper.

   (c) If she reads English news paper, find the probability that she reads Hindi news paper.

Choose the correct answer in Exercises 17 and 18.

17. The probability of obtaining an even prime number on each die, when a pair of dice is rolled is

   (A) 0　　　　　(B) $\dfrac{1}{3}$　　　　　(C) $\dfrac{1}{12}$　　　　　(D) $\dfrac{1}{36}$

18. Two events A and B will be independent, if

   (A) A and B are mutually exclusive

   (B) $P(A'B') = [1 - P(A)] [1 - P(B)]$

   (C) $P(A) = P(B)$

   (D) $P(A) + P(B) = 1$

13.5 Bayes' Theorem

Consider that there are two bags I and II. Bag I contains 2 white and 3 red balls and Bag II contains 4 white and 5 red balls. One ball is drawn at random from one of the bags. We can find the probability of selecting any of the bags (i.e. $\dfrac{1}{2}$) or probability of drawing a ball of a particular colour (say white) from a particular bag (say Bag I). In other words, we can find the probability that the ball drawn is of a particular colour, if we are given the bag from which the ball is drawn. But, can we find the probability that the ball drawn is from a particular bag (say Bag II), if the colour of the ball drawn is given? Here, we have to find the reverse probability of Bag II to be selected when an event occurred after it is known. Famous mathematician, John Bayes' solved the problem of finding reverse probability by using conditional probability. The formula developed by him is known as 'Bayes theorem' which was published posthumously in 1763. Before stating and proving the Bayes' theorem, let us first take up a definition and some preliminary results.

13.5.1 *Partition of a sample space*

A set of events E_1, E_2, ..., E_n is said to represent a partition of the sample space S if

   (a) $E_i \cap E_j = \phi$, $i \neq j$, $i, j = 1, 2, 3, ..., n$

(b) $E_1 \cup E_2 \cup ... \cup E_n = S$ and

(c) $P(E_i) > 0$ for all $i = 1, 2, ..., n$.

In other words, the events $E_1, E_2, ..., E_n$ represent a partition of the sample space S if they are pairwise disjoint, exhaustive and have nonzero probabilities.

As an example, we see that any nonempty event E and its complement E' form a partition of the sample space S since they satisfy $E \cap E' = \phi$ and $E \cup E' = S$.

From the Venn diagram in Fig 13.3, one can easily observe that if E and F are any two events associated with a sample space S, then the set $\{E \cap F', E \cap F, E' \cap F, E' \cap F'\}$ is a partition of the sample space S. It may be mentioned that the partition of a sample space is not unique. There can be several partitions of the same sample space.

We shall now prove a theorem known as *Theorem of total probability*.

13.5.2 *Theorem of total probability*

Let $\{E_1, E_2, ..., E_n\}$ be a partition of the sample space S, and suppose that each of the events $E_1, E_2, ..., E_n$ has nonzero probability of occurrence. Let A be any event associated with S, then

$$P(A) = P(E_1) \, P(A|E_1) + P(E_2) \, P(A|E_2) + ... + P(E_n) \, P(A|E_n)$$

$$= \sum_{j=1}^{n} P(E_j) P(A|E_j)$$

Proof Given that $E_1, E_2, ..., E_n$ is a partition of the sample space S (Fig 13.4). Therefore,

$$S = E_1 \cup E_2 \cup ... \cup E_n \qquad ... (1)$$

and $\quad E_i \cap E_j = \phi, \, i \neq j, \, i, j = 1, 2, ..., n$

Now, we know that for any event A,

$A = A \cap S$

$= A \cap (E_1 \cup E_2 \cup ... \cup E_n)$

$= (A \cap E_1) \cup (A \cap E_2) \cup ... \cup (A \cap E_n)$

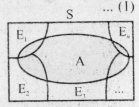

Fig 13.4

Also $A \cap E_i$ and $A \cap E_j$ are respectively the subsets of E_i and E_j. We know that E_i and E_j are disjoint, for $i \neq j$, therefore, $A \cap E_i$ and $A \cap E_j$ are also disjoint for all $i \neq j$, $i, j = 1, 2, ..., n$.

Thus, $\qquad P(A) = P[(A \cap E_1) \cup (A \cap E_2) \cup ..... \cup (A \cap E_n)]$

$= P(A \cap E_1) + P(A \cap E_2) + ... + P(A \cap E_n)$

Now, by multiplication rule of probability, we have

$$P(A \cap E_i) = P(E_i) \, P(A|E_i) \text{ as } P(E_i) \neq 0 \forall i = 1, 2, ..., n$$

Therefore, $P(A) = P(E_1) P(A|E_1) + P(E_2) P(A|E_2) + ... + P(E_n)P(A|E_n)$

or $$P(A) = \sum_{j=1}^{n} P(E_j)P(A|E_j)$$

Example 15 A person has undertaken a construction job. The probabilities are 0.65 that there will be strike, 0.80 that the construction job will be completed on time if there is no strike, and 0.32 that the construction job will be completed on time if there is a strike. Determine the probability that the construction job will be completed on time.

Solution Let A be the event that the construction job will be completed on time, and B be the event that there will be a strike. We have to find $P(A)$.
We have

$$P(B) = 0.65, P(\text{no strike}) = P(B') = 1 - P(B) = 1 - 0.65 = 0.35$$
$$P(A|B) = 0.32, P(A|B') = 0.80$$

Since events B and B' form a partition of the sample space S, therefore, by theorem on total probability, we have

$$P(A) = P(B) \ P(A|B) + P(B') \ P(A|B')$$
$$= 0.65 \times 0.32 + 0.35 \times 0.8$$
$$= 0.208 + 0.28 = 0.488$$

Thus, the probability that the construction job will be completed in time is 0.488.

We shall now state and prove the Bayes' theorem.

Bayes' Theorem If E_1, E_2, ..., E_n are n non empty events which constitute a partition of sample space S, i.e. E_1, E_2, ..., E_n are pairwise disjoint and $E_1 \cup E_2 \cup ... \cup E_n = S$ and A is any event of nonzero probability, then

$$P(E_i|A) = \frac{P(E_i)P(A|E_i)}{\sum_{j=1}^{n} P(E_j)P(A|E_j)} \quad \text{for any } i = 1, 2, 3, ..., n$$

Proof By formula of conditional probability, we know that

$$P(E_i|A) = \frac{P(A \cap E_i)}{P(A)}$$

$$= \frac{P(E_i)P(A|E_i)}{P(A)} \quad \text{(by multiplication rule of probability)}$$

$$= \frac{P(E_i)P(A|E_i)}{\sum_{j=1}^{n} P(E_j)P(A|E_j)} \quad \text{(by the result of theorem of total probability)}$$

Remark The following terminology is generally used when Bayes' theorem is applied.

The events $E_1, E_2, ..., E_n$ are called *hypotheses*.

The probability $P(E_i)$ is called the *priori probability* of the hypothesis E_i

The conditional probability $P(E_i|A)$ is called *a posteriori probability* of the hypothesis E_i.

Bayes' theorem is also called the formula for the probability of "causes". Since the E_i's are a partition of the sample space S, one and only one of the events E_i occurs (i.e. one of the events E_i must occur and only one can occur). Hence, the above formula gives us the probability of a particular E_i (i.e. a "Cause"), given that the event A has occurred.

The Bayes' theorem has its applications in variety of situations, few of which are illustrated in following examples.

Example 16 Bag I contains 3 red and 4 black balls while another Bag II contains 5 red and 6 black balls. One ball is drawn at random from one of the bags and it is found to be red. Find the probability that it was drawn from Bag II.

Solution Let E_1 be the event of choosing the bag I, E_2 the event of choosing the bag II and A be the event of drawing a red ball.

Then
$$P(E_1) = P(E_2) = \frac{1}{2}$$

Also
$$P(A|E_1) = P(\text{drawing a red ball from Bag I}) = \frac{3}{7}$$

and
$$P(A|E_2) = P(\text{drawing a red ball from Bag II}) = \frac{5}{11}$$

Now, the probability of drawing a ball from Bag II, being given that it is red, is $P(E_2|A)$

By using Bayes' theorem, we have

$$P(E_2|A) = \frac{P(E_2)P(A|E_2)}{P(E_1)P(A|E_1)+P(E_2)P(A|E_2)} = \frac{\frac{1}{2}\times\frac{5}{11}}{\frac{1}{2}\times\frac{3}{7}+\frac{1}{2}\times\frac{5}{11}} = \frac{35}{68}$$

Example 17 Given three identical boxes I, II and III, each containing two coins. In box I, both coins are gold coins, in box II, both are silver coins and in the box III, there is one gold and one silver coin. A person chooses a box at random and takes out a coin. If the coin is of gold, what is the probability that the other coin in the box is also of gold?

Solution Let E_1, E_2 and E_3 be the events that boxes I, II and III are chosen, respectively.

Then $P(E_1) = P(E_2) = P(E_3) = \dfrac{1}{3}$

Also, let A be the event that 'the coin drawn is of gold'

Then $P(A|E_1) = P(\text{a gold coin from bag I}) = \dfrac{2}{2} = 1$

$P(A|E_2) = P(\text{a gold coin from bag II}) = 0$

$P(A|E_3) = P(\text{a gold coin from bag III}) = \dfrac{1}{2}$

Now, the probability that the other coin in the box is of gold

$= $ the probability that gold coin is drawn from the box I.

$= P(E_1|A)$

By Bayes' theorem, we know that

$$P(E_1|A) = \frac{P(E_1)\,P(A|E_1)}{P(E_1)\,P(A|E_1) + P(E_2)\,P(A|E_2) + P(E_3)\,P(A|E_3)}$$

$$= \frac{\dfrac{1}{3} \times 1}{\dfrac{1}{3} \times 1 + \dfrac{1}{3} \times 0 + \dfrac{1}{3} \times \dfrac{1}{2}} = \frac{2}{3}$$

Example 18 Suppose that the reliability of a HIV test is specified as follows:

Of people having HIV, 90% of the test detect the disease but 10% go undetected. Of people free of HIV, 99% of the test are judged HIV–ive but 1% are diagnosed as showing HIV+ive. From a large population of which only 0.1% have HIV, one person is selected at random, given the HIV test, and the pathologist reports him/her as HIV+ive. What is the probability that the person actually has HIV?

Solution Let E denote the event that the person selected is actually having HIV and A the event that the person's HIV test is diagnosed as +ive. We need to find $P(E|A)$.

Also E' denotes the event that the person selected is actually not having HIV.

Clearly, $\{E, E'\}$ is a partition of the sample space of all people in the population. We are given that

$$P(E) = 0.1\% = \frac{0.1}{100} = 0.001$$

$$P(E') = 1 - P(E) = 0.999$$

$P(A|E)$ = P(Person tested as HIV+ive given that he/she is actually having HIV)

$$= 90\% = \frac{90}{100} = 0.9$$

and $\quad P(A|E')$ = P(Person tested as HIV +ive given that he/she is actually not having HIV)

$$= 1\% = \frac{1}{100} = 0.01$$

Now, by Bayes' theorem

$$P(E|A) = \frac{P(E)P(A|E)}{P(E)P(A|E)+P(E')P(A|E')}$$

$$= \frac{0.001\times0.9}{0.001\times0.9+0.999\times0.01} = \frac{90}{1089}$$

$$= 0.083 \text{ approx.}$$

Thus, the probability that a person selected at random is actually having HIV given that he/she is tested HIV+ive is 0.083.

Example 19 In a factory which manufactures bolts, machines A, B and C manufacture respectively 25%, 35% and 40% of the bolts. Of their outputs, 5, 4 and 2 percent are respectively defective bolts. A bolt is drawn at random from the product and is found to be defective. What is the probability that it is manufactured by the machine B?

Solution Let events B_1, B_2, B_3 be the following :

B_1 : the bolt is manufactured by machine A

B_2 : the bolt is manufactured by machine B

B_3 : the bolt is manufactured by machine C

Clearly, B_1, B_2, B_3 are mutually exclusive and exhaustive events and hence, they represent a partition of the sample space.

Let the event E be 'the bolt is defective'.

The event E occurs with B_1 or with B_2 or with B_3. Given that,

$$P(B_1) = 25\% = 0.25, \quad P(B_2) = 0.35 \text{ and } P(B_3) = 0.40$$

Again $P(E|B_1)$ = Probability that the bolt drawn is defective given that it is manufactured by machine A = 5% = 0.05

Similarly, $\quad P(E|B_2) = 0.04, \quad P(E|B_3) = 0.02.$

Hence, by Bayes' Theorem, we have

$$P(B_2|E) = \frac{P(B_2)P(E|B_2)}{P(B_1)P(E|B_1)+P(B_2)P(E|B_2)+P(B_3)P(E|B_3)}$$

$$= \frac{0.35 \times 0.04}{0.25 \times 0.05 + 0.35 \times 0.04 + 0.40 \times 0.02}$$

$$= \frac{0.0140}{0.0345} = \frac{28}{69}$$

Example 26 A doctor is to visit a patient. From the past experience, it is known that the probabilities that he will come by train, bus, scooter or by other means of transport are respectively $\frac{3}{10}, \frac{1}{5}, \frac{1}{10}$ and $\frac{2}{5}$. The probabilities that he will be late are $\frac{1}{4}, \frac{1}{3}$, and $\frac{1}{12}$, if he comes by train, bus and scooter respectively, but if he comes by other means of transport, then he will not be late. When he arrives, he is late. What is the probability that he comes by train?

Solution Let E be the event that the doctor visits the patient late and let T_1, T_2, T_3, T_4 be the events that the doctor comes by train, bus, scooter, and other means of transport respectively.

Then $P(T_1) = \frac{3}{10}, P(T_2) = \frac{1}{5}, P(T_3) = \frac{1}{10}$ and $P(T_4) = \frac{2}{5}$ (given)

$P(E|T_1)$ = Probability that the doctor arriving late comes by train = $\frac{1}{4}$

Similarly, $P(E|T_2) = \frac{1}{3}$, $P(E|T_3) = \frac{1}{12}$ and $P(E|T_4) = 0$, since he is not late if he comes by other means of transport.

Therefore, by Bayes' Theorem, we have

$P(T_1|E)$ = Probability that the doctor arriving late comes by train

$$= \frac{P(T_1)P(E|T_1)}{P(T_1)P(E|T_1)+P(T_2)P(E|T_2)+P(T_3)P(E|T_3)+P(T_4)P(E|T_4)}$$

$$= \frac{\frac{3}{10} \times \frac{1}{4}}{\frac{3}{10} \times \frac{1}{4} + \frac{1}{5} \times \frac{1}{3} + \frac{1}{10} \times \frac{1}{12} + \frac{2}{5} \times 0} = \frac{3}{40} \times \frac{120}{18} = \frac{1}{2}$$

Hence, the required probability is $\frac{1}{2}$.

Example 21 A man is known to speak truth 3 out of 4 times. He throws a die and reports that it is a six. Find the probability that it is actually a six.

Solution Let E be the event that the man reports that six occurs in the throwing of the die and let S_1 be the event that six occurs and S_2 be the event that six does not occur.

Then

$$P(S_1) = \text{Probability that } six \text{ occurs} = \frac{1}{6}$$

$$P(S_2) = \text{Probability that } six \text{ does not occur} = \frac{5}{6}$$

$P(E|S_1)$ = Probability that the man reports that *six* occurs when *six* has actually occurred on the die

= Probability that the man speaks the truth = $\dfrac{3}{4}$

$P(E|S_2)$ = Probability that the man reports that *six* occurs when *six* has not actually occurred on the die

= Probability that the man does not speak the truth $= 1 - \dfrac{3}{4} = \dfrac{1}{4}$

Thus, by Bayes' theorem, we get

$P(S_1|E)$ = Probability that the report of the man that *six* has occurred is actually a *six*

$$= \frac{P(S_1)P(E|S_1)}{P(S_1)P(E|S_1) + P(S_2)P(E|S_2)}$$

$$= \frac{\dfrac{1}{6} \times \dfrac{3}{4}}{\dfrac{1}{6} \times \dfrac{3}{4} + \dfrac{5}{6} \times \dfrac{1}{4}} = \frac{1}{8} \times \frac{24}{8} = \frac{3}{8}$$

Hence, the required probability is $\dfrac{3}{8}$.

EXERCISE 13.3

1. An urn contains 5 red and 5 black balls. A ball is drawn at random, its colour is noted and is returned to the urn. Moreover, 2 additional balls of the colour drawn are put in the urn and then a ball is drawn at random. What is the probability that the second ball is red?

2. A bag contains 4 red and 4 black balls, another bag contains 2 red and 6 black balls. One of the two bags is selected at random and a ball is drawn from the bag which is found to be red. Find the probability that the ball is drawn from the first bag.

3. Of the students in a college, it is known that 60% reside in hostel and 40% are day scholars (not residing in hostel). Previous year results report that 30% of all students who reside in hostel attain A grade and 20% of day scholars attain A grade in their annual examination. At the end of the year, one student is chosen at random from the college and he has an A grade, what is the probability that the student is a hostlier?

4. In answering a question on a multiple choice test, a student either knows the answer or guesses. Let $\frac{3}{4}$ be the probability that he knows the answer and $\frac{1}{4}$ be the probability that he guesses. Assuming that a student who guesses at the answer will be correct with probability $\frac{1}{4}$. What is the probability that the student knows the answer given that he answered it correctly?

5. A laboratory blood test is 99% effective in detecting a certain disease when it is in fact, present. However, the test also yields a false positive result for 0.5% of the healthy person tested (i.e. if a healthy person is tested, then, with probability 0.005, the test will imply he has the disease). If 0.1 percent of the population actually has the disease, what is the probability that a person has the disease given that his test result is positive ?

6. There are three coins. One is a two headed coin (having head on both faces), another is a biased coin that comes up heads 75% of the time and third is an unbiased coin. One of the three coins is chosen at random and tossed, it shows heads, what is the probability that it was the two headed coin ?

7. An insurance company insured 2000 scooter drivers, 4000 car drivers and 6000 truck drivers. The probability of an accidents are 0.01, 0.03 and 0.15 respectively. One of the insured persons meets with an accident. What is the probability that he is a scooter driver?

8. A factory has two machines A and B. Past record shows that machine A produced 60% of the items of output and machine B produced 40% of the items. Further, 2% of the items produced by machine A and 1% produced by machine B were defective. All the items are put into one stockpile and then one item is chosen at random from this and is found to be defective. What is the probability that it was produced by machine B?

9. Two groups are competing for the position on the Board of directors of a corporation. The probabilities that the first and the second groups will win are

0.6 and 0.4 respectively. Further, if the first group wins, the probability of introducing a new product is 0.7 and the corresponding probability is 0.3 if the second group wins. Find the probability that the new product introduced was by the second group.

10. Suppose a girl throws a die. If she gets a 5 or 6, she tosses a coin three times and notes the number of heads. If she gets 1, 2, 3 or 4, she tosses a coin once and notes whether a head or tail is obtained. If she obtained exactly one head, what is the probability that she threw 1, 2, 3 or 4 with the die?

11. A manufacturer has three machine operators A, B and C. The first operator A produces 1% defective items, where as the other two operators B and C produce 5% and 7% defective items respectively. A is on the job for 50% of the time, B is on the job for 30% of the time and C is on the job for 20% of the time. A defective item is produced, what is the probability that it was produced by A?

12. A card from a pack of 52 cards is lost. From the remaining cards of the pack, two cards are drawn and are found to be both diamonds. Find the probability of the lost card being a diamond.

13. Probability that A speaks truth is $\frac{4}{5}$. A coin is tossed. A reports that a head appears. The probability that actually there was head is

(A) $\frac{4}{5}$ (B) $\frac{1}{2}$ (C) $\frac{1}{5}$ (D) $\frac{2}{5}$

14. If A and B are two events such that $A \subset B$ and $P(B) \neq 0$, then which of the following is correct?

(A) $P(A|B) = \dfrac{P(B)}{P(A)}$ (B) $P(A|B) < P(A)$

(C) $P(A|B) \geq P(A)$ (D) None of these

13.6 Random Variables and its Probability Distributions

We have already learnt about random experiments and formation of sample spaces. In most of these experiments, we were not only interested in the particular outcome that occurs but rather in some number associated with that outcomes as shown in following examples/experiments.

(i) In tossing two dice, we may be interested in the sum of the numbers on the two dice.

(ii) In tossing a coin 50 times, we may want the number of heads obtained.

(iii) In the experiment of taking out four articles (one after the other) at random from a lot of 20 articles in which 6 are defective, we want to know the number of defectives in the sample of four and not in the particular sequence of defective and nondefective articles.

In all of the above experiments, we have a rule which assigns to each outcome of the experiment a single real number. This single real number may vary with different outcomes of the experiment. Hence, it is a variable. Also its value depends upon the outcome of a random experiment and, hence, is called random variable. A random variable is usually denoted by X.

If you recall the definition of a function, you will realise that the random variable X is really speaking a function whose domain is the set of outcomes (or sample space) of a random experiment. A random variable can take any real value, therefore, its co-domain is the set of real numbers. Hence, a random variable can be defined as follows :

Definition 4 A random variable is a real valued function whose domain is the sample space of a random experiment.

For example, let us consider the experiment of tossing a coin two times in succession. The sample space of the experiment is $S = \{HH, HT, TH, TT\}$.

If X denotes the number of heads obtained, then X is a random variable and for each outcome, its value is as given below :

$$X(HH) = 2, X(HT) = 1, X(TH) = 1, X(TT) = 0.$$

More than one random variables can be defined on the same sample space. For example, let Y denote the number of heads minus the number of tails for each outcome of the above sample space S.

Then $Y(HH) = 2, Y(HT) = 0, Y(TH) = 0, Y(TT) = -2.$

Thus, X and Y are two different random variables defined on the same sample space S.

Example 22 A person plays a game of tossing a coin thrice. For each head, he is given Rs 2 by the organiser of the game and for each tail, he has to give Rs 1.50 to the organiser. Let X denote the amount gained or lost by the person. Show that X is a random variable and exhibit it as a function on the sample space of the experiment.

Solution X is a number whose values are defined on the outcomes of a random experiment. Therefore, X is a random variable.

Now, sample space of the experiment is

$$S = \{HHH, HHT, HTH, THH, HTT, THT, TTH, TTT\}$$

Then $X(HHH) = Rs (2 \times 3) = Rs 6$

$X(HHT) = X(HTH) = X(THH) = Rs (2 \times 2 - 1 \times 1.50) = Rs 2.50$

$X(HTT) = X(THT) = (TTH) = Rs (1 \times 2) - (2 \times 1.50) = - Re 1$

and $X(TTT) = - Rs (3 \times 1.50) = - Rs 4.50$

where, minus sign shows the loss to the player. Thus, for each element of the sample space, X takes a unique value, hence, X is a function on the sample space whose range is

$$\{-1,\ 2.50,\ -4.50,\ 6\}$$

Example 23 A bag contains 2 white and 1 red balls. One ball is drawn at random and then put back in the box after noting its colour. The process is repeated again. If X denotes the number of red balls recorded in the two draws, describe X.

Solution Let the balls in the bag be denoted by w_1, w_2, r. Then the sample space is

$$S = \{w_1\,w_1,\ w_1\,w_2,\ w_2\,w_2,\ w_2\,w_1,\ w_1\,r,\ w_2\,r,\ r\,w_1,\ r\,w_2,\ r\,r\}$$

Now, for $\omega \in S$

$X(\omega) =$ number of red balls

Therefore

$$X(\{w_1\,w_1\}) = X(\{w_1\,w_2\}) = X(\{w_2\,w_2\}) = X(\{w_2\,w_1\}) = 0$$

$$X(\{w_1\,r\}) = X(\{w_2\,r\}) = X(\{r\,w_1\}) = X(\{r\,w_2\}) = 1 \text{ and } X(\{r\,r\}) = 2$$

Thus, X is a random variable which can take values 0, 1 or 2.

13.6.1 *Probability distribution of a random variable*

Let us look at the experiment of selecting one family out of ten families $f_1, f_2, ..., f_{10}$ in such a manner that each family is equally likely to be selected. Let the families $f_1, f_2, ..., f_{10}$ have 3, 4, 3, 2, 5, 4, 3, 6, 4, 5 members, respectively.

Let us select a family and note down the number of members in the family denoting X. Clearly, X is a random variable defined as below :

$$X(f_1) = 3,\ X(f_2) = 4,\ X(f_3) = 3,\ X(f_4) = 2,\ X(f_5) = 5,$$

$$X(f_6) = 4,\ X(f_7) = 3,\ X(f_8) = 6,\ X(f_9) = 4,\ X(f_{10}) = 5$$

Thus, X can take any value 2,3,4,5 or 6 depending upon which family is selected.

Now, X will take the value 2 when the family f_4 is selected. X can take the value 3 when any one of the families f_1, f_3, f_7 is selected.

Similarly, $X = 4$, when family f_2, f_6 or f_9 is selected,

$X = 5$, when family f_5 or f_{10} is selected

and $X = 6$, when family f_8 is selected.

Since we had assumed that each family is equally likely to be selected, the probability that family f_4 is selected is $\dfrac{1}{10}$.

Thus, the probability that X can take the value 2 is $\dfrac{1}{10}$. We write $P(X = 2) = \dfrac{1}{10}$

Also, the probability that any one of the families f_1, f_3 or f_7 is selected is

$$P(\{f_1, f_3, f_7\}) = \frac{3}{10}$$

Thus, the probability that X can take the value 3 $= \dfrac{3}{10}$

We write $\qquad P(X = 3) = \dfrac{3}{10}$

Similarly, we obtain

$$P(X = 4) = P(\{f_2, f_6, f_9\}) = \frac{3}{10}$$

$$P(X = 5) = P(\{f_5, f_{10}\}) = \frac{2}{10}$$

and $\qquad P(X = 6) = P(\{f_8\}) = \dfrac{1}{10}$

Such a description giving the values of the random variable along with the corresponding probabilities is called the *probability distribution of the random variable X.*

In general, the probability distribution of a random variable X is defined as follows:

Definition 5 The probability distribution of a random variable X is the system of numbers

X	:	x_1	x_2	$\cdots$	x_n
P(X)	:	p_1	p_2	$\cdots$	p_n

where, $\qquad p_i > 0, \; \displaystyle\sum_{i=1}^{n} p_i = 1, \, i = 1, 2,..., n$

The real numbers $x_1, x_2,..., x_n$ are the possible values of the random variable X and p_i ($i = 1, 2,..., n$) is the probability of the random variable X taking the value x_i i.e., $P(X = x_i) = p_i$

Note If x_i is one of the possible values of a random variable X, the statement $X = x_i$ is true only at some point (s) of the sample space. Hence, the probability that X takes value x_i is always nonzero, i.e. $P(X = x_i) \neq 0$.

Also for all possible values of the random variable X, all elements of the sample space are covered. Hence, the sum of all the probabilities in a probability distribution must be one,

Example 24 Two cards are drawn successively with replacement from a well-shuffled deck of 52 cards. Find the probability distribution of the number of aces.

Solution The number of aces is a random variable. Let it be denoted by X. Clearly, X can take the values 0, 1, or 2.

Now, since the draws are done with replacement, therefore, the two draws form independent experiments.

Therefore,
$$P(X = 0) = P(\text{non-ace and non-ace})$$
$$= P(\text{non-ace}) \times P(\text{non-ace})$$
$$= \frac{48}{52} \times \frac{48}{52} = \frac{144}{169}$$

$$P(X = 1) = P(\text{ace and non-ace or non-ace and ace})$$
$$= P(\text{ace and non-ace}) + P(\text{non-ace and ace})$$
$$= P(\text{ace}). P(\text{non-ace}) + P(\text{non-ace}) . P(\text{ace})$$
$$= \frac{4}{52} \times \frac{48}{52} + \frac{48}{52} \times \frac{4}{52} = \frac{24}{169}$$

and
$$P(X = 2) = P(\text{ace and ace})$$
$$= \frac{4}{52} \times \frac{4}{52} = \frac{1}{169}$$

Thus, the required probability distribution is

X	0	1	2
P(X)	$\frac{144}{169}$	$\frac{24}{169}$	$\frac{1}{169}$

Example 25 Find the probability distribution of number of doublets in three throws of a pair of dice.

Solution Let X denote the number of doublets. Possible doublets are

$$(1,1), (2,2), (3,3), (4,4), (5,5), (6,6)$$

Clearly, X can take the value 0, 1, 2, or 3.

Probability of getting a doublet $= \dfrac{6}{36} = \dfrac{1}{6}$

Probability of not getting a doublet $= 1 - \dfrac{1}{6} = \dfrac{5}{6}$

Now $P(X = 0) = P \text{ (no doublet)} = \dfrac{5}{6} \times \dfrac{5}{6} \times \dfrac{5}{6} = \dfrac{125}{216}$

$P(X = 1) = P \text{ (one doublet and two non-doublets)}$

$$= \dfrac{1}{6} \times \dfrac{5}{6} \times \dfrac{5}{6} + \dfrac{5}{6} \times \dfrac{1}{6} \times \dfrac{5}{6} + \dfrac{5}{6} \times \dfrac{5}{6} \times \dfrac{1}{6}$$

$$= 3\left(\dfrac{1}{6} \times \dfrac{5^2}{6^2} \right) = \dfrac{75}{216}$$

$P(X = 2) = P \text{ (two doublets and one non-doublet)}$

$$= \dfrac{1}{6} \times \dfrac{1}{6} \times \dfrac{5}{6} + \dfrac{1}{6} \times \dfrac{5}{6} \times \dfrac{1}{6} + \dfrac{5}{6} \times \dfrac{1}{6} \times \dfrac{1}{6} = 3\left(\dfrac{1}{6^2} \times \dfrac{5}{6} \right) = \dfrac{15}{216}$$

and $P(X = 3) = P \text{ (three doublets)}$

$$= \dfrac{1}{6} \times \dfrac{1}{6} \times \dfrac{1}{6} = \dfrac{1}{216}$$

Thus, the required probability distribution is

X	0	1	2	3
P(X)	$\dfrac{125}{216}$	$\dfrac{75}{216}$	$\dfrac{15}{216}$	$\dfrac{1}{216}$

Verification Sum of the probabilities

$$\sum_{i=1}^{n} p_i = \dfrac{125}{216} + \dfrac{75}{216} + \dfrac{15}{216} + \dfrac{1}{216}$$

$$= \dfrac{125 + 75 + 15 + 1}{216} = \dfrac{216}{216} = 1$$

Example 26 Let X denote the number of hours you study during a randomly selected school day. The probability that X can take the values x, has the following form, where k is some unknown constant.

$$P(X = x) = \begin{cases} 0.1, \text{ if } x = 0 \\ kx, \text{ if } x = 1 \text{ or } 2 \\ k(5-x), \text{ if } x = 3 \text{ or } 4 \\ 0, \text{ otherwise} \end{cases}$$

(a)   Find the value of k.

(b)   What is the probability that you study at least two hours ? Exactly two hours? At most two hours?

Solution The probability distribution of X is

X	0	1	2	3	4
P(X)	0.1	k	$2k$	$2k$	k

(a)   We know that $\qquad\qquad \displaystyle\sum_{i=1}^{n} p_i = 1$

Therefore $\qquad 0.1 + k + 2k + 2k + k = 1$

i.e. $\qquad\qquad\qquad\qquad k = 0.15$

(b)   P(you study at least two hours) $\quad = P(X \geq 2)$

$\qquad\qquad\qquad = P(X = 2) + P(X = 3) + P(X = 4)$

$\qquad\qquad\qquad = 2k + 2k + k = 5k = 5 \times 0.15 = 0.75$

P(you study exactly two hours) $\qquad = P(X = 2)$

$\qquad\qquad\qquad = 2k = 2 \times 0.15 = 0.3$

P(you study at most two hours) $\qquad = P(X \leq 2)$

$\qquad\qquad\qquad = P(X = 0) + P(X = 1) + P(X = 2)$

$\qquad\qquad\qquad = 0.1 + k + 2k = 0.1 + 3k = 0.1 + 3 \times 0.15$

$\qquad\qquad\qquad = 0.55$

13.6.2 *Mean of a random variable*

In many problems, it is desirable to describe some feature of the random variable by means of a single number that can be computed from its probability distribution. Few such numbers are mean, median and mode. In this section, we shall discuss mean only. Mean is a measure of location or central tendency in the sense that it roughly locates a *middle* or *average value* of the random variable.

Definition 6 Let X be a random variable whose possible values $x_1, x_2, x_3, ..., x_n$ occur with probabilities $p_1, p_2, p_3, ..., p_n$, respectively. The mean of X, denoted by μ, is the number $\sum_{i=1}^{n} x_i p_i$ i.e. the mean of X is the weighted average of the possible values of X, each value being weighted by its probability with which it occurs.

The mean of a random variable X is also called the expectation of X, denoted by E(X).

Thus,
$$E(X) = \mu = \sum_{i=1}^{n} x_i p_i = x_1 p_1 + x_2 p_2 + ... + x_n p_n.$$

In other words, the mean or expectation of a random variable X is the sum of the products of all possible values of X by their respective probabilities.

Example 27 Let a pair of dice be thrown and the random variable X be the sum of the numbers that appear on the two dice. Find the mean or expectation of X.

Solution The sample space of the experiment consists of 36 elementary events in the form of ordered pairs (x_i, y_i), where $x_i = 1, 2, 3, 4, 5, 6$ and $y_i = 1, 2, 3, 4, 5, 6$.

The random variable X i.e. the sum of the numbers on the two dice takes the values 2, 3, 4, 5, 6, 7, 8, 9, 10, 11 or 12.

Now $P(X = 2) = P(\{(1,1)\}) = \dfrac{1}{36}$

$P(X = 3) = P(\{(1,2), (2,1)\}) = \dfrac{2}{36}$

$P(X = 4) = P(\{(1,3), (2,2), (3,1)\}) = \dfrac{3}{36}$

$P(X = 5) = P(\{(1,4), (2,3), (3,2), (4,1)\}) = \dfrac{4}{36}$

$P(X = 6) = P(\{(1,5), (2,4), (3,3), (4,2), (5,1)\}) = \dfrac{5}{36}$

$P(X = 7) = P(\{(1,6), (2,5), (3,4), (4,3), (5,2), (6,1)\}) = \dfrac{6}{36}$

$P(X = 8) = P(\{(2,6), (3,5), (4,4), (5,3), (6,2)\}) = \dfrac{5}{36}$

$$P(X = 9) = \ P(\{(3,6), (4,5), (5,4), (6,3)\}) = \frac{4}{36}$$

$$P(X = 10) = P(\{(4,6), (5,5), (6,4)\}) = \frac{3}{36}$$

$$P(X = 11) = P(\{(5,6), (6,5)\}) = \frac{2}{36}$$

$$P(X = 12) = P(\{(6,6)\}) \ = \frac{1}{36}$$

The probability distribution of X is

X or x_i	2	3	4	5	6	7	8	9	10	11	12
P(X) or p_i	$\frac{1}{36}$	$\frac{2}{36}$	$\frac{3}{36}$	$\frac{4}{36}$	$\frac{5}{36}$	$\frac{6}{36}$	$\frac{5}{36}$	$\frac{4}{36}$	$\frac{3}{36}$	$\frac{2}{36}$	$\frac{1}{36}$

Therefore,

$$\mu = E(X) = \sum_{i=1}^{n} x_i p_i = 2 \times \frac{1}{36} + 3 \times \frac{2}{36} + 4 \times \frac{3}{36} + 5 \times \frac{4}{36}$$

$$+ 6 \times \frac{5}{36} + 7 \times \frac{6}{36} + 8 \times \frac{5}{36} + 9 \times \frac{4}{36} + 10 \times \frac{3}{36} + 11 \times \frac{2}{36} + 12 \times \frac{1}{36}$$

$$= \frac{2 + 6 + 12 + 20 + 30 + 42 + 40 + 36 + 30 + 22 + 12}{36} = 7$$

Thus, the mean of the sum of the numbers that appear on throwing two fair dice is 7.

13.6.3 *Variance of a random variable*

The mean of a random variable does not give us information about the variability in the values of the random variable. In fact, if the variance is small, then the values of the random variable are close to the mean. Also random variables with different probability distributions can have equal means, as shown in the following distributions of X and Y.

X	1	2	3	4
P(X)	$\frac{1}{8}$	$\frac{2}{8}$	$\frac{3}{8}$	$\frac{2}{8}$

Y	−1	0	4	5	6
P(Y)	$\dfrac{1}{8}$	$\dfrac{2}{8}$	$\dfrac{3}{8}$	$\dfrac{1}{8}$	$\dfrac{1}{8}$

Clearly $E(X) = 1\times\dfrac{1}{8}+2\times\dfrac{2}{8}+3\times\dfrac{3}{8}+4\times\dfrac{2}{8}=\dfrac{22}{8}=2.75$

and $E(Y) = -1\times\dfrac{1}{8}+0\times\dfrac{2}{8}+4\times\dfrac{3}{8}+5\times\dfrac{1}{8}=6\times\dfrac{1}{8}=\dfrac{22}{8}=2.75$

The variables X and Y are different, however their means are same. It is also easily observable from the diagramatic representation of these distributions (Fig 13.5).

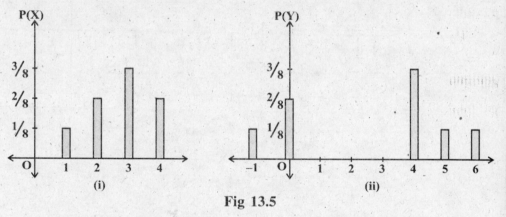

Fig 13.5

To distinguish X from Y, we require a measure of the extent to which the values of the random variables spread out. In Statistics, we have studied that the variance is a measure of the spread or scatter in data. Likewise, the variability or spread in the values of a random variable may be measured by variance.

Definition 7 Let X be a random variable whose possible values $x_1, x_2,....,x_n$ occur with probabilities $p(x_1), p(x_2),..., p(x_n)$ respectively.

Let $\mu = E(X)$ be the mean of X. The variance of X, denoted by Var (X) or σ_x^2 is defined as

$$\sigma_x^2 = Var(X)=\sum_{i=1}^{n}(x_i-\mu)^2\, p(x_i)$$

or equivalently $\sigma_x^2 = E(X - \mu)^2$

The non-negative number

$$\sigma_x = \sqrt{\mathrm{Var(X)}} = \sqrt{\sum_{i=1}^{n}(x_i - \mu)^2\, p(x_i)}$$

is called the *standard deviation* of the random variable X.

Another formula to find the variance of a random variable. We know that,

$$\mathrm{Var\ (X)} = \sum_{i=1}^{n}(x_i - \mu)^2\, p(x_i)$$

$$= \sum_{i=1}^{n}(x_i^2 + \mu^2 - 2\mu\, x_i)\, p(x_i)$$

$$= \sum_{i=1}^{n}x_i^2\, p(x_i) + \sum_{i=1}^{n}\mu^2\, p(x_i) - \sum_{i=1}^{n}2\mu x_i\, p(x_i)$$

$$= \sum_{i=1}^{n}x_i^2\, p(x_i) + \mu^2\sum_{i=1}^{n}p(x_i) - 2\mu\sum_{i=1}^{n}x_i\, p(x_i)$$

$$= \sum_{i=1}^{n}x_i^2\, p(x_i) + \mu^2 - 2\mu^2\left[\text{since}\sum_{i=1}^{n}p\ (x_i)=1\,\text{and}\,\mu = \sum_{i=1}^{n}x_i p(x_i)\right]$$

$$= \sum_{i=1}^{n}x_i^2\, p(x_i) - \mu^2$$

or

$$\mathrm{Var\ (X)} = \sum_{i=1}^{n}x_i^2\, p(x_i) - \left(\sum_{i=1}^{n}x_i\, p(x_i)\right)^2$$

or

$$\mathrm{Var\ (X)} = \mathrm{E(X^2)} - [\mathrm{E(X)}]^2, \text{ where } \mathrm{E(X^2)} = \sum_{i=1}^{n}x_i^2\, p(x_i)$$

Example 28 Find the variance of the number obtained on a throw of an unbiased die.

Solution The sample space of the experiment is S = {1, 2, 3, 4, 5, 6}.

Let X denote the number obtained on the throw. Then X is a random variable which can take values 1, 2, 3, 4, 5, or 6.

Also $P(1) = P(2) = P(3) = P(4) = P(5) = P(6) = \dfrac{1}{6}$

Therefore, the Probability distribution of X is

X	1	2	3	4	5	6
P(X)	$\dfrac{1}{6}$	$\dfrac{1}{6}$	$\dfrac{1}{6}$	$\dfrac{1}{6}$	$\dfrac{1}{6}$	$\dfrac{1}{6}$

Now $E(X) = \displaystyle\sum_{i=1}^{n} x_i\, p(x_i)$

$$= 1\times\frac{1}{6}+2\times\frac{1}{6}+3\times\frac{1}{6}+4\times\frac{1}{6}+5\times\frac{1}{6}+6\times\frac{1}{6}=\frac{21}{6}$$

Also $E(X^2) = 1^2\times\dfrac{1}{6}+2^2\times\dfrac{1}{6}+3^2\times\dfrac{1}{6}+4^2\times\dfrac{1}{6}+5^2\times\dfrac{1}{6}+6^2\times\dfrac{1}{6}=\dfrac{91}{6}$

Thus,   Var $(X) = E(X^2) - (E(X))^2$

$$= \frac{91}{6}-\left(\frac{21}{6}\right)^2=\frac{91}{6}-\frac{441}{36}=\frac{35}{12}$$

Example 29 Two cards are drawn simultaneously (or successively without replacement) from a well shuffled pack of 52 cards. Find the mean, variance and standard deviation of the number of kings.

Solution Let X denote the number of kings in a draw of two cards. X is a random variable which can assume the values 0, 1 or 2.

Now $P(X = 0) = P\text{ (no king)} = \dfrac{^{48}C_2}{^{52}C_2} = \dfrac{\dfrac{48!}{2!(48-2)!}}{\dfrac{52!}{2!(52-2)!}} = \dfrac{48\times47}{52\times51} = \dfrac{188}{221}$

$P(X = 1) = P\text{ (one king and one non-king)} = \dfrac{^4C_1\,^{48}C_1}{^{52}C_2}$

$$= \frac{4\times48\times2}{52\times51}=\frac{32}{221}$$

and $\qquad$ P(X = 2) = P (two kings) $= \dfrac{^4C_2}{^{52}C_2} = \dfrac{4\times3}{52\times51} = \dfrac{1}{221}$

Thus, the probability distribution of X is

X	0	1	2
P(X)	$\dfrac{188}{221}$	$\dfrac{32}{221}$	$\dfrac{1}{221}$

Now $\qquad$ Mean of $\;$ X = E(X) = $\displaystyle\sum_{i=1}^{n} x_i\, p(x_i)$

$$= 0\times\frac{188}{221}+1\times\frac{32}{221}+2\times\frac{1}{221}=\frac{34}{221}$$

Also $\qquad$ $E(X^2) = \displaystyle\sum_{i=1}^{n} x_i^2\, p(x_i)$

$$= 0^2\times\frac{188}{221}+1^2\times\frac{32}{221}+2^2\times\frac{1}{221}=\frac{36}{221}$$

Now $\qquad$ Var(X) = E(X^2) $-$ [E(X)]^2

$$= \frac{36}{221}-\left(\frac{34}{221}\right)^2=\frac{6800}{(221)^2}$$

Therefore $\qquad$ $\sigma_x = \sqrt{\text{Var(X)}} = \dfrac{\sqrt{6800}}{221}=0.37$

EXERCISE 13.4

1. State which of the following are not the probability distributions of a random variable. Give reasons for your answer.

    (i)

X	0	1	2
P(X)	0.4	0.4	0.2

    (ii)

X	0	1	2	3	4
P(X)	0.1	0.5	0.2	-0.1	0.3

(iii)

Y	− 1	0	1
P(Y)	0.6	0.1	0.2

(iv)

Z	3	2	1	0	−1
P(Z)	0.3	0.2	0.4	0.1	0.05

2. An urn contains 5 red and 2 black balls. Two balls are randomly drawn. Let X represent the number of black balls. What are the possible values of X? Is X a random variable ?

3. Let X represent the difference between the number of heads and the number of tails obtained when a coin is tossed 6 times. What are possible values of X?

4. Find the probability distribution of
   (i) number of heads in two tosses of a coin.
   (ii) number of tails in the simultaneous tosses of three coins.
   (iii) number of heads in four tosses of a coin.

5. Find the probability distribution of the number of successes in two tosses of a die, where a success is defined as
   (i) number greater than 4
   (ii) six appears on at least one die

6. From a lot of 30 bulbs which include 6 defectives, a sample of 4 bulbs is drawn at random with replacement. Find the probability distribution of the number of defective bulbs.

7. A coin is biased so that the head is 3 times as likely to occur as tail. If the coin is tossed twice, find the probability distribution of number of tails.

8. A random variable X has the following probability distribution:

X	0	1	2	3	4	5	6	7
P(X)	0	k	$2k$	$2k$	$3k$	k^2	$2k^2$	$7k^2+k$

Determine
   (i) k (ii) $P(X < 3)$
   (iii) $P(X > 6)$ (iv) $P(0 < X < 3)$

9. The random variable X has a probability distribution P(X) of the following form, where k is some number :

$$P(X) = \begin{cases} k, & if \ x=0 \\ 2k, & if \ x=1 \\ 3k, & if \ x=2 \\ 0, & otherwise \end{cases}$$

(a) Determine the value of k.

(b) Find P (X < 2), P (X ≤ 2), P(X ≥ 2).

10. Find the mean number of heads in three tosses of a fair coin.

11. Two dice are thrown simultaneously. If X denotes the number of sixes, find the expectation of X.

12. Two numbers are selected at random (without replacement) from the first six positive integers. Let X denote the larger of the two numbers obtained. Find E(X).

13. Let X denote the sum of the numbers obtained when two fair dice are rolled. Find the variance and standard deviation of X.

14. A class has 15 students whose ages are 14, 17, 15, 14, 21, 17, 19, 20, 16, 18, 20, 17, 16, 19 and 20 years. One student is selected in such a manner that each has the same chance of being chosen and the age X of the selected student is recorded. What is the probability distribution of the random variable X? Find mean, variance and standard deviation of X.

15. In a meeting, 70% of the members favour and 30% oppose a certain proposal. A member is selected at random and we take X = 0 if he opposed, and X = 1 if he is in favour. Find E(X) and Var (X).

Choose the correct answer in each of the following:

16. The mean of the numbers obtained on throwing a die having written 1 on three faces, 2 on two faces and 5 on one face is

(A) 1   (B) 2   (C) 5   (D) $\dfrac{8}{3}$

17. Suppose that two cards are drawn at random from a deck of cards. Let X be the number of aces obtained. Then the value of E(X) is

(A) $\dfrac{37}{221}$ (B) $\dfrac{5}{13}$ (C) $\dfrac{1}{13}$ (D) $\dfrac{2}{13}$

13.7 Bernoulli Trials and Binomial Distribution

13.7.1 *Bernoulli trials*

Many experiments are dichotomous in nature. For example, a tossed coin shows a 'head' or 'tail', a manufactured item can be 'defective' or 'non-defective', the response to a question might be 'yes' or 'no', an egg has 'hatched' or 'not hatched', the decision is 'yes' or 'no' etc. In such cases, it is customary to call one of the outcomes a 'success' and the other 'not success' or 'failure'. For example, in tossing a coin, if the occurrence of the head is considered a success, then occurrence of tail is a failure.

Each time we toss a coin or roll a die or perform any other experiment, we call it a trial. If a coin is tossed, say, 4 times, the number of trials is 4, each having exactly two outcomes, namely, success or failure. The outcome of any trial is independent of the outcome of any other trial. In each of such trials, the probability of success or failure remains constant. Such independent trials which have only two outcomes usually referred as 'success' or 'failure' are called *Bernoulli trials*.

Definition 8 Trials of a random experiment are called Bernoulli trials, if they satisfy the following conditions :

(i)   There should be a finite number of trials.

(ii) The trials should be independent.

(iii) Each trial has exactly two outcomes : success or failure.

(iv) The probability of success remains the same in each trial.

For example, throwing a die 50 times is a case of 50 Bernoulli trials, in which each trial results in success (say an even number) or failure (an odd number) and the probability of success (p) is same for all 50 throws. Obviously, the successive throws of the die are independent experiments. If the die is fair and have six numbers 1 to 6 written on six faces, then $p = \dfrac{1}{2}$ and $q = 1 - p = \dfrac{1}{2}$ = probability of failure.

Example 30 Six balls are drawn successively from an urn containing 7 red and 9 black balls. Tell whether or not the trials of drawing balls are Bernoulli trials when after each draw the ball drawn is

(i) replaced   (ii) not replaced in the urn.

Solution

(i) The number of trials is finite. When the drawing is done with replacement, the probability of success (say, red ball) is $p = \dfrac{7}{16}$ which is same for all six trials (draws). Hence, the drawing of balls with replacements are Bernoulli trials.

(ii)   When the drawing is done without replacement, the probability of success
(i.e., red ball) in first trial is $\dfrac{7}{16}$, in 2nd trial is $\dfrac{6}{15}$ if the first ball drawn is red or
$\dfrac{7}{15}$ if the first ball drawn is black and so on. Clearly, the probability of success is
not same for all trials, hence the trials are not Bernoulli trials.

13.7.2 Binomial distribution

Consider the experiment of tossing a coin in which each trial results in success (say, heads) or failure (tails). Let S and F denote respectively success and failure in each trial. Suppose we are interested in finding the ways in which we have one success in six trials.

Clearly, six different cases are there as listed below:

SFFFFF, FSFFFF, FFSFFF, FFFSFF, FFFFSF, FFFFFS.

Similarly, two successes and four failures can have $\dfrac{6!}{4! \times 2!}$ combinations. It will be

lengthy job to list all of these ways. Therefore, calculation of probabilities of 0, 1, 2,..., n number of successes may be lengthy and time consuming. To avoid the lengthy calculations and listing of all the possible cases, for the probabilities of number of successes in n-Bernoulli trials, a formula is derived. For this purpose, let us take the experiment made up of three Bernoulli trials with probabilities p and $q = 1 - p$ for success and failure respectively in each trial. The sample space of the experiment is the set

S = {SSS, SSF, SFS, FSS, SFF, FSF, FFS, FFF}

The number of successes is a random variable X and can take values 0, 1, 2, or 3. The probability distribution of the number of successes is as below :

$P(X = 0)$ = P(no success)

   $= P(\{FFF\}) = P(F) \, P(F) \, P(F)$

   $= q \cdot q \cdot q = q^3$ since the trials are independent

$P(X = 1)$ = P(one successes)

   $= P(\{SFF, FSF, FFS\})$

   $= P(\{SFF\}) + P(\{FSF\}) + P(\{FFS\})$

   $= P(S) \, P(F) \, P(F) + P(F) \, P(S) \, P(F) + P(F) \, P(F) \, P(S)$

   $= p.q.q + q.p.q + q.q.p = 3pq^2$

$P(X = 2)$ = P (two successes)

   $= P(\{SSF, SFS, FSS\})$

   $= P(\{SSF\}) + P (\{SFS\}) + P(\{FSS\})$

$$= P(S)\ P(S)\ P(F) + P(S)\ P(F)\ P(S) + P(F)\ P(S)\ P(S)$$

$$= p.p.q. + p.q.p + q.p.p = 3p^2q$$

and $P(X = 3) = P(\text{three success}) = P\ (\{SSS\})$

$$= P(S)\ .\ P(S)\ .\ P(S) = p^3$$

Thus, the probability distribution of X is

X	0	1	2	3
P(X)	q^3	$3q^2p$	$3qp^2$	p^3

Also, the binominal expansion of $(q + p)^3$ is

$$q^3 + 3q^2 p + 3qp^2 + p^3$$

Note that the probabilities of 0, 1, 2 or 3 successes are respectively the 1st, 2nd, 3rd and 4th term in the expansion of $(q + p)^3$.

Also, since $q + p = 1$, it follows that the sum of these probabilities, as expected, is 1.

Thus, we may conclude that in an experiment of n-Bernoulli trials, the probabilities of 0, 1, 2,..., n successes can be obtained as 1st, 2nd,...,$(n + 1)^{th}$ terms in the expansion of $(q + p)^n$. To prove this assertion (result), let us find the probability of x-successes in an experiment of n-Bernoulli trials.

Clearly, in case of x successes (S), there will be $(n - x)$ failures (F).

Now, x successes (S) and $(n - x)$ failures (F) can be obtained in $\dfrac{n!}{x!(n-x)!}$ ways.

In each of these ways, the probability of x successes and $(n - x)$ failures is

$$= P(x\ \text{successes})\ .\ P(n{-}x)\ \text{failures is}$$

$$= \underbrace{P(S).P(S)...P(S)}_{x\ \text{times}} \cdot \underbrace{P(F).P(F)...P(F)}_{(n-x)\ \text{times}} = p^x\ q^{n-x}$$

Thus, the probability of x successes in n-Bernoulli trials is $\dfrac{n!}{x!(n-x)!} p^x\ q^{n-x}$

or $^nC_x p^x\ q^{n-x}$

Thus $P(x\ \text{successes}) = {}^nC_x p^x\ q^{n-x},\quad x = 0, 1, 2,....,n.\ (q = 1 - p)$

Clearly, P(x successes), i.e. $^nC_x p^x\ q^{n-x}$ is the $(x + 1)^{th}$ term in the binomial expansion of $(q + p)^n$.

Thus, the probability distribution of number of successes in an experiment consisting of n Bernoulli trials may be obtained by the binomial expansion of $(q + p)^n$. Hence, this distribution of number of successes X can be written as

X	0	1	2	...	x	...	n
P(X)	$^nC_0\, q^n$	$^nC_1\, q^{n-1}p^1$	$^nC_2\, q^{n-2}p^2$		$^nC_x\, q^{n-x}p^x$		$^nC_n\, p^n$

The above probability distribution is known as *binomial distribution* with parameters n and p, because for given values of n and p, we can find the complete probability distribution.

The probability of x successes $P(X = x)$ is also denoted by $P(x)$ and is given by

$$P(x) = {^nC_x}\, q^{n-x}p^x, \quad x = 0, 1,..., n. \ (q = 1 - p)$$

This $P(x)$ is called the *probability function* of the binomial distribution.

A binomial distribution with n-Bernoulli trials and probability of success in each trial as p, is denoted by $B(n, p)$.

Let us now take up some examples.

Example 31 If a fair coin is tossed 10 times, find the probability of

(i)   exactly six heads

(ii) at least six heads

(iii) at most six heads

Solution The repeated tosses of a coin are Bernoulli trials. Let X denote the number of heads in an experiment of 10 trials.

Clearly, X has the binomial distribution with $n = 10$ and $p = \dfrac{1}{2}$

Therefore $P(X = x) = {^nC_x}\, q^{n-x}p^x, x = 0, 1, 2,...,n$

Here $n = 10, \ p = \dfrac{1}{2}, \ q = 1 - p = \dfrac{1}{2}$

Therefore $P(X = x) = {^{10}C_x}\left(\dfrac{1}{2}\right)^{10-x}\left(\dfrac{1}{2}\right)^{x} = {^{10}C_x}\left(\dfrac{1}{2}\right)^{10}$

Now   (i) $P(X = 6) = {^{10}C_6}\left(\dfrac{1}{2}\right)^{10} = \dfrac{10!}{6! \times 4!}\dfrac{1}{2^{10}} = \dfrac{105}{512}$

(ii) P(at least six heads) $= P(X \geq 6)$

$= P(X = 6) + P(X = 7) + P(X = 8) + P(X = 9) + P(X = 10)$

$$= {}^{10}C_6 \left(\frac{1}{2}\right)^{10} + {}^{10}C_7 \left(\frac{1}{2}\right)^{10} + {}^{10}C_8 \left(\frac{1}{2}\right)^{10} + {}^{10}C_9 \left(\frac{1}{2}\right)^{10} + {}^{10}C_{10} \left(\frac{1}{2}\right)^{10}$$

$$= \left[\left(\frac{10!}{6! \times 4!}\right) + \left(\frac{10!}{7! \times 3!}\right) + \left(\frac{10!}{8! \times 2!}\right) + \left(\frac{10!}{9! \times 1!}\right) + \left(\frac{10!}{10!}\right)\right]\frac{1}{2^{10}} = \frac{193}{512}$$

(iii) P(at most six heads) = $P(X \le 6)$

$= P(X = 0) + P(X = 1) + P(X = 2) + P(X = 3)$

$+ P(X = 4) + P(X = 5) + P(X = 6)$

$$= \left(\frac{1}{2}\right)^{10} + {}^{10}C_1 \left(\frac{1}{2}\right)^{10} + {}^{10}C_2 \left(\frac{1}{2}\right)^{10} + {}^{10}C_3 \left(\frac{1}{2}\right)^{10}$$

$$+ {}^{10}C_4 \left(\frac{1}{2}\right)^{10} + {}^{10}C_5 \left(\frac{1}{2}\right)^{10} + {}^{10}C_6 \left(\frac{1}{2}\right)^{10}$$

$$= \frac{848}{1024} = \frac{53}{64}$$

Example 32 Ten eggs are drawn successively with replacement from a lot containing 10% defective eggs. Find the probability that there is at least one defective egg.

Solution Let X denote the number of defective eggs in the 10 eggs drawn. Since the drawing is done with replacement, the trials are Bernoulli trials. Clearly, X has the

binomial distribution with $n = 10$ and $p = \dfrac{10}{100} = \dfrac{1}{10}$.

Therefore $\qquad\qquad\qquad q = 1 - p = \dfrac{9}{10}$

Now $\qquad$ P(at least one defective egg) = $P(X \ge 1) = 1 - P(X = 0)$

$$= 1 - {}^{10}C_0 \left(\frac{9}{10}\right)^{10} = 1 - \frac{9^{10}}{10^{10}}$$

EXERCISE 13.5

1. A die is thrown 6 times. If 'getting an odd number' is a success, what is the probability of

    (i) 5 successes? $\qquad\qquad$ (ii) at least 5 successes?

    (iii) at most 5 successes?

2. A pair of dice is thrown 4 times. If getting a doublet is considered a success, find the probability of two successes.

3. There are 5% defective items in a large bulk of items. What is the probability that a sample of 10 items will include not more than one defective item?

4. Five cards are drawn successively with replacement from a well-shuffled deck of 52 cards. What is the probability that
    (i) all the five cards are spades?
    (ii) only 3 cards are spades?
    (iii) none is a spade?

5. The probability that a bulb produced by a factory will fuse after 150 days of use is 0.05. Find the probability that out of 5 such bulbs
    (i) none
    (ii) not more than one
    (iii) more than one
    (iv) at least one
    will fuse after 150 days of use.

6. A bag consists of 10 balls each marked with one of the digits 0 to 9. If four balls are drawn successively with replacement from the bag, what is the probability that none is marked with the digit 0?

7. In an examination, 20 questions of true-false type are asked. Suppose a student tosses a fair coin to determine his answer to each question. If the coin falls heads, he answers 'true'; if it falls tails, he answers 'false'. Find the probability that he answers at least 12 questions correctly.

8. Suppose X has a binomial distribution $B\left(6, \dfrac{1}{2}\right)$. Show that X = 3 is the most likely outcome.
    (Hint : P(X = 3) is the maximum among all $P(x_i)$, $x_i = 0,1,2,3,4,5,6$)

9. On a multiple choice examination with three possible answers for each of the five questions, what is the probability that a candidate would get four or more correct answers just by guessing ?

10. A person buys a lottery ticket in 50 lotteries, in each of which his chance of winning a prize is $\dfrac{1}{100}$. What is the probability that he will win a prize
    (a) at least once (b) exactly once (c) at least twice?

11. Find the probability of getting 5 exactly twice in 7 throws of a die.

12. Find the probability of throwing at most 2 sixes in 6 throws of a single die.

13. It is known that 10% of certain articles manufactured are defective. What is the probability that in a random sample of 12 such articles, 9 are defective?

In each of the following, choose the correct answer:

14. In a box containing 100 bulbs, 10 are defective. The probability that out of a sample of 5 bulbs, none is defective is

(A) 10^{-1}
(B) $\left(\dfrac{1}{2}\right)^5$
(C) $\left(\dfrac{9}{10}\right)^5$
(D) $\dfrac{9}{10}$

15. The probability that a student is not a swimmer is $\dfrac{1}{5}$. Then the probability that out of five students, four are swimmers is

(A) $^5C_4\left(\dfrac{4}{5}\right)^4\dfrac{1}{5}$
(B) $\left(\dfrac{4}{5}\right)^4\dfrac{1}{5}$

(C) $^5C_1\dfrac{1}{5}\left(\dfrac{4}{5}\right)^4$
(D) None of these

Miscellaneous Examples

Example 33 Coloured balls are distributed in four boxes as shown in the following table:

Box	Colour			
	Black	White	Red	Blue
I	3	4	5	6
II	2	2	2	2
III	1.	2	3	1
IV	4	3	1	5

A box is selected at random and then a ball is randomly drawn from the selected box. The colour of the ball is black, what is the probability that ball drawn is from the box III?

Solution Let A, E_1, E_2, E_3 and E_4 be the events as defined below :

    A : a black ball is selected E_1 : box I is selected

    E_2 : box II is selected E_3 : box III is selected

    E_4 : box IV is selected

Since the boxes are chosen at random,

Therefore $P(E_1) = P(E_2) = P(E_3) = P(E_4) = \dfrac{1}{4}$

Also $P(A|E_1) = \dfrac{3}{18}, \ P(A|E_2) = \dfrac{2}{8}, \ P(A|E_3) = \dfrac{1}{7}$ and $P(A|E_4) = \dfrac{4}{13}$

P(box III is selected, given that the drawn ball is black) = $P(E_3|A)$. By Bayes' theorem,

$$P(E_3|A) = \frac{P(E_3) \cdot P(A|E_3)}{P(E_1)P(A|E_1) + P(E_2)P(A|E_2) + P(E_3)P(A|E_3) + P(E_4)P(A|E_4)}$$

$$= \frac{\dfrac{1}{4} \times \dfrac{1}{7}}{\dfrac{1}{4} \times \dfrac{3}{18} + \dfrac{1}{4} \times \dfrac{1}{4} + \dfrac{1}{4} \times \dfrac{1}{7} + \dfrac{1}{4} \times \dfrac{4}{13}} = 0.165$$

Example 34 Find the mean of the Binomial distribution $B\left(4, \dfrac{1}{3}\right)$.

Solution Let X be the random variable whose probability distribution is $B\left(4, \dfrac{1}{3}\right)$.

Here $n = 4, p = \dfrac{1}{3}$ and $q = 1 - \dfrac{1}{3} = \dfrac{2}{3}$

We know that $P(X = x) = {}^4C_x \left(\dfrac{2}{3}\right)^{4-x} \left(\dfrac{1}{3}\right)^x, x = 0, 1, 2, 3, 4.$

i.e. the distribution of X is

x_i	$P(x_i)$		$x_i \ P(x_i)$
0	${}^4C_0 \left(\dfrac{2}{3}\right)^4$		0
1	${}^4C_1 \left(\dfrac{2}{3}\right)^3 \left(\dfrac{1}{3}\right)$		${}^4C_1 \left(\dfrac{2}{3}\right)^3 \left(\dfrac{1}{3}\right)$

2	$^4C_2\left(\dfrac{2}{3}\right)^2\left(\dfrac{1}{3}\right)^2$	$2\left(^4C_2\left(\dfrac{2}{3}\right)^2\left(\dfrac{1}{3}\right)^2\right)$
3	$^4C_3\left(\dfrac{2}{3}\right)\left(\dfrac{1}{3}\right)^3$	$3\left(^4C_3\left(\dfrac{2}{3}\right)\left(\dfrac{1}{3}\right)^3\right)$
4	$^4C_4\left(\dfrac{1}{3}\right)^4$	$\cdot\ 4\left(^4C_4\left(\dfrac{1}{3}\right)^4\right)$

(I)

Now Mean $(\mu) = \displaystyle\sum_{i=1}^{4} x_i\, p(x_i)$

$$= 0 + {}^4C_1\left(\frac{2}{3}\right)^3\left(\frac{1}{3}\right) + 2\cdot {}^4C_2\left(\frac{2}{3}\right)^2\left(\frac{1}{3}\right)^2 + 3\cdot {}^4C_3\left(\frac{2}{3}\right)\left(\frac{1}{3}\right)^3 + 4\cdot {}^4C_4\left(\frac{1}{3}\right)^4$$

$$= 4\times\frac{2^3}{3^4} + 2\times 6\times\frac{2^2}{3^4} + 3\times 4\times\frac{2}{3^4} + 4\times 1\times\frac{1}{3^4}$$

$$= \frac{32 + 48 + 24 + 4}{3^4} = \frac{108}{81} = \frac{4}{3}$$

Example 35 The probability of a shooter hitting a target is $\dfrac{3}{4}$. How many minimum number of times must he/she fire so that the probability of hitting the target at least once is more than 0.99?

Solution Let the shooter fire n times. Obviously, n fires are n Bernoulli trials. In each trial, $p =$ probability of hitting the target $= \dfrac{3}{4}$ and $q =$ probability of not hitting the

target $= \dfrac{1}{4}$. Then $P(X = x) = {}^nC_x\, q^{n-x}\, p^x = {}^nC_x\left(\dfrac{1}{4}\right)^{n-x}\left(\dfrac{3}{4}\right)^x = {}^nC_x\,\dfrac{3^x}{4^n}$.

Now, given that,

P(hitting the target at least once) > 0.99

i.e. $P(x \geq 1) > 0.99$

Therefore, $\qquad\qquad 1 - P(x = 0) > 0.99$

or $\qquad\qquad\qquad 1 - {}^nC_0 \dfrac{1}{4^n} > 0.99$

or $\qquad\qquad {}^nC_0 \dfrac{1}{4^n} < 0.01$ i.e. $\dfrac{1}{4^n} < 0.01$

or $\qquad\qquad\qquad 4^n > \dfrac{1}{0.01} = 100 \qquad\qquad\qquad\qquad$ ... (1)

The minimum value of n to satisfy the inequality (1) is 4.

Thus, the shooter must fire 4 times.

Example 36 A and B throw a die alternatively till one of them gets a '6' and wins the game. Find their respective probabilities of winning, if A starts first.

Solution Let S denote the success (getting a '6') and F denote the failure (not getting a '6').

Thus, $\qquad\qquad\qquad P(S) = \dfrac{1}{6}, P(F) = \dfrac{5}{6}$

$\qquad$ P(A wins in the first throw) = $P(S) = \dfrac{1}{6}$

A gets the third throw, when the first throw by A and second throw by B result into failures.

Therefore, $\quad$ P(A wins in the 3rd throw) = $P(FFS) = P(F)P(F)P(S) = \dfrac{5}{6} \times \dfrac{5}{6} \times \dfrac{1}{6}$

$$= \left(\dfrac{5}{6}\right)^2 \times \dfrac{1}{6}$$

$\qquad$ P(A wins in the 5th throw) = $P(FFFFS) = \left(\dfrac{5}{6}\right)^4 \left(\dfrac{1}{6}\right)$ and so on.

Hence, $\qquad\qquad$ P(A wins) = $\dfrac{1}{6} + \left(\dfrac{5}{6}\right)^2 \left(\dfrac{1}{6}\right) + \left(\dfrac{5}{6}\right)^4 \left(\dfrac{1}{6}\right) + \ldots$

$$= \dfrac{\dfrac{1}{6}}{1 - \dfrac{25}{36}} = \dfrac{6}{11}$$

$$P(B \text{ wins}) = 1 - P (A \text{ wins}) = 1 - \frac{6}{11} = \frac{5}{11}$$

Remark If $a + ar + ar^2 + ... + ar^{n-1} + ...$, where $|r| < 1$, then sum of this infinite G.P.

is given by $\dfrac{a}{1-r}$. (Refer A.1.3 of Class XI Text book).

Example 37 If a machine is correctly set up, it produces 90% acceptable items. If it is incorrectly set up, it produces only 40% acceptable items. Past experience shows that 80% of the set ups are correctly done. If after a certain set up, the machine produces 2 acceptable items, find the probability that the machine is correctly setup.

Solution Let A be the event that the machine produces 2 acceptable items.

Also let B_1 represent the event of correct set up and B_2 represent the event of incorrect setup.

Now $P(B_1) = 0.8, P(B_2) = 0.2$

$P(A|B_1) = 0.9 \times 0.9$ and $P(A|B_2) = 0.4 \times 0.4$

Therefore $P(B_1|A) = \dfrac{P(B_1)\, P(A|B_1)}{P(B_1)\, P(A|B_1) + P(B_2)\, P(A|B_2)}$

$$= \frac{0.8 \times 0.9 \times 0.9}{0.8 \times 0.9 \times 0.9 + 0.2 \times 0.4 \times 0.4} = \frac{648}{680} = 0.95$$

Miscellaneous Exercise on Chapter 13

1. A and B are two events such that $P (A) \neq 0$. Find $P(B|A)$, if
   (i) A is a subset of B   (ii) $A \cap B = \phi$

2. A couple has two children,
   (i) Find the probability that both children are males, if it is known that at least one of the children is male.
   (ii) Find the probability that both children are females, if it is known that the elder child is a female.

3. Suppose that 5% of men and 0.25% of women have grey hair. A grey haired person is selected at random. What is the probability of this person being male? Assume that there are equal number of males and females.

4. Suppose that 90% of people are right-handed. What is the probability that at most 6 of a random sample of 10 people are right-handed?

5. An urn contains 25 balls of which 10 balls bear a mark 'X' and the remaining 15 bear a mark 'Y'. A ball is drawn at random from the urn, its mark is noted down and it is replaced. If 6 balls are drawn in this way, find the probability that

    (i) all will bear 'X' mark.

    (ii) not more than 2 will bear 'Y' mark.

    (iii) at least one ball will bear 'Y' mark.

    (iv) the number of balls with 'X' mark and 'Y' mark will be equal.

6. In a hurdle race, a player has to cross 10 hurdles. The probability that he will clear each hurdle is $\frac{5}{6}$. What is the probability that he will knock down fewer than 2 hurdles?

7. A die is thrown again and again until three sixes are obtained. Find the probability of obtaining the third six in the sixth throw of the die.

8. If a leap year is selected at random, what is the chance that it will contain 53 tuesdays?

9. An experiment succeeds twice as often as it fails. Find the probability that in the next six trials, there will be atleast 4 successes.

10. How many times must a man toss a fair coin so that the probability of having at least one head is more than 90%?

11. In a game, a man wins a rupee for a six and loses a rupee for any other number when a fair die is thrown. The man decided to throw a die thrice but to quit as and when he gets a six. Find the expected value of the amount he wins / loses.

12. Suppose we have four boxes A,B,C and D containing coloured marbles as given below:

Box	Marble colour		
	Red	White	Black
A	1	6	3
B	6	2	2
C	8	1	1
D	0	6	4

    One of the boxes has been selected at random and a single marble is drawn from it. If the marble is red, what is the probability that it was drawn from box A?, box B?, box C?

13. Assume that the chances of a patient having a heart attack is 40%. It is also assumed that a meditation and yoga course reduce the risk of heart attack by 30% and prescription of certain drug reduces its chances by 25%. At a time a patient can choose any one of the two options with equal probabilities. It is given that after going through one of the two options the patient selected at random suffers a heart attack. Find the probability that the patient followed a course of meditation and yoga?

14. If each element of a second order determinant is either zero or one, what is the probability that the value of the determinant is positive? (Assume that the individual entries of the determinant are chosen independently, each value being assumed with probability $\frac{1}{2}$).

15. An electronic assembly consists of two subsystems, say, A and B. From previous testing procedures, the following probabilities are assumed to be known:

$$P(A \text{ fails}) = 0.2$$
$$P(B \text{ fails alone}) = 0.15$$
$$P(A \text{ and B fail}) = 0.15$$

Evaluate the following probabilities

(i) P(A fails|B has failed)   (ii) P(A fails alone)

16. Bag I contains 3 red and 4 black balls and Bag II contains 4 red and 5 black balls. One ball is transferred from Bag I to Bag II and then a ball is drawn from Bag II. The ball so drawn is found to be red in colour. Find the probability that the transferred ball is black.

Choose the correct answer in each of the following:

17. If A and B are two events such that $P(A) \neq 0$ and $P(B \mid A) = 1$, then

(A) $A \subset B$ (B) $B \subset A$ (C) $B = \phi$ (D) $A = \phi$

18. If $P(A|B) > P(A)$, then which of the following is correct :

(A) $P(B|A) < P(B)$ (B) $P(A \cap B) < P(A) . P(B)$

(C) $P(B|A) > P(B)$ (D) $P(B|A) = P(B)$

19. If A and B are any two events such that $P(A) + P(B) - P(A \text{ and } B) = P(A)$, then

(A) $P(B|A) = 1$ (B) $P(A|B) = 1$

(C) $P(B|A) = 0$ (D) $P(A|B) = 0$

Summary

The salient features of the chapter are –

♦ The conditional probability of an event E, given the occurrence of the event F

   is given by $P(E|F) = \dfrac{P(E \cap F)}{P(F)}$, $P(F) \neq 0$

♦ $0 \leq P(E|F) \leq 1,$ $P(E'|F) = 1 - P(E|F)$

   $P((E \cup F)|G) = P(E|G) + P(F|G) - P((E \cap F)|G)$

♦ $P(E \cap F) = P(E) \, P(F|E), P(E) \neq 0$

   $P(E \cap F) = P(F) \, P(E|F), P(F) \neq 0$

♦ If E and F are independent, then

   $P(E \cap F) = P(E) \, P(F)$

   $P(E|F) = P(E), P(F) \neq 0$

   $P(F|E) = P(F), P(E) \neq 0$

♦ **Theorem of total probability**

   Let $\{E_1, E_2, ..., E_n\}$ be a partition of a sample space and suppose that each of $E_1, E_2, ..., E_n$ has nonzero probability. Let A be any event associated with S, then

   $P(A) = P(E_1) \, P(A|E_1) + P(E_2) \, P(A|E_2) + ... + P(E_n) \, P(A|E_n)$

♦ **Bayes' theorem** If $E_1, E_2, ..., E_n$ are events which constitute a partition of sample space S, i.e. $E_1, E_2, ..., E_n$ are pairwise disjoint and $E_1 \cup E_2 \cup ... \cup E_n = S$ and A be any event with nonzero probability, then

   $$P(E_i | A) = \dfrac{P(E_i) P(A|E_i)}{\displaystyle\sum_{j=1}^{n} P(E_j) P(A|E_j)}$$

♦ A random variable is a real valued function whose domain is the sample space of a random experiment.

♦ The probability distribution of a random variable X is the system of numbers

X	:	x_1	x_2	...	x_n
P(X)	:	p_1	p_2	...	p_n

   where, $p_i > 0,\ \displaystyle\sum_{i=1}^{n} p_i = 1,\ i = 1, 2, ..., n$

◆ Let X be a random variable whose possible values $x_1, x_2, x_3, ..., x_n$ occur with probabilities $p_1, p_2, p_3, ... p_n$ respectively. The mean of X, denoted by μ, is the number $\sum_{i=1}^{n} x_i p_i$.

The mean of a random variable X is also called the expectation of X, denoted by E (X).

◆ Let X be a random variable whose possible values $x_1, x_2, ..., x_n$ occur with probabilities $p(x_1), p(x_2), ..., p(x_n)$ respectively.

Let $\mu = E(X)$ be the mean of X. The variance of X, denoted by Var (X) or σ_x^2, is defined as $\sigma_x^2 = \text{Var}(X) = \sum_{i=1}^{n} (x_i - \mu)^2 p(x_i)$

or equivalently $\sigma_x^2 = E (X - \mu)^2$

The non-negative number

$$\sigma_x = \sqrt{\text{Var}(X)} = \sqrt{\sum_{i=1}^{n} (x_i - \mu)^2 p(x_i)}$$

is called the standard deviation of the random variable X.

◆ Var (X) = E (X²) – [E(X)]²

◆ Trials of a random experiment are called Bernoulli trials, if they satisfy the following conditions :

(i) There should be a finite number of trials.

(ii) The trials should be independent.

(iii) Each trial has exactly two outcomes : success or failure.

(iv) The probability of success remains the same in each trial.

For Binomial distribution B (n, p), P $(X = x) = {}^nC_x \, q^{n-x} \, p^x$, $x = 0, \ 1,..., n$ $(q = 1 - p)$

Historical Note

The earliest indication on measurement of chances in game of dice appeared in 1477 in a commentary on Dante's Divine Comedy. A treatise on gambling named *liber de Ludo Alcae*, by Geronimo Carden (1501-1576) was published posthumously in 1663. In this treatise, he gives the number of favourable cases for each event when two dice are thrown.

Galileo (1564-1642) gave casual remarks concerning the correct evaluation of chance in a game of three dice. Galileo analysed that when three dice are thrown, the sum of the number that appear is more likely to be 10 than the sum 9, because the number of cases favourable to 10 are more than the number of cases for the appearance of number 9.

Apart from these early contributions, it is generally acknowledged that the true origin of the science of probability lies in the correspondence between two great men of the seventeenth century, Pascal (1623-1662) and Pierre de Fermat (1601-1665). A French gambler, Chevalier de Metre asked Pascal to explain some seeming contradiction between his theoretical reasoning and the observation gathered from gambling. In a series of letters written around 1654, Pascal and Fermat laid the first foundation of science of probability. Pascal solved the problem in algebraic manner while Fermat used the method of combinations.

Great Dutch Scientist, Huygens (1629-1695), became acquainted with the content of the correspondence between Pascal and Fermat and published a first book on probability, "*De Ratiociniis in Ludo Aleae*" containing solution of many interesting rather than difficult problems on probability in games of chances.

The next great work on probability theory is by Jacob Bernoulli (1654-1705), in the form of a great book, "*Ars Conjectendi*" published posthumously in 1713 by his nephew, Nicholes Bernoulli. To him is due the discovery of one of the most important probility distribution known as Binomial distribution. The next remarkable work on probability lies in 1993. A. N. Kolmogorov (1903-1987) is credited with the axiomatic theory of probability. His book, 'Foundations of probability' published in 1933, introduces probability as a set function and is considered a 'classic!'.

ANSWERS

EXERCISE 7.1

1. $-\dfrac{1}{2}\cos 2x$

2. $\dfrac{1}{3}\sin 3x$

3. $\dfrac{1}{2}e^{2x}$

4. $\dfrac{1}{3a}(ax+b)^3$

5. $-\dfrac{1}{2}\cos 2x - \dfrac{4}{3}e^{3x}$

6. $\dfrac{4}{3}e^{3x}+x+C$

7. $\dfrac{x^3}{3}-x+C$

8. $\dfrac{ax^3}{3}+\dfrac{bx^2}{2}+cx+C$

9. $\dfrac{2}{3}x^{\frac{3}{2}}+e^x+C$

10. $\dfrac{x^2}{2}+\log|x|-2x+C$

11. $\dfrac{x^2}{2}+5x+\dfrac{4}{x}+C$

12. $\dfrac{2}{7}x^{\frac{7}{2}}+2x^{\frac{3}{2}}+8\sqrt{x}+C$

13. $\dfrac{x^3}{3}+x+C$

14. $\dfrac{2}{3}x^{\frac{3}{2}}-\dfrac{2}{5}x^{\frac{5}{2}}+C$

15. $\dfrac{6}{7}x^{\frac{7}{2}}+\dfrac{4}{5}x^{\frac{5}{2}}+2x^{\frac{3}{2}}+C$

16. $x^2-3\sin x+e^x+C$

17. $\dfrac{2}{3}x^3+3\cos x+\dfrac{10}{3}x^{\frac{3}{2}}+C$

18. $\tan x + \sec x + C$

19. $\tan x - x + C$

20. $2\tan x - 3\sec x + C$

21. C

22. A

EXERCISE 7.2

1. $\log(1+x^2)+C$

2. $\dfrac{1}{3}(\log|x|)^3+C$

3. $\log|1+\log x|+C$

4. $\cos(\cos x)+C$

5. $-\dfrac{1}{4a}\cos 2(ax+b)+C$

6. $\dfrac{2}{3a}(ax+b)^{\frac{3}{2}}+C$

7. $\dfrac{2}{5}(x+2)^{\frac{5}{2}}-\dfrac{4}{3}(x+2)^{\frac{3}{2}}+C$

8. $\frac{1}{6}(1+2x^2)^{\frac{3}{2}}+C$ 9. $\frac{4}{3}(x^2+x+1)^{\frac{3}{2}}+C$ 10. $2\log\left|\sqrt{x}-1\right|+C$

11. $\frac{2}{3}\sqrt{x+4}(x-8)+C$

12. $\frac{1}{7}(x^3-1)^{\frac{7}{3}}+\frac{1}{4}(x^3-1)^{\frac{4}{3}}+C$ 13. $-\frac{1}{18(2+3x^3)^2}+C$

14. $\frac{(\log x)^{1-m}}{1-m}+C$ 15. $-\frac{1}{8}\log|9-4x^2|+C$ 16. $\frac{1}{2}e^{2x+3}+C$

17. $-\frac{1}{2e^{x^2}}+C$ 18. $e^{\tan^{-1}x}+C$ 19. $\log(e^x+e^{-x})+C$

20. $\frac{1}{2}\log(e^{2x}+e^{-2x})+C$ 21. $\frac{1}{2}\tan(2x-3)-x+C$

22. $-\frac{1}{4}\tan(7-4x)+C$ 23. $\frac{1}{2}(\sin^{-1}x)^2+C$

24. $\frac{1}{2}\log|2\sin x+3\cos x|+C$ 25. $\frac{1}{(1-\tan x)}+C$

26. $2\sin\sqrt{x}+C$ 27. $\frac{1}{3}(\sin 2x)^{\frac{3}{2}}+C$ 28. $2\sqrt{1+\sin x}+C$

29. $\frac{1}{2}(\log\sin x)^2+C$ 30. $-\log|1+\cos x|+C$ 31. $\frac{1}{1+\cos x}+C$

32. $\frac{x}{2}-\frac{1}{2}\log|\cos x+\sin x|+C$ 33. $\frac{x}{2}-\frac{1}{2}\log|\cos x-\sin x|+C$

34. $2\sqrt{\tan x}+C$ 35. $\frac{1}{3}(1+\log x)^3+C$ 36. $\frac{1}{3}(x+\log x)^3+C$

37. $-\frac{1}{4}\cos(\tan^{-1}x^4)+C$ 38. D

39. B

EXERCISE 7.3

1. $\dfrac{x}{2} - \dfrac{1}{8}\sin(4x+10)+C$

2. $-\dfrac{1}{14}\cos 7x + \dfrac{1}{2}\cos x + C$

3. $\dfrac{1}{4}\left[\dfrac{1}{12}\sin 12x + x + \dfrac{1}{8}\sin 8x + \dfrac{1}{4}\sin 4x\right]+C$

4. $-\dfrac{1}{2}\cos(2x+1)+\dfrac{1}{6}\cos^3(2x+1)+C$

5. $\dfrac{1}{6}\cos^6 x - \dfrac{1}{4}\cos^4 x + C$

6. $\dfrac{1}{4}\left[\dfrac{1}{6}\cos 6x - \dfrac{1}{4}\cos 4x - \dfrac{1}{2}\cos 2x\right]+C$

7. $\dfrac{1}{2}\left[\dfrac{1}{4}\sin 4x - \dfrac{1}{12}\sin 12x\right]+C$

8. $2\tan\dfrac{x}{2} - x + C$

9. $x - \tan\dfrac{x}{2}+C$

10. $\dfrac{3x}{8} - \dfrac{1}{4}\sin 2x + \dfrac{1}{32}\sin 4x + C$

11. $\dfrac{3x}{8} + \dfrac{1}{8}\sin 4x + \dfrac{1}{64}\sin 8x + C$

12. $x - \sin x + C$

13. $2(\sin x + x\cos\alpha)+C$

14. $-\dfrac{1}{\cos x + \sin x}+C$

15. $\dfrac{1}{6}\sec^3 2x - \dfrac{1}{2}\sec 2x + C$

16. $\dfrac{1}{3}\tan^3 x - \tan x + x + C$

17. $\sec x - \operatorname{cosec} x + C$

18. $\tan x + C$

19. $\log|\tan x| + \dfrac{1}{2}\tan^2 x + C$

20. $\log|\cos x + \sin x| + C$

21. $\dfrac{\pi x}{2} - \dfrac{x^2}{2}+C$

22. $\dfrac{1}{\sin(a-b)}\log\left|\dfrac{\cos(x-a)}{\cos(x-b)}\right|+C$

23. A

24. B

EXERCISE 7.4

1. $\tan^{-1} x^3 + C$

2. $\dfrac{1}{2}\log\left|2x+\sqrt{1+4x^2}\right|+C$

3. $\log\left|\dfrac{1}{2-x+\sqrt{x^2-4x+5}}\right|+C$

4. $\dfrac{1}{5}\sin^{-1}\dfrac{5x}{3}+C$

5. $\dfrac{3}{2\sqrt{2}}\tan^{-1}\sqrt{2}\,x^2+C$

6. $\dfrac{1}{6}\log\left|\dfrac{1+x^3}{1-x^3}\right|+C$

7. $\sqrt{x^2-1}-\log\left|x+\sqrt{x^2-1}\right|+C$

8. $\dfrac{1}{3}\log\left|x^3+\sqrt{x^6+a^6}\right|+C$

9. $\log\left|\tan x+\sqrt{\tan^2 x+4}\right|+C$

10. $\log\left|x+1+\sqrt{x^2+2x+2}\right|+C$

11. $\dfrac{1}{6}\tan^{-1}\left(\dfrac{3x+1}{2}\right)+C$

12. $\sin^{-1}\left(\dfrac{x+3}{2}\right)+C$

13. $\log\left|x-\dfrac{3}{2}+\sqrt{x^2-3x+2}\right|+C$

14. $\sin^{-1}\left(\dfrac{2x-3}{\sqrt{41}}\right)+C$

15. $\log\left|x-\dfrac{a+b}{2}+\sqrt{(x-a)(x-b)}\right|+C$

16. $2\sqrt{2x^2+x-3}+C$

17. $\sqrt{x^2-1}+2\log\left|x+\sqrt{x^2-1}\right|+C$

18. $\dfrac{5}{6}\log\left|3x^2+2x+1\right|-\dfrac{11}{3\sqrt{2}}\tan^{-1}\left(\dfrac{3x+1}{\sqrt{2}}\right)+C$

19. $6\sqrt{x^2-9x+20}+34\log\left|x-\dfrac{9}{2}+\sqrt{x^2-9x+20}\right|+C$

20. $-\sqrt{4x-x^2}+4\sin^{-1}\left(\dfrac{x-2}{2}\right)+C$

21. $\sqrt{x^2+2x+3}+\log\left|x+1+\sqrt{x^2+2x+3}\right|+C$

22. $\dfrac{1}{2}\log\left|x^2-2x-5\right|+\dfrac{2}{\sqrt{6}}\log\left|\dfrac{x-1-\sqrt{6}}{x-1+\sqrt{6}}\right|+C$

23. $5\sqrt{x^2+4x+10} - 7\log\left|x+2+\sqrt{x^2+4x+10}\right| + C$

24. B   25. B

EXERCISE 7.5

1. $\log\dfrac{(x+2)^2}{|x+1|} + C$ 2. $\dfrac{1}{6}\log\left|\dfrac{x-3}{x+3}\right| + C$

3. $\log|x-1| - 5\log|x-2| + 4\log|x-3| + C$

4. $\dfrac{1}{2}\log|x-1| - 2\log|x-2| + \dfrac{3}{2}\log|x-3| + C$

5. $4\log|x+2| - 2\log|x+1| + C$ 6. $\dfrac{x}{2} + \log|x| - \dfrac{3}{4}\log|1-2x| + C$

7. $\dfrac{1}{2}\log|x-1| - \dfrac{1}{4}\log(x^2+1) + \dfrac{1}{2}\tan^{-1}x + C$

8. $\dfrac{2}{9}\log\left|\dfrac{x-1}{x+2}\right| - \dfrac{1}{3(x-1)} + C$ 9. $\dfrac{1}{2}\log\left|\dfrac{x+1}{x-1}\right| - \dfrac{4}{x-1} + C$

10. $\dfrac{5}{2}\log|x+1| - \dfrac{1}{10}\log|x-1| - \dfrac{12}{5}\log|2x+3| + C$

11. $\dfrac{5}{3}\log|x+1| - \dfrac{5}{2}\log|x+2| + \dfrac{5}{6}\log|x-2| + C$

12. $\dfrac{x^2}{2} + \dfrac{1}{2}\log|x+1| + \dfrac{3}{2}\log|x-1| + C$

13. $-\log|x-1| + \dfrac{1}{2}\log(1+x^2) + \tan^{-1}x + C$

14. $3\log|x-2| + \dfrac{7}{x+2} + C$ 15. $\dfrac{1}{4}\log\left|\dfrac{x-1}{x+1}\right| - \dfrac{1}{2}\tan^{-1}x + C$

16. $\dfrac{1}{n}\log\left|\dfrac{x^n}{x^n+1}\right| + C$ 17. $\log\left|\dfrac{2-\sin x}{1-\sin x}\right| + C$

18. $x + \dfrac{2}{\sqrt{3}}\tan^{-1}\dfrac{x}{\sqrt{3}} - 3\tan^{-1}\dfrac{x}{2} + C$ 19. $\dfrac{1}{2}\log\left(\dfrac{x^2+1}{x^2+3}\right) + C$

20. $\dfrac{1}{4}\log\left|\dfrac{x^4-1}{x^4}\right|+C$

21. $\log\left(\dfrac{e^x-1}{e^x}\right)+C$

22. B

23. A

EXERCISE 7.6

1. $-x\cos x+\sin x+C$

2. $-\dfrac{x}{3}\cos 3x+\dfrac{1}{9}\sin 3x+C$

3. $e^x(x^2-2x+2)+C$

4. $\dfrac{x^2}{2}\log x-\dfrac{x^2}{4}+C$

5. $\dfrac{x^2}{2}\log 2x-\dfrac{x^2}{4}+C$

6. $\dfrac{x^3}{3}\log x-\dfrac{x^3}{9}+C$

7. $\dfrac{1}{4}(2x^2-1)\sin^{-1}x+\dfrac{x\sqrt{1-x^2}}{4}+C$

8. $\dfrac{x^2}{2}\tan^{-1}x-\dfrac{x}{2}+\dfrac{1}{2}\tan^{-1}x+C$

9. $(2x^2-1)\dfrac{\cos^{-1}x}{4}-\dfrac{x}{4}\sqrt{1-x^2}+C$

10. $\left(\sin^{-1}x\right)^2 x+2\sqrt{1-x^2}\,\sin^{-1}x-2x+C$

11. $-\left[\sqrt{1-x^2}\cos^{-1}x+x\right]+C$

12. $x\tan x+\log|\cos x|+C$

13. $x\tan^{-1}x-\dfrac{1}{2}\log(1+x^2)+C$

14. $\dfrac{x^2}{2}(\log x)^2-\dfrac{x^2}{2}\log x+\dfrac{x^2}{4}+C$

15. $\left(\dfrac{x^3}{3}+x\right)\log x-\dfrac{x^3}{9}-x+C$

16. $e^x\sin x+C$

17. $\dfrac{e^x}{1+x}+C$

18. $e^x\tan\dfrac{x}{2}+C$

19. $\dfrac{e^x}{x}+C$

20. $\dfrac{e^x}{(x-1)^2}+C$

21. $\dfrac{e^{2x}}{5}(2\sin x-\cos x)+C$

22. $2x\tan^{-1}x-\log(1+x^2)+C$

23. A

24. B

EXERCISE 7.7

1. $\frac{1}{2}x\sqrt{4-x^2}+2\sin^{-1}\frac{x}{2}+C$

2. $\frac{1}{4}\sin^{-1}2x+\frac{1}{2}x\sqrt{1-4x^2}+C$

3. $\frac{(x+2)}{2}\sqrt{x^2+4x+6}+\log\left|x+2+\sqrt{x^2+4x+6}\right|+C$

4. $\frac{(x+2)}{2}\sqrt{x^2+4x+1}-\frac{3}{2}\log\left|x+2+\sqrt{x^2+4x+1}\right|+C$

5. $\frac{5}{2}\sin^{-1}\left(\frac{x+2}{\sqrt{5}}\right)+\frac{x+2}{2}\sqrt{1-4x-x^2}+C$

6. $\frac{(x+2)}{2}\sqrt{x^2+4x-5}-\frac{9}{2}\log\left|x+2+\sqrt{x^2+4x-5}\right|+C$

7. $\frac{(2x-3)}{4}\sqrt{1+3x-x^2}+\frac{13}{8}\sin^{-1}\left(\frac{2x-3}{\sqrt{13}}\right)+C$

8. $\frac{2x+3}{4}\sqrt{x^2+3x}-\frac{9}{8}\log\left|x+\frac{3}{2}+\sqrt{x^2+3x}\right|+C$

9. $\frac{x}{6}\sqrt{x^2+9}+\frac{3}{2}\log\left|x+\sqrt{x^2+9}\right|+C$

10. A

11. D

EXERCISE 7.8

1. $\frac{1}{2}(b^2-a^2)$

2. $\frac{35}{2}$

3. $\frac{19}{3}$

4. $\frac{27}{2}$

5. $e-\frac{1}{e}$

6. $\frac{15+e^8}{2}$

EXERCISE 7.9

1. 2

2. $\log\frac{3}{2}$

3. $\frac{64}{3}$

4. $\frac{1}{2}$

5. 0

6. $e^4(e-1)$

7. $\dfrac{1}{2}\log 2$

8. $\log\left(\dfrac{\sqrt{2}-1}{2-\sqrt{3}}\right)$

9. $\dfrac{\pi}{2}$

10. $\dfrac{\pi}{4}$

11. $\dfrac{1}{2}\log\dfrac{3}{2}$

12. $\dfrac{\pi}{4}$

13. $\dfrac{1}{2}\log 2$

14. $\dfrac{1}{5}\log 6+\dfrac{3}{\sqrt{5}}\tan^{-1}\sqrt{5}$

15. $\dfrac{1}{2}(e-1)$

16. $5-\dfrac{5}{2}\left(9\log\dfrac{5}{4}-\log\dfrac{3}{2}\right)$

17. $\dfrac{\pi^4}{1024}+\dfrac{\pi}{2}+2$

18. 0

19. $3\log 2+\dfrac{3\pi}{8}$

20. $1+\dfrac{4}{\pi}-\dfrac{2\sqrt{2}}{\pi}$

21. D

22. C

EXERCISE 7.10

1. $\dfrac{1}{2}\log 2$

2. $\dfrac{64}{231}$

3. $\dfrac{\pi}{2}-\log 2$

4. $\dfrac{16\sqrt{2}}{15}(\sqrt{2}+1)$

5. $\dfrac{\pi}{4}$

6. $\dfrac{1}{\sqrt{17}}\log\dfrac{21+5\sqrt{17}}{4}$

7. $\dfrac{\pi}{8}$

8. $\dfrac{e^2(e^2-2)}{4}$

9. D

10. B

EXERCISE 7.11

1. $\dfrac{\pi}{4}$

2. $\dfrac{\pi}{4}$

3. $\dfrac{\pi}{4}$

4. $\dfrac{\pi}{4}$

5. 29

6. 9

7. $\dfrac{1}{(n+1)(n+2)}$

8. $\dfrac{\pi}{8}\log 2$

9. $\dfrac{16\sqrt{2}}{15}$

10. $\dfrac{\pi}{2}\log\dfrac{1}{2}$

11. $\dfrac{\pi}{2}$

12. π

13. 0

14. 0

15. 0

16. $-\pi \log 2$

17. $\dfrac{a}{2}$

18. 5

20. C

21. C

MISCELLANEOUS EXERCISE ON CHAPTER 7

1. $\dfrac{1}{2}\log\left|\dfrac{x^2}{1-x^2}\right|+C$

2. $\dfrac{2}{3(a-b)}\left[(x+a)^{\frac{3}{2}}-(x+b)^{\frac{3}{2}}\right]+C$

3. $-\dfrac{2}{a}\sqrt{\dfrac{(a-x)}{x}}+C$

4. $-\left(1+\dfrac{1}{x^4}\right)^{\frac{1}{4}}+C$

5. $2\sqrt{x}-3x^{\frac{1}{3}}+6x^{\frac{1}{6}}-6\log(1+x^{\frac{1}{6}})+C$

6. $-\dfrac{1}{2}\log|x+1|+\dfrac{1}{4}\log(x^2+9)+\dfrac{3}{2}\tan^{-1}\dfrac{x}{3}+C$

7. $\sin a\log|\sin(x-a)|+x\cos a+C$

8. $\dfrac{x^3}{3}+C$

9. $\sin^{-1}\left(\dfrac{\sin x}{2}\right)+C$

10. $-\dfrac{1}{2}\sin 2x+C$

11. $\dfrac{1}{\sin(a-b)}\log\left|\dfrac{\cos(x+b)}{\cos(x+a)}\right|+C$

12. $\dfrac{1}{4}\sin^{-1}(x^4)+C$

13. $\log\left(\dfrac{1+e^x}{2+e^x}\right)+C$

14. $\dfrac{1}{3}\tan^{-1}x-\dfrac{1}{6}\tan^{-1}\dfrac{x}{2}+C$

15. $-\dfrac{1}{4}\cos^4 x+C$

16. $\dfrac{1}{4}\log(x^4+1)+C$

17. $\dfrac{[f(ax+b)]^{n+1}}{a(n+1)}+C$

18. $\dfrac{-2}{\sin\alpha}\sqrt{\dfrac{\sin(x+\alpha)}{\sin x}}+C$

19. $\dfrac{2(2x-1)}{\pi}\sin^{-1}\sqrt{x}+\dfrac{2\sqrt{x-x^2}}{\pi}-x+C$

20. $-2\sqrt{1-x}+\cos^{-1}\sqrt{x}+\sqrt{x-x^2}+C$

21. $e^x \tan x + C$

22. $-2\log|x+1|-\dfrac{1}{x+1}+3\log|x+2|+C$

23. $\dfrac{1}{2}\left[x\cos^{-1}x-\sqrt{1-x^2}\right]+C$

24. $-\dfrac{1}{3}\left(1+\dfrac{1}{x^2}\right)^{\frac{3}{2}}\left[\log\left(1+\dfrac{1}{x^2}\right)-\dfrac{2}{3}\right]+C$

25. $e^{\frac{\pi}{2}}$

26. $\dfrac{\pi}{8}$

27. $\dfrac{\pi}{6}$

28. $2\sin^{-1}\dfrac{(\sqrt{3}-1)}{2}$

29. $\dfrac{4\sqrt{2}}{3}$

30. $\dfrac{1}{40}\log 9$

31. $\dfrac{\pi}{2}-1$

32. $\dfrac{\pi}{2}(\pi-2)$

33. $\dfrac{19}{2}$

40. $\dfrac{1}{3}\left(e^2-\dfrac{1}{e}\right)$

41. A

42. B

43. D

44. B

EXERCISE 8.1

1. $\dfrac{14}{3}$

2. $16-4\sqrt{2}$

3. $\dfrac{32-8\sqrt{2}}{3}$

4. 12π

5. 6π

6. $\dfrac{\pi}{3}$

7. $\dfrac{a^2}{2}\left(\dfrac{\pi}{2}-1\right)$

8. $(4)^{\frac{2}{3}}$

9. $\dfrac{1}{3}$

10. $\dfrac{9}{8}$

11. $8\sqrt{3}$

12. A

13. B

EXERCISE 8.2

1. $\dfrac{\sqrt{2}}{6} + \dfrac{9}{4}\sin^{-1}\dfrac{2\sqrt{2}}{3}$

2. $\left(\dfrac{2\pi}{3} - \dfrac{\sqrt{3}}{2}\right)$

3. $\dfrac{21}{2}$

4. 4

5. 8

6. B

7. B

Miscellaneous Exercise on Chapter 8

1. (i) $\dfrac{7}{3}$ (ii) 624.8

2. $\dfrac{1}{6}$

3. $\dfrac{7}{3}$

4. 9

5. 4

6. $\dfrac{8}{3}\dfrac{a^2}{m^3}$

7. 27

8. $\dfrac{3}{2}(\pi - 2)$

9. $\dfrac{ab}{4}(\pi - 2)$

10. $\dfrac{9}{2}$

11. 2

12. $\dfrac{1}{3}$

13. 7

14. $\dfrac{7}{2}$

15. $\dfrac{9\pi}{8} - \dfrac{9}{4}\sin^{-1}\left(\dfrac{1}{3}\right) + \dfrac{1}{3\sqrt{2}}$

16. D

17. C

18. C

19. B

EXERCISE 9.1

1. Order 4; Degree not defined

2. Order 1; Degree 1

3. Order 2; Degree 1

4. Order 2; Degree not defined

5. Order 2; Degree 1

6. Order 3; Degree 2

7. Order 3; Degree 1

8. Order 1; Degree 1

9. Order 2; Degree 1

10. Order 2; Degree 1

11. D

12. A

EXERCISE 9.2

11. D

12. D

1. $y'' = 0$

2. $xy\, y'' + x\, (y')^2 - y\, y' = 0$

3. $y'' - y' - 6y = 0$

4. $y'' - 4y' + 4y = 0$

5. $y'' - 2y' + 2y = 0$

6. $2xyy' + x^2 = y^2$

7. $xy' - 2y = 0$

8. $xyy'' + x(y')^2 - yy' = 0$

9. $xyy'' + x(y')^2 - yy' = 0$

10. $(x^2 - 9)(y')^2 + x^2 = 0$

11. B

12. C

1. $y = 2 \tan \dfrac{x}{2} - x + C$

2. $y = 2 \sin (x + C)$

3. $y = 1 + Ae^{-x}$

4. $\tan x \tan y = C$

5. $y = \log (e^x + e^{-x}) + C$

6. $\tan^{-1} y = x + \dfrac{x^3}{3} + C$

7. $y = e^{cx}$

8. $x^{-4} + y^{-4} = C$

9. $y = x \sin^{-1}x + \sqrt{1 - x^2} + C$

10. $\tan y = C(1 - e^x)$

11. $y = \dfrac{1}{4} \log\left[(x+1)^2 (x^2 + 1)^3\right] - \dfrac{1}{2} \tan^{-1} x + 1$

12. $y = \dfrac{1}{2} \log\left(\dfrac{x^2 - 1}{x^2}\right) - \dfrac{1}{2} \log \dfrac{3}{4}$

13. $\cos\left(\dfrac{y-2}{x}\right) = a$

14. $y = \sec x$

15. $2y - 1 = e^x(\sin x - \cos x)$

16. $y - x + 2 = \log (x^2 (y + 2)^2)$

17. $y^2 - x^2 = 4$

18. $(x + 4)^2 = y + 3$

19. $(63t + 27)^{\frac{1}{3}}$

20. 6.93%

21. Rs 1648

22. $\dfrac{2 \log 2}{\log\left(\dfrac{11}{10}\right)}$

23. A

1. $(x - y)^2 = Cx\, e^{\frac{-y}{x}}$

2. $y = x \log|x| + Cx$

3. $\tan^{-1}\left(\dfrac{y}{x}\right)=\dfrac{1}{2}\log(x^2+y^2)+C$ 4. $x^2+y^2=Cx$

5. $\dfrac{1}{2\sqrt{2}}\log\left|\dfrac{x+\sqrt{2}y}{x-\sqrt{2}y}\right|=\log|x|+C$ 6. $y+\sqrt{x^2+y^2}=Cx^2$

7. $xy\cos\left|\dfrac{y}{x}\right|=C$ 8. $x\left[1-\cos\left(\dfrac{y}{x}\right)\right]=C\sin\left(\dfrac{y}{x}\right)$

9. $cy=\log\left|\dfrac{y}{x}\right|-1$ 10. $ye^{\frac{x}{y}}+x=C$

11. $\log(x^2+y^2)+2\tan^{-1}\dfrac{y}{x}=\dfrac{\pi}{2}+\log 2$

12. $y+2x=3x^2y$ 13. $\cot\left(\dfrac{y}{x}\right)=\log|ex|$

14. $\cos\left(\dfrac{y}{x}\right)=\log|ex|$ 15. $y=\dfrac{2x}{1-\log|x|}(x\neq 0,\ x\neq e)$

16. C   17. D

EXERCISE 9.6

1. $y=\dfrac{1}{5}(2\sin x-\cos x)+C\,e^{-2x}$ 2. $y=e^{-2x}+Ce^{-3x}$

3. $xy=\dfrac{x^4}{4}+C$ 4. $y(\sec x+\tan x)=\sec x+\tan x-x+C$

5. $y=(\tan x-1)+Ce^{-\tan x}$ 6. $y=\dfrac{x^2}{16}(4\log|x|-1)+Cx^{-2}$

7. $y\log x=\dfrac{-2}{x}(1+\log|x|)+C$ 8. $y=(1+x^2)^{-1}\log|\sin x|+C(1+x^2)^{-1}$

9. $y=\dfrac{1}{x}-\cot x+\dfrac{C}{x\sin x}$ 10. $(x+y+1)=C\,e^y$

11. $x=\dfrac{y^2}{3}+\dfrac{C}{y}$ 12. $x=3y^2+Cy$

13. $y = \cos x - 2 \cos^2 x$

14. $y (1 + x^2) = \tan^{-1} x - \dfrac{\pi}{4}$

15. $y = 4 \sin^3 x - 2 \sin^2 x$

16. $x + y + 1 = e^x$

17. $y = 4 - x - 2 e^x$

18. C

19. D

Miscellaneous Exercise on Chapter 9

1. (i) Order 2; Degree 1   (ii) Order 1; Degree 3
(iii) Order 4; Degree not defined

3. $y' = \dfrac{2y^2 - x^2}{4xy}$

5. $(x + yy')^2 = (x - y)^2 (1 + (y')^2)$

6. $\sin^{-1}y + \sin^{-1}x = C$

8. $\cos y = \dfrac{\sec x}{\sqrt{2}}$

9. $\tan^{-1} y + \tan^{-1}(e^x) = \dfrac{\pi}{2}$

10. $e^{\frac{x}{y}} = y + C$

11. $\log |x - y| = x + y + 1$

12. $y e^{2\sqrt{x}} = (2\sqrt{x} + C)$

13. $y \sin x = 2x^2 - \dfrac{\pi^2}{2} \ (\sin x \neq 0)$

14. $y = \log \left| \dfrac{2x+1}{x+1} \right|, x \neq -1$

15. 31250

16. C

17. C

18. C

EXERCISE 10.1

1. In the adjoining figure, the vector $\overrightarrow{OP}$ represents the required displacement.

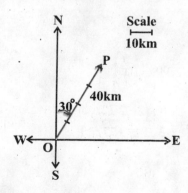

2. (i) scalar   (ii) vector   (iii) scalar   (iv) scalar   (v) scalar
    (vi) vector

3. (i) scalar   (ii) scalar   (iii) vector   (iv) vector   (v) scalar

4. (i) Vectors $\vec{a}$ and $\vec{b}$ are coinitial

    (ii) Vectors $\vec{b}$ and $\vec{d}$ are equal

    (iii) Vectors $\vec{a}$ and $\vec{c}$ are collinear but not equal

5. (i) True   (ii) False   (iii) False   (iv) False

EXERCISE 10.2

1. $|\vec{a}|=\sqrt{3}, |\vec{b}|=\sqrt{62}, |\vec{c}|=1$

2. An infinite number of possible answers.
3. An infinite number of possible answers.

4. $x = 2, y = 3$

5. -7 and 6; $-7\hat{i}$ and $6\hat{j}$

6. $-4\hat{j}-\hat{k}$

7. $\dfrac{1}{\sqrt{6}}\hat{i}+\dfrac{1}{\sqrt{6}}\hat{j}+\dfrac{2}{\sqrt{6}}\hat{k}$

8. $\dfrac{1}{\sqrt{3}}\hat{i}+\dfrac{1}{\sqrt{3}}\hat{j}+\dfrac{1}{\sqrt{3}}\hat{k}$

9. $\dfrac{1}{\sqrt{2}}\hat{i}+\dfrac{1}{\sqrt{2}}\hat{k}$

10. $\dfrac{40}{\sqrt{30}}\hat{i}-\dfrac{8}{\sqrt{30}}\hat{j}+\dfrac{16}{\sqrt{30}}\hat{k}$

12. $\dfrac{1}{\sqrt{14}}, \dfrac{2}{\sqrt{14}}, \dfrac{3}{\sqrt{14}}$

13. $-\dfrac{1}{3}, -\dfrac{2}{3}, \dfrac{2}{3}$

15. (i) $-\dfrac{1}{3}\hat{i}+\dfrac{4}{3}\hat{j}+\dfrac{1}{3}\hat{k}$ (ii) $-3\hat{i}+3\hat{k}$

16. $3\hat{i}+2\hat{j}+\hat{k}$

18. (C)

19. (D)

EXERCISE 10.3

1. $\dfrac{\pi}{4}$

2. $\cos^{-1}\left(\dfrac{5}{7}\right)$

3. 0

4. $\dfrac{60}{\sqrt{114}}$

6. $\dfrac{16\sqrt{2}}{3\sqrt{7}}, \dfrac{2\sqrt{2}}{3\sqrt{7}}$

7. $6|\vec{a}|^2+11\vec{a}.\vec{b}-35|\vec{b}|^2$

8. $|\vec{a}|=1, |\vec{b}|=1$

9. $\sqrt{13}$

10. 8

12. Vector $\vec{b}$ can be any vector

13. $\dfrac{-3}{2}$

14. Take any two non-zero perpendicular vectors $\vec{a}$ and $\vec{b}$

15. $\cos^{-1}\left(\dfrac{10}{\sqrt{102}}\right)$ 18.   (D)

EXERCISE 10.4

1. $19\sqrt{2}$

2. $\pm\dfrac{2}{3}\hat{i}\mp\dfrac{2}{3}\hat{j}\mp\dfrac{1}{3}\hat{k}$ 3. $\dfrac{\pi}{3};\ \dfrac{1}{2},\dfrac{1}{\sqrt{2}},\dfrac{1}{2}$

5. $3,\dfrac{27}{2}$

6. Either $|\vec{a}|=0$ or $|\vec{b}|=0$

8. No; take any two nonzero collinear vectors

9. $\dfrac{\sqrt{61}}{2}$ 10. $15\sqrt{2}$ 11.   (B)   12.   (C)

Miscellaneous Exercise on Chapter 10

1. $\dfrac{\sqrt{3}}{2}\hat{i}+\dfrac{1}{2}\hat{j}$

2. $x_2-x_1,y_2-y_1,z_2-z_1;\sqrt{(x_2-x_1)^2+(y_2-y_1)^2+(z_2-z_1)^2}$

3. $\dfrac{-5}{2}\hat{i}+\dfrac{3\sqrt{3}}{2}\hat{j}$

4. No; take $\vec{a}$, $\vec{b}$ and $\vec{c}$ to represent the sides of a triangle.

5. $\pm\dfrac{1}{\sqrt{3}}$ 6. $\dfrac{3}{2}\sqrt{10}\,\hat{i}+\dfrac{\sqrt{10}}{2}\hat{j}$ 7. $\dfrac{3}{\sqrt{22}}\hat{i}-\dfrac{3}{\sqrt{22}}\hat{j}+\dfrac{2}{\sqrt{22}}\hat{k}$

8. $2:3$ 9. $3\vec{a}+5\vec{b}$ 10. $\dfrac{1}{7}(3\hat{i}-6\hat{j}+2\hat{k});\ 11\sqrt{5}$

12. $\dfrac{1}{3}(160\hat{i}-5\hat{j}+70\hat{k})$ 13. $\lambda=1$ 16.   (B)

17.   (D)   18.   (C)   19.   (B)

EXERCISE 11.1

1. $0, \dfrac{-1}{\sqrt{2}}, \dfrac{1}{\sqrt{2}}$

2. $\pm\dfrac{1}{\sqrt{3}}, \pm\dfrac{1}{\sqrt{3}}, \pm\dfrac{1}{\sqrt{3}}$

3. $\dfrac{-9}{11}, \dfrac{6}{11}, \dfrac{-2}{11}$

5. $\dfrac{-2}{\sqrt{17}}, \dfrac{-2}{\sqrt{17}}, \dfrac{3}{17}; \dfrac{-2}{\sqrt{17}}, \dfrac{-3}{\sqrt{17}}, \dfrac{-2}{\sqrt{17}}; \dfrac{4}{\sqrt{42}}, \dfrac{5}{\sqrt{42}}, \dfrac{-1}{\sqrt{42}}$

EXERCISE 11.2

4. $\vec{r} = \hat{i} + 2\,\hat{j} + 3\,\hat{k} + \lambda\,(3\,\hat{i} + 2\,\hat{j} - 2\,\hat{k})$, where λ is a real number

5. $\vec{r} = 2\,\hat{i} - \hat{j} + 4\,\hat{k} + \lambda\,(\hat{i} + 2\,\hat{j} - \hat{k})$ and cartesian form is

$$\dfrac{x-2}{1} = \dfrac{y+1}{2} = \dfrac{z-4}{-1}$$

6. $\dfrac{x+2}{3} = \dfrac{y-4}{5} = \dfrac{z+5}{6}$

7. $\vec{r} = (5\hat{i} - 4\,\hat{j} + 6\,\hat{k}) + \lambda\,(3\,\hat{i} + 7\hat{j} + 2\hat{k})$

8. Vector equation of the line: $\vec{r} = \lambda\,(5\,\hat{i} - 2\,\hat{j} + 3\hat{k})$;

Cartesian equation of the line: $\dfrac{x}{5} = \dfrac{y}{-2} = \dfrac{z}{3}$.

9. Vector equation of the line: $\vec{r} = 3\hat{i} - 2\hat{j} - 5\hat{k} + \lambda(11\hat{k})$

Cartesian equation of the line: $\dfrac{x-3}{0} = \dfrac{y+2}{0} = \dfrac{z+5}{11}$

10. (i) $\theta = \cos^{-1}\left(\dfrac{19}{21}\right)$ (ii) $\theta = \cos^{-1}\left(\dfrac{8}{5\sqrt{3}}\right)$

11. (i) $\theta = \cos^{-1}\left(\dfrac{26}{9\sqrt{38}}\right)$ (ii) $\theta = \cos^{-1}\left(\dfrac{2}{3}\right)$

12. $p = \dfrac{70}{11}$ 14. $\dfrac{3\sqrt{2}}{2}$ 15. $2\sqrt{29}$

16. $\dfrac{3}{\sqrt{19}}$ 17. $\dfrac{8}{\sqrt{29}}$

EXERCISE 11.3

1. (a) $0, 0, 1; 2$

   (b) $\dfrac{1}{\sqrt{3}}, \dfrac{1}{\sqrt{3}}, \dfrac{1}{\sqrt{3}} ; \dfrac{1}{\sqrt{3}}$

   (c) $\dfrac{2}{\sqrt{14}}, \dfrac{3}{\sqrt{14}}, \dfrac{-1}{\sqrt{14}} ; \dfrac{5}{\sqrt{14}}$

   (d) $0, 1, 0; \dfrac{8}{5}$

2. $\vec{r} \cdot \left(\dfrac{3\hat{i} + 5\hat{j} - 6\hat{k}}{\sqrt{70}} \right) = 7$

3. (a) $x + y - z = 2$
   (b) $2x + 3y - 4z = 1$
   (c) $(s - 2t) x + (3 - t) y + (2s + t) z = 15$

4. (a) $\left(\dfrac{24}{29}, \dfrac{36}{29}, \dfrac{48}{29} \right)$
   (b) $\left(0, \dfrac{18}{25}, \dfrac{24}{25} \right)$

   (c) $\left(\dfrac{1}{3}, \dfrac{1}{3}, \dfrac{1}{3} \right)$
   (d) $\left(0, \dfrac{-8}{5}, 0 \right)$

5. (a) $[\vec{r} - (\hat{i} - 2\hat{k})] \cdot (\hat{i} + \hat{j} - \hat{k}) = 0;\ x + y - z = 3$

   (b) $[\vec{r} - (\hat{i} + 4\hat{j} + 6\hat{k})] \cdot (\hat{i} - 2\hat{j} + \hat{k}) = 0;\ x - 2y + z + 1 = 0$

6. (a) The points are collinear. There will be infinite number of planes passing through the given points.
   (b) $2x + 3y - 3z = 5$

7. $\dfrac{5}{2}, 5, -5$ 8. $y = 3$ 9. $7x - 5y + 4z - 8 = 0$

10. $\vec{r} \cdot \left(38\hat{i} + 68\hat{j} + 3\hat{k} \right) = 153$ 11. $x - z + 2 = 0$

12. $\cos^{-1} \dfrac{15}{\sqrt{731}}$

13. (a) $\cos^{-1} \left(\dfrac{2}{5} \right)$
    (b) The planes are perpendicular

    (c) The planes are parallel
    (d) The planes are parallel
    (e) $45°$

14. (a) $\dfrac{3}{13}$
    (b) $\dfrac{13}{3}$
    (c) 3
    (d) 2

Miscellaneous Exercise on Chapter 11

3. $90°$

4. $\dfrac{x}{1} = \dfrac{y}{0} = \dfrac{z}{0}$

5. $0°$

6. $k = \dfrac{-10}{7}$

7. $\vec{r} = \hat{i} + 2\hat{j} + 3\hat{k} + \lambda(\hat{i} + 2\hat{j} - 5\hat{k})$

8. $x + y + z = a + b + c$

9. 9

10. $\left(0, \dfrac{17}{2}, \dfrac{-13}{2}\right)$

11. $\left(\dfrac{17}{3}, 0, \dfrac{23}{3}\right)$

12. $(1, -2, 7)$

13. $7x - 8y + 3z + 25 = 0$

14. $p = \dfrac{3}{2}$ or $\dfrac{11}{6}$ or $\dfrac{7}{3}$

15. $y - 3z + 6 = 0$

16. $x + 2y - 3z - 14 = 0$

17. $33x + 45y + 50z - 41 = 0$

18. 13

19. $\vec{r} = \hat{i} + 2\hat{j} + 3\hat{k} + \lambda(-3\hat{i} + 5\hat{j} + 4\hat{k})$

20. $\vec{r} = \hat{i} + 2\hat{j} - 4\hat{k} + \lambda(2\hat{i} + 3\hat{j} + 6\hat{k})$

22. D

23. B

EXERCISE 12.1

1. Maximum $Z = 16$ at $(0, 4)$

2. Minimum $Z = -12$ at $(4, 0)$

3. Maximum $Z = \dfrac{235}{19}$ at $\dfrac{20}{19}, \dfrac{45}{19}$

4. Minimum $Z = 7$ at $\dfrac{3}{2}, \dfrac{1}{2}$

5. Maximum $Z = 18$ at $(4, 3)$

6. Minimum $Z = 6$ at all the points on the line segment joining the points $(6, 0)$ and $(0, 3)$.

7. Minimum $Z = 300$ at $(60, 0)$;

Maximum $Z = 600$ at all the points on the line segment joining the points $(120, 0)$ and $(60, 30)$.

8. Minimum Z = 100 at all the points on the line segment joining the points (0, 50) and (20, 40);

   Maximum Z = 400 at (0, 200)

9. Z has no maximum value

10. No feasible region, hence no maximum value of Z.

EXERCISE 12.2

1. Minimum cost = Rs 160 at all points lying on segment joining $\frac{8}{3}, 0$ and $2, \frac{1}{2}$.

2. Maximum number of cakes = 30 of kind one and 10 cakes of another kind.

3. (i) 4 tennis rackets and 12 cricket bats

   (ii) Maximum profit = Rs 200

4. 3 packages of nuts and 3 packages of bolts; Maximum profit = Rs 73.50.

5. 30 packages of screws A and 20 packages of screws B; Maximum profit = Rs 410

6. 4 Pedestal lamps and 4 wooden shades; Maximum profit = Rs 32

7. 8 Souvenir of types A and 20 of Souvenir of type B; Maximum profit = Rs 160.

8. 200 units of desktop model and 50 units of portable model; Maximum profit = Rs 1150000.

9. Minimise Z = 4x + 6y

   subject to $3x + 6y \geq 80$, $4x + 3y \geq 100$, $x \geq 0$ and $y \geq 0$, where x and y denote the number of units of food F_1 and food F_2 respectively; Minimum cost = Rs 104

10. 100 kg of fertiliser F_1 and 80 kg of fertiliser F_2; Minimum cost = Rs 1000

11. (D)

Miscellaneous Exercise on Chapter 12

1. 40 packets of food P and 15 packets of food Q; Maximum amount of vitamin A = 285 units.

2. 3 bags of brand P and 6 bags of brand Q; Minimum cost of the mixture = Rs 1950

3. Least cost of the mixture is Rs 112 (2 kg of Food X and 4 kg of food Y).

5. 40 tickets of executive class and 160 tickets of economy class; Maximum profit = Rs 136000.

6. From A : 10,50, 40 units; From B: 50,0,0 units to D, E and F respectively and minimum cost = Rs 510

7. From A: 500, 3000 and 3500 litres; From B: 4000, 0, 0 litres to D, E and F respectively; Minimum cost = Rs 4400

8. 40 bags of brand P and 100 bags of brand Q; Minimum amount of nitrogen = 470 kg.

9. 140 bags of brand P and 50 bags of brand Q; Maximum amount of nitrogen = 595 kg.

10. 800 dolls of type A and 400 dolls of type B; Maximum profit = Rs 16000

EXERCISE 13.1

1. $P(E|F) = \dfrac{2}{3}, P(F|E) = \dfrac{1}{3}$ 2. $P(A|B) = \dfrac{16}{25}$

3. (i) 0.32   (ii) 0.64   (iii) 0.98

4. $\dfrac{11}{26}$

5. (i) $\dfrac{4}{11}$ (ii) $\dfrac{4}{5}$ (iii) $\dfrac{2}{3}$

6. (i) $\dfrac{1}{2}$ (ii) $\dfrac{3}{7}$ (iii) $\dfrac{6}{7}$

7. (i) 1   (ii) 0

8. $\dfrac{1}{6}$ 9. 1   10. (a) $\dfrac{1}{3}$, (b) $\dfrac{1}{9}$

11. (i) $\dfrac{1}{2}, \dfrac{1}{3}$ (ii) $\dfrac{1}{2}, \dfrac{2}{3}$ (iii) $\dfrac{3}{4}, \dfrac{1}{4}$

12. (i) $\dfrac{1}{2}$ (ii) $\dfrac{1}{3}$ 13. $\dfrac{5}{9}$

14. $\dfrac{1}{15}$ 15. 0   16. C   17. D

EXERCISE 13.2

1. $\dfrac{3}{25}$ 2. $\dfrac{25}{102}$ 3. $\dfrac{44}{91}$

4. A and B are independent   5. A and B are not independent

6. E and F are not independent

7. (i) $p = \dfrac{1}{10}$ (ii) $p = \dfrac{1}{5}$

8. (i) 0.12   (ii) 0.58   (iii) 0.3   (iv) 0.4

9. $\dfrac{3}{8}$ 10. A and B are not independent

11. (i) 0.18   (ii) 0.12   (iii) 0.72   (iv) 0.28

12. $\dfrac{7}{8}$ 13. (i) $\dfrac{16}{81}$, (ii) $\dfrac{20}{81}$, (iii) $\dfrac{40}{81}$

14. (i) $\dfrac{2}{3}$, (ii) $\dfrac{1}{2}$ 15. (i), (ii)   16. (a) $\dfrac{1}{5}$, (b) $\dfrac{1}{3}$, (c) $\dfrac{1}{2}$

17. D   18. B

EXERCISE 13.3

1. $\dfrac{1}{2}$ 2. $\dfrac{2}{3}$ 3. $\dfrac{9}{13}$ 4. $\dfrac{12}{13}$

5. $\dfrac{22}{133}$ 6. $\dfrac{4}{9}$ 7. $\dfrac{1}{52}$ 8. $\dfrac{1}{4}$

9. $\dfrac{2}{9}$ 10. $\dfrac{8}{11}$ 11. $\dfrac{5}{34}$ 12. $\dfrac{11}{50}$

13. A   14. C

EXERCISE 13.4

1. (ii), (iii) and (iv)   2. X = 0, 1, 2; yes   3. X = 6, 4, 2, 0

4. (i)

X	0	1	2
P(X)	$\dfrac{1}{4}$	$\dfrac{1}{2}$	$\dfrac{1}{4}$

(ii)

X	0	1	2	3
P(X)	$\dfrac{1}{8}$	$\dfrac{3}{8}$	$\dfrac{3}{8}$	$\dfrac{1}{8}$

(iii)

X	0	1	2	3	4
P(X)	$\dfrac{1}{16}$	$\dfrac{1}{4}$	$\dfrac{3}{8}$	$\dfrac{1}{4}$	$\dfrac{1}{16}$

5. (i)

X	0	1	2
P(X)	$\dfrac{4}{9}$	$\dfrac{4}{9}$	$\dfrac{1}{9}$

(ii)

X	0	1
P(X)	$\dfrac{25}{36}$	$\dfrac{11}{36}$

6.

X	0	1	2	3	4
P(X)	$\dfrac{256}{625}$	$\dfrac{256}{625}$	$\dfrac{96}{625}$	$\dfrac{16}{625}$	$\dfrac{1}{625}$

7.

X	0	1	2
P(X)	$\dfrac{9}{16}$	$\dfrac{6}{16}$	$\dfrac{1}{16}$

8. (i) $k = \dfrac{1}{10}$ (ii) $P(X < 3) = \dfrac{3}{10}$ (iii) $P(X > 6) = \dfrac{17}{100}$

   (iv) $P(0 < X < 3) = \dfrac{3}{10}$

9. (a) $k = \dfrac{1}{6}$ (b) $P(X < 2) = \dfrac{1}{2}, P(X \le 2) = 1, P(X \ge 2) = \dfrac{1}{2}$

10. 1.5   11. $\dfrac{1}{3}$ 12. $\dfrac{14}{3}$

13. Var(X) = 5.833, S.D = 2.415

14.

X	14	15	16	17	18	19	20	21
P(X)	$\dfrac{2}{15}$	$\dfrac{1}{15}$	$\dfrac{2}{15}$	$\dfrac{3}{15}$	$\dfrac{1}{15}$	$\dfrac{2}{15}$	$\dfrac{3}{15}$	$\dfrac{1}{15}$

Mean = 17.53, Var(X) = 4.78 and S.D(X) = 2.19

15. E(X) = 0.7 and Var (X) = 0.21   16. B   17. D

EXERCISE 13.5

1. (i) $\dfrac{3}{32}$ (ii) $\dfrac{7}{64}$ (iii) $\dfrac{63}{64}$

2. $\dfrac{25}{216}$

3. $\left(\dfrac{29}{20}\right)\left(\dfrac{19}{20}\right)^9$

4. (i) $\dfrac{1}{1024}$ (ii) $\dfrac{45}{512}$ (iii) $\dfrac{243}{1024}$

5. (i) $(0.95)^5$ (ii) $(0.95)^4 \times 1.2$ (iii) $1 - (0.95)^4 \times 1.2$
   (iv) $1 - (0.95)^5$

6. $\left(\dfrac{9}{10}\right)^4$

7. $\left(\dfrac{1}{2}\right)^{20}\left[20C_{12} + {}^{20}C_{13} + ... + {}^{20}C_{20}\right]$

9. $\dfrac{11}{243}$

10. (a) $1 - \left(\dfrac{99}{100}\right)^{50}$ (b) $\dfrac{1}{2}\left(\dfrac{99}{100}\right)^{49}$ (c) $1 - \dfrac{149}{100}\left(\dfrac{99}{100}\right)^{49}$

11. $\dfrac{7}{12}\left(\dfrac{5}{6}\right)^5$ 12. $\dfrac{35}{18}\left(\dfrac{5}{6}\right)^4$ 13. $\dfrac{22 \times 9^3}{10^{11}}$

14. C   15. A

Miscellaneous Exercise on Chapter 13

1. (i) 1   (ii) 0

2. (i) $\dfrac{1}{3}$ (ii) $\dfrac{1}{2}$

3. $\dfrac{20}{21}$

4. $1 - \sum\limits_{r=7}^{10} {}^{10}C_r (0.9)^r (0.1)^{10-r}$

5. (i) $\left(\dfrac{2}{5}\right)^6$ (ii) $7\left(\dfrac{2}{5}\right)^4$ (iii) $1 - \left(\dfrac{2}{5}\right)^6$ (iv) $\dfrac{864}{3125}$

6. $\dfrac{5^{10}}{2\times6^9}$　　　　7. $\dfrac{625}{23328}$　　　　8. $\dfrac{2}{7}$

9. $\dfrac{31}{9}\left(\dfrac{2}{3}\right)^4$ 　　　10. $n \geq 4$　　　11. $\dfrac{11}{216}$

12. $\dfrac{1}{15},\dfrac{2}{5},\dfrac{8}{15}$　　　13. $\dfrac{14}{29}$　　　14. $\dfrac{3}{16}$

15. (i)　0.5　　(ii)　0.05　　　16. $\dfrac{16}{31}$

17. A　　　　18. C　　　　19. B

— ❖ —

SUPPLEMENTARY MATERIAL

CHAPTER 7

7.6.3 $\int (px + q)\sqrt{ax^2 + bx + c}\ dx.$

We choose constants A and B such that

$$px + q = A\left[\frac{d}{dx}(ax^2 + bx + c)\right] + B$$

$$= A(2ax + b) + B$$

Comparing the coefficients of x and the constant terms on both sides, we get

$$2a\text{A} = p \text{ and } \text{A}b + \text{B} = q$$

Solving these equations, the values of A and B are obtained. Thus, the integral reduces to

$$\text{A} \int (2ax + b)\sqrt{ax^2 + bx + c}\ dx + \text{B} \int \sqrt{ax^2 + bx + c}\ dx$$

$$= \text{AI}_1 + \text{BI}_2$$

where $\quad \text{I}_1 = \int (2ax + b)\sqrt{ax^2 + bx + c}\ dx$

Put $ax^2 + bx + c = t$, then $(2ax + b)dx = dt$

So, $\quad \text{I}_1 = \frac{2}{3}(ax^2 + bx + c)^{\frac{3}{2}} + \text{C}_1$

Similarly, $\quad \text{I}_2 = \int \sqrt{ax^2 + bx + c}\ dx$

is found, using the integral formulae discussed in [7.6.2, Page 328 of the textbook].

Thus $\int (px + q)\sqrt{ax^2 + bx + c}\; dx$ is finally worked out.

Example 25 Find $\int x\sqrt{1 + x - x^2}\; dx$

Solution Following the procedure as indicated above, we write

$$x \quad = \quad A\left[\frac{d}{dx}\left(1 + x - x^2\right)\right] + B$$

$$= \quad A\left(1 - 2x\right) + B$$

Equating the coefficients of x and constant terms on both sides,

We get $-2A = 1$ and $A + B = 0$

Solving these equations, we get $A = -\dfrac{1}{2}$ and $B = \dfrac{1}{2}$. Thus the integral reduces to

$$\int x\sqrt{1 + x - x^2}\, dx = -\frac{1}{2}\int (1 - 2x)\sqrt{1 + x - x^2}\, dx + \frac{1}{2}\int \sqrt{1 + x - x^2}\, dx$$

$$= -\frac{1}{2}I_1 + \frac{1}{2}I_2 \tag{1}$$

Consider $\qquad I_1 = \int (1 - 2x)\sqrt{1 + x - x^2}\, dx$

Put $1 + x - x^2 = t$, then $(1 - 2x)dx = dt$

Thus $\quad I_1 = \int (1 - 2x)\sqrt{1 + x - x^2}\, dx = \int t^{\frac{1}{2}} dt = \frac{2}{3} t^{\frac{3}{2}} + C_1$

$$= \quad \frac{2}{3}\left(1 + x - x^2\right)^{\frac{3}{2}} + C_1, \text{ where } C_1 \text{ is some constant.}$$

Further, consider $I_2 = \int\sqrt{1 + x - x^2}\, dx = \int\sqrt{\dfrac{5}{4} - \left(x - \dfrac{1}{2}\right)^2}\, dx$

Put $x - \dfrac{1}{2} = t$. Then $dx = dt$

Therefore, $I_2 = \int\sqrt{\left(\dfrac{\sqrt{5}}{2}\right)^2 - t^2}\, dt$

$= \dfrac{1}{2}t\sqrt{\dfrac{5}{4} - t^2} + \dfrac{1}{2}\cdot\dfrac{5}{4}\sin^{-1}\dfrac{2t}{\sqrt{5}} + C_2$

$= \dfrac{1}{2}\dfrac{(2x - 1)}{2}\sqrt{\dfrac{5}{4} - (x - \dfrac{1}{2})^2} + \dfrac{5}{8}\sin^{-1}\left(\dfrac{2x - 1}{\sqrt{5}}\right) + C_2$

$= \dfrac{1}{4}(2x - 1)\sqrt{1 + x - x^2} + \dfrac{5}{8}\sin^{-1}\left(\dfrac{2x - 1}{\sqrt{5}}\right) + C_2,$

where C_2 is some constant.

Putting values of I_1 and I_2 in (1), we get

$\int x\sqrt{1 + x} - x^2\, dx = -\dfrac{1}{3}(1 + x - x^2)^{\frac{3}{2}} + \dfrac{1}{8}(2x - 1)\sqrt{1 + x - x^2}$

$+ \dfrac{5}{16}\sin^{-1}\left(\dfrac{2x - 1}{\sqrt{5}}\right) + C,$

where $C = -\dfrac{C_1 + C_2}{2}$ is another arbitrary constant.

Insert the following exercises at the end of EXERCISE 7.7 as follows:

12. $x\sqrt{x+x^2}$ 13. $(x+1)\sqrt{2x^2+3}$ 14. $(x+3)\sqrt{3-4x-x^2}$

Answers

12. $\dfrac{1}{3}(x^2+x)^{\frac{3}{2}} - \dfrac{(2x+1)\sqrt{x^2+x}}{8} + \dfrac{1}{16}\log|x+\dfrac{1}{2}+\sqrt{x^2+x}|+C$

13. $\dfrac{1}{6}(2x^2+3)^{\frac{3}{2}} + \dfrac{x}{2}\sqrt{2x^2+3} + \dfrac{3\sqrt{2}}{4}\log\left|x+\sqrt{x^2+\dfrac{3}{2}}\right|+C$

14. $-\dfrac{1}{3}(3-4x-x^2)^{\frac{3}{2}} + \dfrac{7}{2}\sin^{-1}\left(\dfrac{x+2}{\sqrt{7}}\right) + \dfrac{(x+2)\sqrt{3-4x-x^2}}{2}+C$

CHAPTER 10

10.7 Scalar Triple Product

Let $\vec{a}, \vec{b}$ and $\vec{c}$ be any three vectors. The scalar product of $\vec{a}$ and $(\vec{b}\times\vec{c})$, i.e., $\vec{a}\cdot(\vec{b}\times\vec{c})$ is called the scalar triple product of $\vec{a}, \vec{b}$ and $\vec{c}$ in this order and is denoted by $[\vec{a}, \vec{b}, \vec{c}]$ (or $[\vec{a}\,\vec{b}\,\vec{c}\cdot]$). We thus have

$$[\vec{a},\vec{b},\vec{c}] = \vec{a}\cdot(\vec{b}\times\vec{c})$$

Observations

1. Since $(\vec{b}\times\vec{c})$ is a vector, $\vec{a}\cdot(\vec{b}\times\vec{c})$ is a scalar quantity, i.e. $[\vec{a}, \vec{b}, \vec{c}]$ is a scalar quantity.

2. Geometrically, the magnitude of the scalar triple product is the volume of a parallelopiped formed by adjacent sides given by the three

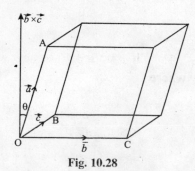

Fig. 10.28

vectors $\vec{a}$, $\vec{b}$ and $\vec{c}$ (Fig. 10.28). Indeed, the area of the parallelogram forming

the base of the parallelopiped is $\left|\vec{b} \times \vec{c}\right|$. The height is the projection of $\vec{a}$ along

the normal to the plane containing $\vec{b}$ and $\vec{c}$ which is the magnitude of the

component of $\vec{a}$ in the direction of $\vec{b} \times \vec{c}$ i.e., $\dfrac{\left|\vec{a} \cdot (\vec{b} \times \vec{c})\right|}{\left|(\vec{b} \times \vec{c})\right|}$. So the required

volume of the parallelopiped is $\dfrac{\left|\vec{a} \cdot (\vec{b} \times \vec{c})\right|}{\left|(\vec{b} \times \vec{c})\right|} \,|\, \vec{b} \times \vec{c} \,|=\left|\vec{a} \cdot (\vec{b} \times \vec{c})\right|,$

3.   If $\vec{a} = a_1 \hat{i} + a_2 \hat{j} + a_3 \hat{k}$, $\vec{b} = b_1 \hat{i} + b_2 \hat{j} + b_3 \hat{k}$ and $\vec{c} = c_1 \hat{i} + c_2 \hat{j} + c_3 \hat{k}$,
then

$$\vec{b} \times \vec{c} = \begin{vmatrix} \hat{i} & \hat{j} & \hat{k} \\ b_1 & b_2 & b_3 \\ c_1 & c_2 & c_3 \end{vmatrix}$$

$$= (b_2 c_3 - b_3 c_2)\, \hat{i} + (b_3 c_1 - b_1 c_3)\, \hat{j} + (b_1 c_2 - b_2 c_1)\, \hat{k}$$

and so

$$\vec{a} \cdot (\vec{b} \times \vec{c}) = a_1 (b_2 c_3 - b_3 c_2) + a_2 (b_3 c_1 - b_1 c_3) + a_3 (b_1 c_2 - b_2 c_1)$$

$$= \begin{vmatrix} a_1 & a_2 & a_3 \\ b_1 & b_2 & b_3 \\ c_1 & c_2 & c_3 \end{vmatrix}$$

4.   If $\vec{a}, \vec{b}$ and $\vec{c}$ be any three vectors, then

$$[\vec{a}, \vec{b}, \vec{c}] = [\vec{b}, \vec{c}, \vec{a}] = [\vec{c}, \vec{a}, \vec{b}]$$

(cyclic permutation of three vectors does not change the value of the scalar triple product).

Let $\vec{a} = a_1 \hat{i} + a_2 \hat{j} + a_3 \hat{k}$, $\vec{b} = b_1 \hat{i} + b_2 \hat{j} + b_3 \hat{k}$ and $\vec{c} = c_1 \hat{i} + c_2 \hat{j}_3 \hat{k}.$

Then, just by observation above, we have

$$[\vec{a},\vec{b},\vec{c}] = \begin{vmatrix} a_1 & a_2 & a_3 \\ b_1 & b_2 & b_3 \\ c_1 & c_2 & c_3 \end{vmatrix}$$

$$= a_1 (b_2c_3 - b_3c_2) + a_2 (b_3c_1 - b_1c_3) + a_3 (b_1c_2 - b_2c_1)$$

$$= b_1 (a_3c_2 - a_2c_3) + b_2 (a_1c_3 - a_3c_1) + b_3 (a_2c_1 - a_1c_2)$$

$$= \begin{vmatrix} b_1 & b_2 & b_3 \\ c_1 & c_2 & c_3 \\ a_1 & a_2 & a_3 \end{vmatrix}$$

$$= [\vec{b},\vec{c},\vec{a}]$$

Similarly, the reader may verify that

$$= [\vec{a},\vec{b}, \vec{c}] = [\vec{c},\vec{a},\vec{b}]$$

Hence $\qquad [\vec{a},\vec{b}, \vec{c}] = [\vec{b},\vec{c},\vec{a}] = [\vec{c},\vec{a},\vec{b}]$

5. In scalar triple product $\vec{a}.(\vec{b}\times\vec{c})$, the dot and cross can be interchanged. Indeed,

$$\vec{a}.(\vec{b}\times\vec{c}) = [\vec{a},\vec{b},\vec{c}] = [\vec{b},\vec{c},\vec{a}] = [\vec{c},\vec{a},\vec{b}] = \vec{c}.(\vec{a}\times\vec{b}) = (\vec{a}\times\vec{b}).\vec{c}$$

6. $= [\vec{a},\vec{b},\vec{c}] = -[\vec{a}, \vec{c},\vec{b}]$. Indeed

$$= [\vec{a},\vec{b},\vec{c}] = \vec{a}.(\vec{b}\times\vec{c})$$

$$= \vec{a}.(-\vec{c}\times\vec{b})$$

$$= -(\vec{a}.(\vec{c}\times\vec{b}))$$

$$= -\left[\vec{a},\vec{c},\vec{b}\right]$$

7. $[\vec{a},\vec{a},\vec{b}]=0$. Indeed

$$[\vec{a},\vec{a},\vec{b}]=[\vec{a},\vec{b},\vec{a},]$$

$$=[\vec{b},\vec{a},\vec{a}]$$

$$=\vec{b}\cdot(\vec{a}\times\vec{a})$$

$$=\vec{b}\cdot\vec{0}=0. \qquad\qquad (\text{as } \vec{a}\times\vec{a}=\vec{0})$$

Note: The result in 7 above is true irrespective of the position of two equal vectors.

10.7.1 Coplanarity of Three Vectors

Theorem 1 Three vectors $\vec{a}$, $\vec{b}$ and $\vec{c}$ are coplanar if and only if $\vec{a}\cdot(\vec{b}\times\vec{c})=0$.

Proof Suppose first that the vectors $\vec{a}$, $\vec{b}$ and $\vec{c}$ are coplanar.

If $\vec{b}$ and $\vec{c}$ are parallel vectors, then, $\vec{b}\times\vec{c}=\vec{0}$ and so $\vec{a}\cdot(\vec{b}\times\vec{c})=0$.

If $\vec{b}$ and $\vec{c}$ are not parallel then, since $\vec{a}$, $\vec{b}$ and $\vec{c}$ are coplanar, $\vec{b}\times\vec{c}$ is perpendicular to $\vec{a}$.

So $\vec{a}\cdot(\vec{b}\times\vec{c})=0$.

Conversely, suppose that $\vec{a}\cdot(\vec{b}\times\vec{c})=0$. If $\vec{a}$ and $\vec{b}\times\vec{c}$ are both non-zero, then we conclude that $\vec{a}$ and $\vec{b}\times\vec{c}$ are perpendicular vectors. But $\vec{b}\times\vec{c}$ is perpendicular to both $\vec{b}$ and $\vec{c}$. Therefore, $\vec{a}$ and $\vec{b}$ and $\vec{c}$ must lie in the plane, i.e. they are coplanar. If $\vec{a}=0$, then $\vec{a}$ is coplanar with any two vectors, in particular with $\vec{b}$ and $\vec{c}$. If $(\vec{b}\times\vec{c})=0$, then $\vec{b}$ and $\vec{c}$ are parallel vectors and so, $\vec{a}$, $\vec{b}$ and $\vec{c}$ are coplanar since any two vectors always lie in a plane determined by them and a vector which is parallel to any one of it also lies in that plane.

Note: Coplanarity of four points can be discussed using coplanarity of three vectors. Indeed, the four points A, B, C and D are coplanar if the vectors $\overrightarrow{AB}, \overrightarrow{AC}$ and $\overrightarrow{AD}$ are coplanar.

Example 26 Find $\vec{a}.(\vec{b}\times\vec{c})$, if $\vec{a}=2\hat{i}+\hat{j}+3\hat{k}$, $\vec{b}=-\hat{i}+2j+k$ and $\vec{c}=3\hat{i}+\hat{j}+2\hat{k}$.

Solution We have $\vec{a}.(\vec{b}\times\vec{c})=\begin{vmatrix} 2 & 1 & 3 \\ -1 & 2 & 1 \\ 3 & 1 & 2 \end{vmatrix}=-10.$

Example 27 Show that the vectors

$\vec{a}=\hat{i}-2\hat{j}+3\hat{k}$, $\vec{b}=-2\hat{i}+3j-4\hat{k}$ and $\vec{c}=\hat{i}-3\hat{j}+5\hat{k}$ are coplanar.

Solution We have $\vec{a}.(\vec{b}\times\vec{c})=\begin{vmatrix} 1 & -2 & 3 \\ -2 & 3 & -4 \\ 1 & -3 & 5 \end{vmatrix}=0.$

Hence, in view of Theorem 1, $\vec{a},\vec{b}$ and $\vec{c}$ are coplanar vectors.

Example 28 Find λ if the vectors

$\vec{a}=\hat{i}+3\hat{j}+\hat{k}$, $\vec{b}=2\hat{i}-\hat{j}-\hat{k}$ and $\vec{c}=\lambda\hat{i}+7\hat{j}+3\hat{k}$ are coplanar.

Solution Since $\vec{a},\vec{b}$ and $\vec{c}$ are coplanar vectors, we have $\left[\vec{a},\vec{b},\vec{c}\right]=0$, i.e.,

$\begin{vmatrix} 1 & 3 & 1 \\ 2 & -1 & -1 \\ \lambda & 7 & 3 \end{vmatrix}=0.$

$\Rightarrow \qquad 1(-3+7)-3(6+\lambda)+1(14+\lambda)=0$

$\Rightarrow \qquad \lambda=0.$

Example 29 Show that the four points A, B, C and D with position vectors

$4\hat{i}+5\hat{j}+\hat{k},-(\hat{j}+\hat{k}),3\hat{i}+9\hat{j}+4\hat{k}$ and $4(-\hat{i}+\hat{j}+\hat{k})$, respectively are coplanar.

Solution We know that the four points A, B, C and D are coplanar if the three vectors $\overrightarrow{AB},\overrightarrow{AC}$ and $\overrightarrow{AD}$ are coplanar, i.e., if

$$\left[\overrightarrow{AB},\overrightarrow{AC},\overrightarrow{AD}\right]=0$$

Now $\overrightarrow{AB} = -(\hat{j}+\hat{k})-(4\hat{i}+5\hat{j}+\hat{k})=-4\hat{i}-6\hat{j}-2\hat{k})$

$\overrightarrow{AC} = (3\hat{i}+9\hat{j}+4\hat{k})-(4\hat{i}+5\hat{j}+\hat{k})=-\hat{i}+4\hat{j}+3\hat{k}$

and $\overrightarrow{AD} = 4(-\hat{i}+\hat{j}+\hat{k})-(4\hat{i}+5\hat{j}+\hat{k})=-8\hat{i}-\hat{j}+3\hat{k}$

Thus $\left[\overrightarrow{AB},\overrightarrow{AC},\overrightarrow{AD}\right] = \begin{vmatrix} -4 & -6 & -2 \\ -1 & 4 & 3 \\ -8 & -1 & 3 \end{vmatrix} = 0.$

Hence A, B, C and D are coplanar.

Example 30 Prove that $\left[\vec{a}+\vec{b},\vec{b}+\vec{c},\vec{c}+\vec{a}\right]=2\left[\vec{a},\vec{b},\vec{c}\right].$

Solution We have

$$\left[\vec{a}+\vec{b},\vec{b}+\vec{c},\vec{c}+\vec{a}\right]=(\vec{a}+\vec{b}).((\vec{b}+\vec{c})\times(\vec{c}+\vec{a}))$$

$$=(\vec{a}+\vec{b}).(\vec{b}\times\vec{c}+\vec{b}\times\vec{a}+\vec{c}\times\vec{c}+\vec{c}\times\vec{a})$$

$$=(\vec{a}+\vec{b}).(\vec{b}\times\vec{c}+\vec{b}\times\vec{a}+\vec{c}\times\vec{a}) \qquad (\text{as } \vec{c}\times\vec{c}=\vec{0}\ )$$

$$=\vec{a}.(\vec{b}\times\vec{c})+\vec{a}.(\vec{b}\times\vec{a})+\vec{a}.(\vec{c}\times\vec{a})+\vec{b}.(\vec{b}\times\vec{c})+\vec{b}.(\vec{b}\times\vec{a})+\vec{b}.(\vec{c}\times\vec{a})$$

$$=\left[\vec{a},\vec{b},\vec{c}\right]+\left[\vec{a},\vec{b},\vec{a}\right]+[\vec{a},\vec{c},\vec{a}]+\left[\vec{b},\vec{b},\vec{c}\right]+\left[\vec{b},\vec{b},\vec{a}\right]+\left[\vec{b},\vec{c},\vec{a}\right]$$

$$=2\left[\vec{a},\vec{b},\vec{c}\right] \qquad\qquad (\text{Why?})$$

Example 31 Prove that $\left[\vec{a},\vec{b},\vec{c}+\vec{d}\right]=\left[\vec{a},\vec{b},\vec{c}\right]+[\vec{a},\vec{b},\vec{d}]$

Solution We have

$$\left[\vec{a},\vec{b},\vec{c}+\vec{d}\right]=\vec{a}.(\vec{b}\times(\vec{c}+\vec{d}))$$

$$=\vec{a}.(\vec{b}\times\vec{c}+\vec{b}\times\vec{d})$$

$$=\vec{a}.(\vec{b}\times\vec{c})+\vec{a}.(\vec{b}\times\vec{d})$$

$$=\left[\vec{a},\vec{b},\vec{c}\right]+\left[\vec{a},\vec{b},\vec{d}\right].$$

Exercise 10.5

1. Find $\left[\vec{a}\,\vec{b}\,\vec{c}\right]$ if $\vec{a}=\hat{i}-2\hat{j}+3\hat{k}, \vec{b}=2\hat{i}-3\hat{j}+\hat{k}$ and $c=3i+j-2\hat{k}$

    (Ans. 24)

2. Show that the vectors $\vec{a}=\hat{i}-2\hat{j}+3\hat{k}, \vec{b}=-2\hat{i}+3\hat{j}-4\hat{k}$ and $\vec{c}=\hat{i}-3\hat{j}+5\hat{k}$ are coplanar.

3. Find λ if the vectors $\hat{i}-\hat{j}+\hat{k}, 3\hat{i}+\hat{j}+2\hat{k}$ and $\hat{i}+\lambda\hat{j}-3\hat{k}$ are coplanar.

    (Ans. $\lambda = 15$)

4. Let $\vec{a}=\hat{i}+\hat{j}+\hat{k}, \vec{b}=\hat{i}$ and $\vec{c}=c_1\hat{i}+c_2\hat{j}+c_3\hat{k}$ Then

    (a) If $c_1 = 1$ and $c_2 = 2$, find c_3 which makes $\vec{a}, \vec{b}$ and $\vec{c}$ coplanar   (Ans. $c_3 = 2$)

    (b) If $c_2 = -1$ and $c_3 = 1$, show that no value of c_1 can make $\vec{a}, \vec{b}$ and $\vec{c}$ coplanar.

5. Show that the four points with position vectors

    $4\hat{i}+8\hat{j}+12\hat{k}, 2\hat{i}+4\hat{j}+6\hat{k}, 3\hat{i}+5\hat{j}+4\hat{k}$ and $5\hat{i}+8\hat{j}+5\hat{k}$ are coplanar.

6. Find x such that the four points A (3, 2, 1) B (4, x, 5), C (4, 2, –2) and D (6, 5, –1) are coplanar.   (Ans. $x = 5$)

7. Show that the vectors $\vec{a}, \vec{b}$ and $\vec{c}$ coplanar if $\vec{a}+\vec{b}, \vec{b}+\vec{c}$ and $\vec{c}+\vec{a}$ are coplanar.